Our auctions regularly feature an impressive selection of

COINS • TOKENS • BANKNOTES
HISTORICAL and ART MEDALS

We hold regular auctions of coins and medals throughout the year.

Our well-illustrated, expertly researched catalogues reach buyers all over the world. The current buoyant market and a strong international demand ensures the best prices for all types of coins and medals.

If you are thinking of disposing of your collection or any pieces surplus to your requirements, please contact us today.

We also provide valuations for insurance and probate. Fees are refunded if we are instructed to sell within one year.

For a free auction valuation or further information, whether buying or selling, please contact Christopher Webb or Michael Sharp.

For the latest information on all DNW auctions check out our website. See what's coming up for auction long before catalogues are published! Updated daily, **www.dnw.co.uk** features a huge numismatic database, an international auction calendar and much more besides!

subscriptions for 4 catalogues
UK £30
Europe £35
Rest of World £40

DIX ✠ NOONAN ✠ WEBB

16 Bolton Street Piccadilly London W1J 8BQ
Tel: 020 7016 1700 Fax 020 7016 1799
E-mail: coins@dnw.co.uk

DIX • NOONAN • WEBB
DNW
AUCTIONEERS AND VALUERS

www.dnw.co.uk

THE

COIN YEARBOOK 2004

Edited by

James Mackay, MA, DLitt
John W. Mussell, FRGS
and the Editorial Team of COIN NEWS

ISBN 1 870 192 64 8

A *Token* TITLE

Published by
TOKEN PUBLISHING LIMITED
Orchard House, Duchy Road, Heathpark, Honiton, EX14 1YD
Telephone: 01404 46972 Fax: 01404 44788
e-mail: info@tokenpublishing.com. Website: http://www.tokenpublishing.com

Printed in Great Britain by Haynes Publishing, Sparkford, Yeovil

Contents

Index to advertisers

MARK RASMUSSEN MR 2001 NUMISMATIST
Mark Rasmussen
Numismatist
Specialising in British Coins and Medals
also World Coins and Bank Notes
Auction Advice
Wants Lists Managed
Valuations for Insurance
Commission Selling
Outright Purchase
Auction Bidding Service
34 Years Experience
Confidentiality Assured
Current list now available
P. O. Box 42, Betchworth,
Surrey RH3 7YR
Tel/Fax: 01737 841000
Mobile: 07798 611006
e mail: mark.rasmussen@rascoins.com
www.rascoins.com
BNTA
~ Winter list out March 2004 ~

Foreword

'ELCOME to the eleventh edition of the COIN YEARBOOK. Last year we celebrated the important ilestone of our tenth edition, but this year we have even greater cause for celebration. In May 2003 we arked the twentieth anniversary of Token Publishing and launched a medal design competition to lebrate. As we go to press with this edition of the YEARBOOK we are about to have the winning design ruck as a medal.

Back in May 1983 the launch of Token Publishing took place with the minimum of fuss and no nfare. The masthead was discreetly changed to indicate the change from Epic Publishing of London Token Publishing at Liphook, Hampshire. In fact the magazine had had a history going back almost ,o decades earlier, having started out in July 1964 as an octavo format (roughly A5) quarterly under e title of *Coins and Medals*, published by Link House of Croydon. Looking at that first issue which ran a mere 42 pages, we note the names of such contributors as E. C. Joslin, D. J. Crowther and the great oward Linecar, all sadly called to higher things, but a regular contributor from the outset was James ackay (who then wrote a regular column on Treasure Trove as well as paper money features) so in 04, God willing, he will be celebrating 40 years associated with this publication in its various ansformations.

The original magazine soon became a monthly and later expanded to a quarto format. Link House ld the magazine to Stanley Gibbons and they, in turn, disposed of it to Irwin Margolis of Epic iblishing. In 1983 he sold the title to John Mussell who had previously been the Editor. In the past ,enty years the magazine has developed enormously, moving from quarto to A4 format, adopting a uch higher quality of paper and introducing colour. It has got bigger and better, but we are not resting our laurels and are constantly striving to improve its appearance and content.

Looking back to 1983 when Token Publishing was founded, our birth coincided with the launch of e first National Coin Week in Britain and the debut of the circulating pound coin. COIN NEWS cost p and averaged 50 pages each month but there was also a central 16-page section entitled MEDAL EWS which would, of course, eventually be hived off to form a separate publication. Making lowances for inflation over the past 20 years and the tremendous improvements in the size and quality the magazine, we are proud of the fact that we continue to offer such tremendous value for money.

Then, as now, John Pearson Andrew was our Consultant Editor who, as well as contributing imerous features over the years, has very ably compiled the Market Scene round-up of the latest ictions. Among our regular contributors in 1983 was Richard Plant and we are very pleased to have m back on board with the immensely popular Lexicon feature which commenced this year. Howard necar continued to be a staunch supporter and, indeed, this only came to an end with his untimely eath. Among other names which figured prominently in our inaugural year we note the token ecialist George Berry and pioneer notaphilist Colin Narbeth, still going strong.

The market in 1983 was dominated by Glendining's, but Spink held occasional sales while coins and edals also featured prominently in the auction calendar of the leading salerooms, Sotheby's and hristie's. Now Glen's have been subsumed into Bonhams and Christie's are no more, but new names ive come to the fore, with Morton & Eden and Dix Noonan Webb raising the standards of coin and edal sales to new heights. Back in 1983 Wallis & Wallis were the only auctioneers beyond the Greater ondon area providing regular sales of coins and medals but now the auction scene has expanded all ,er the country, with mail order and trading on the Internet adding dimensions undreamed of 20 years go.

In the trade, the biggest name at that time was undoubtedly Seaby, alas now consigned to imismatic history. Baldwin's, Dolphin Coins, Giuseppe Miceli, Knightsbridge Coins, Coincraft, tercol, Lubbocks and David Fletcher were flourishing, then as now, living testament to the resilience id stability of this great hobby of ours.

The year 1983 marked the end of a downturn in the numismatic market which had begun to slide in 81, but things began to improve with renewed interest among the general public, stimulated by the inual changes in the pound coin. After two decades of heraldry and national floral symbolism we are ow on the threshold of a new series with a more thematic and pictorial character and we are confident at this initiative of the Royal Mint will prove a welcome boost to the hobby.

In the larger sphere, in 1983 the British economy was beginning to surge ahead and this was reflected the extremely strong prices at two major sales held in the weeks before Token was founded. However, these were as nothing compared with the sale of Nicholson's unique Battle of Britain VC for £110,0C As the going rate for a Victoria Cross at that time was a tenth of that sum there was a general feeling th the contending bidders had blundered or at least had got carried away. At that time VCs cropped u in most major sales, but today they have been reduced to a trickle and the price for an "average" Cro (if there is such a thing) is now fast approaching the figure paid for the Nicholson VC.

Investment in bullion coins was the height of fashion in 1983 and this phenomenon, triggered by tl Krugerrand, would shortly lead to a spate of such coins, including the Maple Leaf, the Angel, tl Libertad and, of course, the Britannia series. Metal detecting also figured prominently in COIN NEV that year and would eventually spawn a separate periodical. In the first issue of the magazine under tl Token imprint there was a news item about a new Treasure Trove Bill before Parliament, bei strangled at birth by the very MP who had sponsored it. Although this seemed extraordinary at the tim the motive was the realisation that the definition of Treasure Trove needed to be considerably widene The pity is that so many years would then elapse before this was rectified.

The world has changed immeasurably over the past twenty years. Perhaps this is best exemplifi by two of the new issues highlighted in early issues of the magazine. Yugoslavia was releasing coins f the forthcoming Winter Olympics in an obscure, little known town in Bosnia called Sarajevo (thou older readers might have shuddered at the time as they recalled that that was where the Austri archduke was assassinated, the outrage that sparked off World War I). And New Zealand w preparing to welcome the Prince and Princess of Wales with a coin bearing their conjoined profiles

New issues were a mere trickle compared with the torrent of coins, in so many metals and finishe that pour from the mint presses nowadays. The Isle of Man was forever under fire for the frequency its coins, but now prolificity is the name of the game everywhere and even staid old institutions like tl Royal Mint and its Australian and Canadian counterparts seem to be producing new coins almost eve month. Coins have even acquired purposes which, back in 1983, were undreamed of. Philately a numismatics were sister hobbies, but they were sisters that were barely on speaking terms. Nowada we have philanumismatic covers and folders in which stamps, coins and even banknotes are combin to celebrate outstanding events and personalities. We have often wondered who buys and collec PNCs. We have never met numismatists or philatelists who collected them and their absence at su events as the York Coin and Stamp Fairs is conspicuous. We have come to the conclusion that the Roy Mint and Royal Mail have created an entirely new market, aimed at people who do not fall within eith of the traditional categories.

Looking back over the past twelve months we have observed a distinct upsurge in the coin mark at all levels, from the grass roots as evinced in coin fairs to the very acme of the hobby as reflected the constant establishment of new records in the salerooms. The UK economy is buoyant just no unemployment is low, interest rates are at a record low and the stock market continues to wallow in tl doldrums. Despite optimism, the FTSE has struggled to keep above the magic 4000 level over the pa six months. To be sure, global confidence in stocks and shares was sluggish in the months leading u to the Gulf War while continuing uncertainty about terrorism and revolution in the world"s troub spots is not helping the situation. Traditionally such a scenario has been a good thing for numismati as well as the other acquisitive hobbies. Although we have not reached the position of the late 196 when "alternative investment" was a dangerous buzzword, there seems little doubt that a lot of mon has been injected into coins and medals in the past couple of years and this shows no sign of slackenin

The big issue at the moment is not whether, but when, the United Kingdom will embrace the Eu Already the European common currency has made significant inroads into Britain, as anyone travelli to Europe or having business interests in the countries of the single currency zone will testify. T smooth transition from national currencies to the Euro has already led to an acceleration of the potenti schedule for a similar changeover in the UK, and as both the manufacturing and service industries Britain continue to recover from the last economic downturn, the prospect of entering the Eurozo seems more attractive.

When compiling such a publication as COIN YEARBOOK we are inevitably dependent to a lar extent on a number of recognised experts in their chosen fields, for advice and assistance as well as precise assessment of current market values. This year, with the generous help of Patrick Mackenzi ably assisted by Terry Strong, we have completely revised the Decimal section of the English coina and we are sure collectors of this series will find the new information contained in this sectic invaluable. We are indebted to these three dedicated collectors for their invaluable assistance. We al take this opportunity of thanking Royston Norbury of West Essex Coins, Steven Mitchell of Stud Coins (Hammered), Chris Rudd (Celtic), Mike Vosper (Roman), Nick Swabey (Maundy), Patri Mackenzie (Decimal) and Chris Denton (Irish) in particular. Many other friends in the trade have help us in ways too numerous to mention; our grateful and sincere thanks are due to them all for their effor in helping us to maintain the high standard of presentation and factual accuracy in this latest editio Our thanks are also due to the various auction houses, mints and dealers who have permitted us reproduce illustrations from their publications.

31 ecember

The year at a glance!

n at-a-glance résumé of the main events and occurrences that affected the ›in hobby during the past months, as reported in COIN NEWS . . .

ıly 2002

n July 1 the Treasury announces an investigation .to accounting practices at the Royal Mint, ›llowing an internal report conducted by Gerald ıeehan, the new Deputy-Master of the Mint.

ɔp price at the Noble Numismatics sale in Ielbourne on July 9–11 was A$52,000, paid for a ıagnificent specimen set of the four 1916 ustralian coins from the florin to the threepence. n example of the rare Adelaide pound of 1852 ıakes A$25,400.

t the Riccardo Paolucci sale in New York on July I, Roman gold is well to the fore. An aureus of ılius Caesar sells for $34,000 against an estimate f $15,000, while an aureus struck during the civil ʼar between Antony and Octavian sells for $37,000, ıore than twice estimate.

ockdale's sale on July 21 establishes a new record ›r the firm

›hn Williams, the wholesale coin dealer, dies on ıly 21 after a long illness.

ı less than ten minutes on July 30 the celebrated old eagle of 1933 sold for $7.5 million, a world ecord for a single coin. The coin, auctioned by tack's in association with Sotheby's New York, ʼas knocked down to a mystery telephone bidder. 'he previous world record was $4.1 million, for ıe 1804 silver dollar sold by Bowers & Merena in ugust 1999.

t the Annual General Meeting of the British Iumismatic Trade Association, Ernie Parsons of)orset Coins succeeds Stephen Fenton as :hairman. Michael Veissid of Collectors Gallery nd Chris Webb of Dix Noonan Webb join the ;eneral Council.

A quarter gold mohur of 1625 commemorating the hunt celebrating the 20th year of the Mughal Emperor Jehangir is identified as coming from a temporary mint at the hunting grounds, previously unrecorded.

August 2002

The International Numismatic Agency reports that its entire stock of 20,000 sets of Euro coins is completely sold out.

Kevin Clancy, Assistant Curator at the Royal Mint, is awarded the British Numismatic Society Council Prize for his work on the Recoinage of 1816–17, forming part of his doctoral thesis, due to be published later in the year.

A unique hoard of gold angels goes on display at the Museum of London. The hoard, discovered on the site of St Mary's Spital in Spitalfields, is believed to have been buried about 1538 when religious houses were under attack by Henry VIII (pictured right).

Volker Heuchert is appointed Collections Manager at the Heberden Coin Room in the Ashmolean Museum.

The US Mint wins a legal action brought against the private Washington Mint, bringing to an end the latter's marketing ploys of passing off their products as official issues. The outcome of the suit, which lasted three years, was a judgement against the Washington Mint who are ordered to pay over $2 million to the Federal Government. They are required to notify all their customers who bought coins since January 2000 of the true nature of the merchandise and file copies of their marketing material with the Justice Department for the next three years.

The Treasury releases a report on a fast-track timetable for British membership of the European single currency, anticipating a changeover period of only two months if and when Britain joins the Eurozone.

Michael Sharp leaves Baldwin's and joins the staff of Dix Noonan Webb.

September 2002

The 5th International Collectors' Fair takes place in the Industrial Palace, Prague on September 13–15, attracting 155 exhibitors from 25 countries.

Spanish police apprehend a gang of 100 archaeological robbers in a special operation that nets a vast haul of stolen antiquities. More than 200,000 items are recovered from a single collection.

The World Proof Numismatic Association celebrates its 38th anniversary.

A bronze medal (pictured left) in memory of September 11, 2001 is released by Coins of Israel.

At Jean Elsen's sale in Brussels on September 20–21 a rare sestertius of Caligula sells for 4,800 euro. Highest price of the day is 8,500 euro paid for a medal of Frederick II Hohenstauffen dating from the 13th century.

The crown-sized £5 coins celebrating the life of the late Queen Mother go on sale at post offices on September 30.

Denis R. Cooper, one of the foremost experts in minting techniques, dies at the age of 89.

October 2002

The Australian Federal Treasury appoints Dr Vivienne Thom as Controller of the Royal Australian Mint.

Former Vice-President and Manager of Spink America, Antony Wilson, is appointed Dix Noonan Webb's representative in New York.

Coincraft fulfils their 500,000th order on Octob 7, after 20 years in the mail order business.

The 24th annual Coinex takes place over t weekend of October 11–12, major sales being stag by Bonham's/Glendining's (October 3), D Noonan Webb (October 8) and Spink (October 10). In addition Bonham's/Glendining's (Octob 2) and Spink (October 4) stage banknote a scripophily sales in the same period.

Harrington Manville is awarded the annual bo price of the International Association Professional Numismatists for his outstandi work *Tokens of the Industrial Revolution: Forei Silver Coins Countermarked for Use in Great Brita* He receives his award at a reception hosted Spink during Coinex.

Baldwin's hold a major sale of commemorati medals on October 14–15.

Chris Rudd, the Celtic specialist, launches "Li List", concentrating on the cheaper material, response to the growing demand for Ancie British and Gallo-Belgic coins.

A medal given to one of the servants w accompanied the body of David Livingstone on epic journey across Africa is sold for £1,600 Baldwin's on October 14.

The Token Congress takes place at the Carlt Hotel, Cheltenham over the weekend of Octob 18–20.

November 2002

The Malaysian International Money Fair tak place in the World Trade Centre, Kuala Lump on November 1–3.

The second part of the fabled "Serenissim collection of Venetian historical medals goes und the hammer at Arsantiqva on November 8.

The London Coin Fair takes place at the Holid Inn, Bloomsbury, followed by Baldwin's Argentu sale.

Coin Yearbook's tenth edition is launched.

To mark the launch of the second Harry Pott film the Pobjoy Mint strikes a series of legal tend coins for the Isle of Man featuring characters a scenes from the film.

DOLPHIN COINS AND MEDALS
LTD
With the Major U.K. Auctions now charging
15% to the vendor and 15% to the buyer (plus V.A.T. on commission)
it is now financially prohibitive for collectors to sell coins by public auction.
We can now offer an alternative !!!
We will sell your collection through our Double Sovereign magazine and charge you a flat fee of 10%.
The advantage for you is that all the coins will be sold to collectors world wide so you will get a full retail price minus 10%. Our magazine reaches 6500 people worldwide who buy coins, medals and banknotes.
ANNA·DEI· GRATIA
1902
EDWARDVS VII DEI GRA: BRITT: OMN: REX FID: DEF: IND: IMP:
Please call for information
Tel: 01525 383822 Fax: 01525 383872
BUY ONLINE NOW AVAILABLE
Web Site: www.Dolphincoins.com Email: Dave@Dolphincoins.com
22 High Street, Leighton Buzzard, Beds, LU7 1EA, England.

The Shawnee tribe release a $5 gold coin, the first Native American gold coin. The obverse portrays the legendary chief Tecumseh's brother Tenskwatawa, known as "The Prophet". The coins, struck at the Perth Mint, are distributed by Panda America.

The Greek police seize almost 500 ancient coins from traders in the Plaka tourist district. The coins, from hoards which came to light during the redevelopment of Athens and which had not been declared, were being converted into jewellery.

Chris Eimer is awarded the Carl W. A. Carlson Award for research by Medal Collectors of America.

Antony Wilson forms York Coins, specialising in Ancient, English, Scottish and Irish coins.

The Midlands Coin Fair at the National Motor Cycle Museum on November 10 is the largest event of its kind, with over 60 dealers taking tables.

Morton & Eden's sale on November 13–14 includes a number of Soho Mint proof coins and medals from the personal collection of James Watt Junior.

At Spink's sale on November 14 a silver ryal of 1565 with facing busts of Mary Queen of Scots and Henry, Lord Darnley, one of two known examples, sells for £97,750 against an estimate of £60,000–£80,000, a new world record for a Scottish coin. The previous record, set by Spink in November 1997 was £77,000 for a gold ducat of Francis and Mary.

Carol Carter resigns as Secretary of the British Numismatic Trade Association and is succeeded by Rosemary Cooke.

Gerald Sheehan, Chief Executive of the Royal Mint, announces tough measures to boost sales, improve productivity and cut losses, following a disastrous end-of-year trading report.

December 2002

Barry Greenaway, the popular West Count dealer who frequently broadcast about coins Radio Bristol, dies on December 11.

In the twelve months to the end of December 20 fewer than 2,500 counterfeit euro coins we detected. Most frequently forged was the 2 eur with 1,030 examples reported.

January 2003

Dix Noonan Webb move from 1 New Bond Street to larger premises at 16 Bolton Street (right), taking over an entire Georgian building on six floors, but continue to hold sales at the New Connaught Rooms in Great Queen Street.

The most complete collection of Canadian coi and medals ever formed is sold by Herita Auctions on January 13 in connection with t New York International Coin Fair. The collectio was formed by Sid Belzberg, founder of one Canada's leading high-tech companies. At t sale the Canadian silver dollar of 1911 (one of on two recorded) realises $690,000.

The Classical Numismatic Group hold a sale New York on January 13–14 and dispose of the la part of the William B. Conte collection of rare coi of the world.

The York Coin and Stamp Fair takes place at th Racecourse Grandstand on January 17–18.

The Bank of England ceases production of note from its own printing works at Debden and award the contract to De La Rue who take over the enti plant in Essex.

Danielle Wetherup retires as Master of the Roy Canadian Mint. She is swiftly followed by at lea three of the Mint's most senior officials. Pendin the appointment of a successor the Chairman the Board takes over as acting Master. Radic proposals for a new marketing strategy a announced shortly afterwards.

bruary 2003

ıldwin's Argentum sale takes place immediately ter the London Coin Fair at the Holiday Inn, oomsbury on February 8.

ıe Dublin International Coin Fair takes place on bruary 22-23 at the Royal Dublin Society, ıllsbridge.

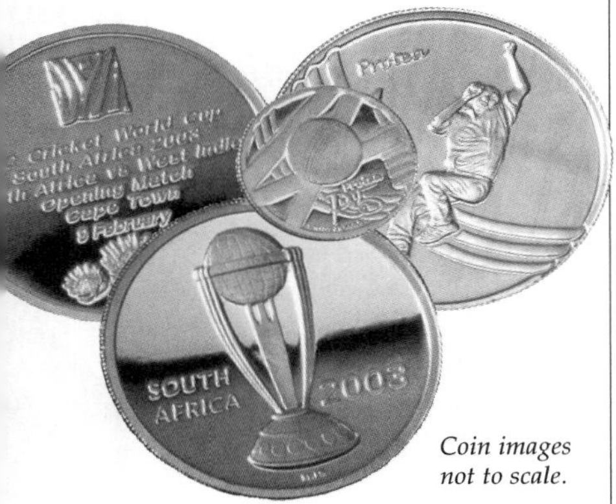

Coin images not to scale.

outh Africa strikes Protea coins to mark the ricket World Cup (above).

he Dorset Coin Company celebrates its silver ıbilee.

larch 2003

burglar is trapped on the premises of Baldwin's, ecoming wedged in the safety glass. He is found ıere on the morning of March 2 by Edward aldwin and remanded in custody to await trial. t Bow Street magistrates court he pleaded guilty.

he Asia Money Fair takes place at the Suntec City onvention Centre in Singapore on March 7–9. everal mints take part in the show as well as umerous dealers. Due to the Gulf War and the ARS epidemic, however, attendance was smaller ıan in previous years.

he Chessington Hoard of Celtic gold coins is cquired by the Kingston Museum.

raham Dyer, OBE, retires as Librarian and luseum Curator of the Royal Mint.

he Royal Canadian Mint releases a silver dollar mark the centenary of the Cobalt Silver Mine, ıe first coin to be struck in .9999 silver.

At Lockdale's auction on March 23 in Norwich a superb collection of George V British coins goes under the hammer, proving the strength of the provincial salerooms.

The 11th North of England Coin & Stamp Fair takes place at the Royal Station Hotel, Newcastle upon Tyne on March 23.

Mark Rasmussen offers the unique 1952 penny for sale on his list.

At Noble's auction in Sydney on March 28–30 a new world record price was paid for a half sovereign when a superb proof example of the 1899 coin from the Perth Mint was sold for A$139,800.

A new two-day fair at the Old Swan Hotel, Harrogate on March 29–30 is organised by Paul Dawson and Simon Monks and takes the place of the popular Coinex North event.

London Coins hold their first auction at Dartford Crossing, Kent on March 30.

The DNA commemorative £2 coin goes into general circulation on March 31.

The Collectibles Expo at Long Beach, California attracts a record attendance, many visitors flocking to see the finest example of the fabled 1885 US trade dollar. This is the first time this coin has been on public show since the US Mint's Bicentennial Exhibition at Philadelphia in 1991.

April 2003

Token Publishing celebrates its 20th anniversary and invites readers of *Coin News* and *Medal News* to design an appropriate medal.

On April 7 the British Museum announces the discovery of the largest hoard of Iron Age silver and gold coinage ever found in Britain. It was found in an area once occupied by the Corieltauvi not far from Leicester.

At Bonham's sale of football memorabilia on April 9 the captain's gold medal presented to Jose Nasazzi for leading his Uruguayan team to victory in the first World Cup (1930) remained unsold.

The magnificent coin collection of Andre Breton, the French poet and founding father of Surrealism who died in 1966, goes under the auctioneer's hammer in Paris.

The Birmingham Mint is placed into administration following cash flow problems arising from the termination of its agreement with the Royal Mint, itself hard hit by over capacity.

Her Majesty the Queen distributes the Royal Maundy at Gloucester Cathedral on April 17. 77 men and 77 women each receive 77 pence in small silver coins.

May 2003

Douglas Liddell, Managing Director of Spink from 1977 to 1989, dies on May 1 at the age of 83.

Spink auction the first part of the Slaney Collection, believed to be the last of the great all-world collections, on May 15. The legendary Petition Crown by Tomas Simon sells for a record £138,000, more than twice the record for any previous English coin.

The tercentenary of the death of Samuel Pepys is marked by the award of a new medal, sculpted by Philip Nathan, at the annual dinner of the Samuel Pepys Club in London on May 28. It is named in memory of the late Robert Latham, former Pepys Librarian at Magdalene College, Oxford. This coincides with the launch of the exhibition Pepys London at the Museum of London till November 3.

An outstanding hoard of English nobles is sold by MPO Auctions in the Netherlands on May 30–31.

June 2003

The annual Congress of the International Association of Professional Numismatists takes place in Munich.

The Royal Australian Mint organises a children's design competition with the theme of Australia, for a forthcoming 50 cent coin. Although stamps have been designed by children since 1958 this is believed to be the first time the idea has been extended to coinage.

The London Coin Fair at the Holiday Inn, Bloomsbury on June 7 attracts a record number of dealers, and a higher than average attendance. Baldwin's hold their Argentum sale at the same venue.

The US Mint announces proposals to alter th designs of the nickel (5 cent coin) for the first tin since 1938. A Bill is presented in Congress change the designs for 2003–5 to mark th bicentennials of the Louisiana Purchase and th Lewis and Clark Expedition. However, it expected that coins will thereafter revert to th Jefferson and Monticello designs.

A sale of coins seized by the US Treasury, includir treasure from such famous shipwrecks as th *Atocha* and the 1715 Fleet, takes place at Tamp Florida on June 25.

July 2003

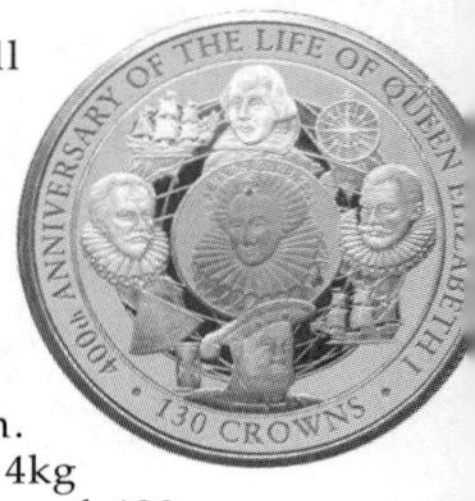

Don Mackay-Coghill retires as Director of the Perth Mint and is succeeded by Edward Harbuz.

The Pobjoy Mint produces the world's largest silver coin. Weighing a massive 4kg and with a face value of 130 crowns, it celebrates the life and times of Elizabet I (illustrated right, actual size 130mm diameter

The latest in the on-going series of state quarte issued by the US Mint celebrates the achievemen of Helen Keller and honours the state of Alabam which joined the Union in 1819.

Ernie Parsons is re-elected Chairman of the Britis Numismatic Trade Association and announc plans to widen the scope of Coinex, in order attract new dealers.

To celebrate their centenary, the Britis Numismatic Society commissions a med designed by Danuta Solowiej-Wedderburn.

A hoard of about 500 Anglo-Saxon coins is reporte from the Doncaster area.

The Royal Mint unveils the designs of the pound coins to be released in 2004–7. The reverses, designed by Edwina Ellis, feature bridges: the Millennium Bridge, Gateshead (2004), the Forth Rail Bridge (2005), the Menai Straits Bridge (2006) and McNeill's Egyptian Arch (2007).

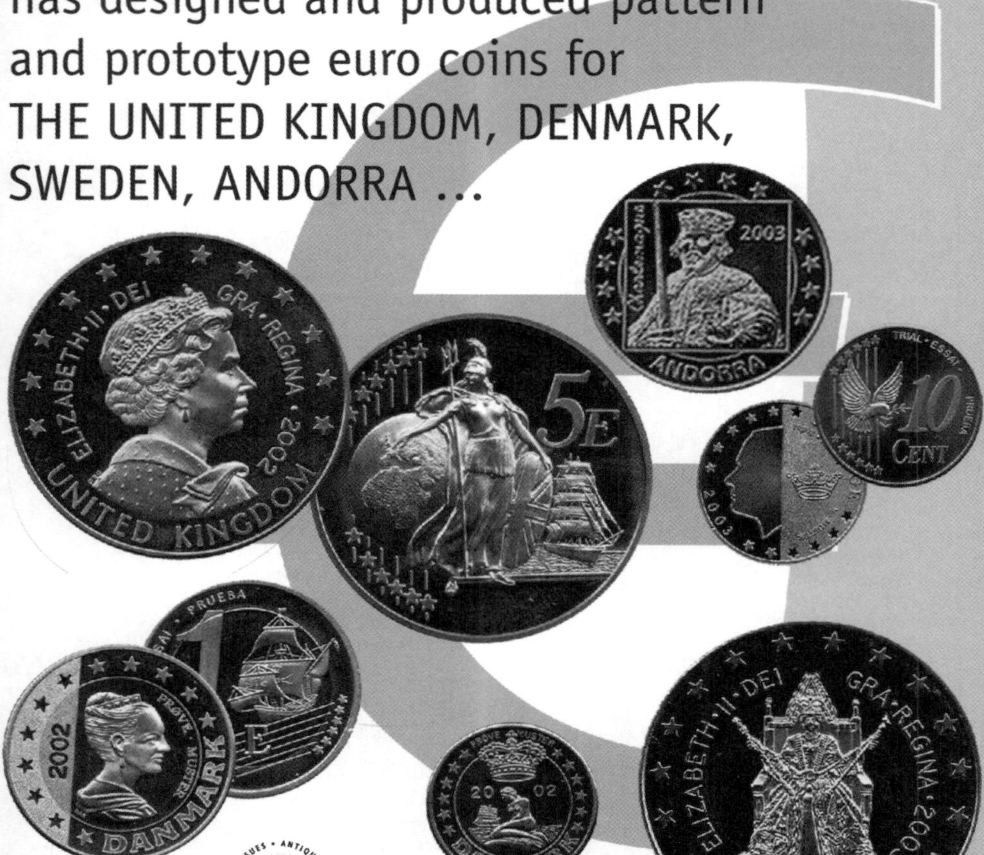
ELIZABETH · II · DEI GRA · REGINA 2002
UNITED KINGDOM
2003
ANDORRA
5E
TRIAL · ESSAI
10 CENT
PRUEBA
2002
PRØVE MUSTER
DANMARK
20 02
DANMARK
ELIZABETH · II · DEI GRA · REGINA 2003
UNITED KINGDOM

The best and worst of recent coin designs

ẗter the welter of coinage in 2002 paying tribute the late Queen Elizabeth the Queen Mother ıd celebrating Her Majesty's Golden Jubilee, 03 seemed set to be something of an anti-climax here royal celebrations were concerned, but at would have been overlooking the useful nd highly lucrative) precedent of the late 1970s hen the Silver Jubilee was followed very ıccessfully with coins marking the 25th ıniversary of the Coronation. At the time, 'ebrows were raised at what was perceived to something of a non-event, in the same genre as ew Zealand's medals celebrating the 75th ıniversary of Victoria's Diamond Jubilee in 1972. ıt it worked extremely well, and so too have the ins which have poured from the world's mints is year to mark the 50th anniversary of the ɔronation.

In fact, the coins marking the Golden Jubilee ere still appearing well into 2003 and in some stances were actually lapped by those ecifically celebrating the Coronation, and with e number of Coronation motifs gracing Jubilee ins in any case there was considerable blurring the edges.

Apart from these twin events connected with e reign of the Queen, this year's secondary yal occasion, and a much more joyous one than e tributes to the Queen Mother, was the 21st rthday of Prince William of Wales. This has oved to be much lower down the scale than the lebration of the life of the Queen Mum. In fact, anything, William has been overshadowed by s mother, judging by the proliferation of coins ɔm the offshore islands publicising the work of e Diana, Princess of Wales Memorial Fund and aring the slogan "The Work Continues". The best of these, by far, were produced by Alderney, Guernsey and Jersey who played it safe with a dignified profile or an upright oval with a three-quarters facing portrait. By contrast, least satisfactory was the crown from the Isle of Man which opted for a full-face portrait, resulting in one of those curiously androgynous images where the gender of the subject is open to question.

After 2,700 years one might assume that the world's mints might have learned the lesson that profile portraiture is what works best in this restrictive medium, and that full-face portraits are very seldom true to life at best, and at worst verge on caricature. A case in point is the Royal Mint's £5 coin for Prince William, arguably the least satisfactory coin to emanate from that august institution this year.

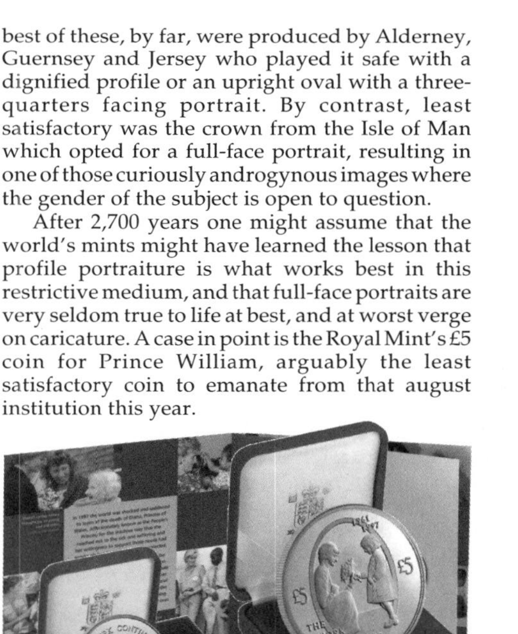

The Royal Mint's Diana, Princess of Wales Memorial Fund Commemorative Coin Collection.

The 2003 Coronation Crown.

Of course, many would argue that this wooden spoon ought to go to the coin marking the 50th anniversary of the Coronation. Both obverse and reverse were designed by Tom Phillips. According to the Mint, "the obverse features a portrait of the Queen in its purest form". In fact, it seems to be a throw-back to the early hammered coinage of the Middle Ages in which the features of the monarch were ingeniously composed of dots and dashes from a variety of punches. Consciously or unconsciously, this is reflected in the mannered lettering, not only on the obverse, but actually forming the subject of the reverse. Half close your eyes as you hold the coin at arm's length and you might be forgiven for thinking you were holding an enlarged version of a silver penny with the name of the mint and the moneyer in artless lettering. All that is missing is the cross.

To refer to the unusual profile as "a portrait in its purist form" is surely stretching the imagination a bit. At best it is a simple pastiche, and the only mitigating feature is that this partial portrait can blame the Netherlands and Sweden for blazing the trail.

Avant-garde it certainly is, but is that really what collectors and the general public want in a coin celebrating the Coronation?

Sometimes it is better to play safe with the tried and tested. Among the last of the Golden Jubilee coins were some outstanding pieces from Australia

Canada's Golden Jubilee $300 Gold Coin, actual size 50mm.

and Canada, both of whom derived inspirati from the various effigies of Her Majesty that h graced coins throughout her long reign. Austra achieved this very neatly in the gold $20 co which showed the four effigies by Mary Gilli Arnold Machin, Raphael Maklouf and Ian Ran Broadley in ascending order of size anti-clockwi Canada's sumptuous $300 gold coin had an obver in which the first three effigies appeared as silv insets, with a Victorian rose in the centre and flo ornament in the intervening spaces, the rever continuing the floral theme with garlands maples cascading from the dates of the Quee reign.

Among the late arrivals were the coins fro the Cayman Islands and the Cook Islands. Bo ostensibly marked the Jubilee but their rever motifs respectively featured the Imperial Crov and a party in a street decorated with festi bunting, the only coins to highlight the mo populist aspects of the celebration.

Apart from the Jubilee-Coronation celebratio there has not been any truly outstanding wor event, falling between the stools of the Olympi and the World Cup. As a result there has beer much wider range of disparate subjects than previous years and a corresponding diversity artistic treatment which makes for a much liveli contemporary scene.

Historic anniversaries, of course, have be well to the fore. The centenary of the womer suffrage movement gave rise to one of the b designs of the year, used for a 50p coin struck the Royal Mint. Economy of line has resulted i reverse that dramatically conveys the spirit of t WSPU in Edwardian times. A close runner-u however, is the bimetallic £2 celebrating the 50 anniversary of the discovery of DNA, the famo double helix lending itself admirably to the rever motif. The most poignant design of the ye however, was that used by the Virgin Islands a series of coins expressing solidarity with t people of New York and depicting the Twin Towe before they were destroyed on September 11, 20 Interestingly, from the same country has come utterly charming dollar marking the centenary the teddy bear!

The Czech Republic belatedly celebrated t centenary of its football association, founded 1901, predictably showing a football and a heral lion. This coin bore a new obverse showing t heraldic shields of the four components that ma up the republic, and this was repeated in the 200 marking the centenary of the death of the explo Emil Holub, portrayed in solar topee with Afric scenes in the background. Rather obscure was t 200kc celebrating the 550th anniversary of Geor

Podebrady as Governor of the Crown Lands in hemia. Not an event to set the world alight, rhaps, but marked by a rather pleasing coin th overlapping heraldic shields on one side and ortrait of the Governor on the other.

Neighbouring Slovakia concentrated on a much ore recent event, the tenth anniversary of the public, with silver 1000sk and gold 10,000sk amond-shaped coins, reminiscent of medieval ppe. Certainly this is a format which is probably ore practical from a designer's viewpoint and e resulting blend of cartography and heraldry is ry strong. The gold coin has central silver inserts aturing a female head and a view of Bratislava stle; it seems that the use of such contrasting etals is becoming almost obligatory.

Poland is rapidly emerging as one of the remost producers of commemorative coins with igh artistic content. Gold 200 zloty and silver 10 oty coins had the theme of the character of Pope hn Paul II—not apparently tied to any specific ent or anniversary, but understandable in view the Pope's Polish origins. At any rate, these ndsome coins provided the opportunity for me of the most evocative religious imagery in cent years. Sometimes, however, it is the most scure subjects that generate the most interesting otifs. Poland's coins celebrating the 750th niversary of municipal rights granted to Poznan a case in point, the gold 100zl featuring the borate door knocker from the west door of the thedral. More recently, a silver 20zl with a dark d-brown ceramic inlay was released to celebrate e Castle of Malbork. The inlay featured detail m St Ann's Chapel with a riverside view in the ver background.

Art is a very popular theme, although it does

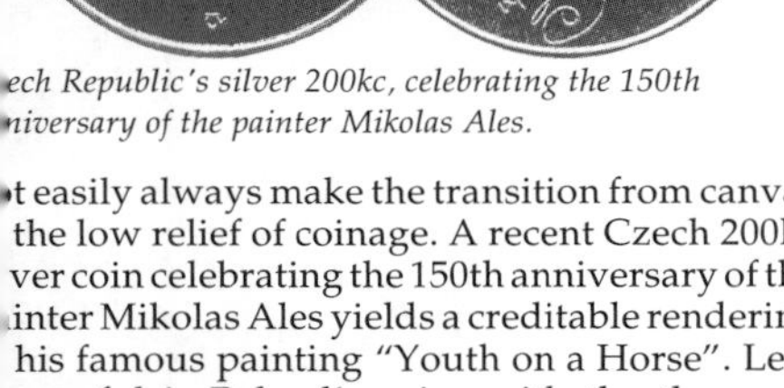

ech Republic's silver 200kc, celebrating the 150th niversary of the painter Mikolas Ales.

t easily always make the transition from canvas the low relief of coinage. A recent Czech 200kc ver coin celebrating the 150th anniversary of the inter Mikolas Ales yields a creditable rendering his famous painting "Youth on a Horse". Less ccessful is Poland's coins with the theme of inters of the 19th and 20th centuries. A 2zl in a conventional circular format reproduces a self-portrait of Jan Matejko which would have been excellent on its own, but unfortunately the Polish Mint succumbed to the temptation to fill the background with a minuscule detail from one of his paintings which did justice neither to the painting nor to Matejko. This was accompanied by a rectangular silver coin repeating the self-portrait but with an artist's palette in the corner, the daubs of paint being picked out in colour. It seems that if you are going to introduce colour (and increasingly this is the norm) you might as well go the whole hog and reproduce the painting itself in that form. Canada has embarked on an art series too, although in this context "art" has been interpreted liberally and began with a $200 gold coin featuring prairie architecture.

The Channel Islands also collaborated in an

The Channel Island's gold £5 coin, celebrating 150th Anniversary of the death of the Duke of Wellington.

issue of coins honouring the 150th anniversary of the death of the Duke of Wellington, an event that was obviously not considered worthy of commemoration by the United Kingdom itself. Alderney, Guernsey and Jersey portrayed the Iron Duke at different stages in his long and illustrious career with stirring scenes of his campaigns in India and the Peninsula. A coin from the UK recalling his services as Prime Minister in his latter years might have been appropriate to complete the set.

A number of coins from Australia in recent years have focused on landmarks in that country's history. Many of these are intended primarily for general circulation (although of course there are also collectors' versions). A prime example of this is the brass dollar marking the 50th anniversary of the signing of the armistice agreement which effectively ended hostilities in Korea. This provides an excellent example of a simple motif, easily understood, and all the more effective for that: the peace dove hovering over the floral emblems of Korea and Australia.

Coins in series are a relatively new phenomenon. While the programme of state quarters from the USA rumbles on (it will not be completed until 2008), Canada launched a series of 13 coins devoted to provincial festivals. The first were released at the end of 2001 with five in 2002 and the others scheduled in 2003. Having exhausted the possibilities of heraldic and floral motifs for pound coins after 20 years of altering the reverses at annual intervals, Britain is now embarking on a series showing famous bridges in each of the four home countries. This notion could easily be extended to castles, town halls, railway stations, post offices, cinemas, supermarkets—the scope for pound coins till the end of time is endless.

Sporting events are perennially popular and in

The gold and silver $5 from Australia for the Rugby World Cup

a period devoid of the very great four-yearly contests lesser championships stand a better chance. This also affords the opportunity to mints to come up with designs that exhibit rather more originality. Switzerland's silver 20 franc coin for the Alpine World Ski Championship at St Moritz shows a skier battling through a blizzard. The most spectacular of this year's sports coins, however, was the gold and silver $5 from Australia for the Rugby World Cup, though South Africa's protea coinage for the Cricket World Cup was also a very creditable performance. Elsewhere Jamaica issued a $25 coin for the ninth International Amateur Athletics Federation World Junior Championships in Kingston. Fortunately that mouthful was partially abbreviated, using the initials IAAF, otherwise it would have been impossible to accommodate the entire title.

Many coins these days are not linked to specific anniversaries or events but are clearly aimed at the thematic market. In this genre we have the magnificent series from Austria featuring historic castles, an idea that has now been borrowed by Lithuania as well. Austria also has its increasingly popular historical series, portraying personalities and alluding to events in its long and colourful history. Latest to get this treatment was the celebrated soldier, Prince Eugene of Savoy (obverse) and the Grand Staircase from his Palace in Vienna, a splendid example of Baroq architecture (reverse).

Most of the coins with a literary theme seem have come from the Pobjoy Mint, with coi celebrating the centenary of Peter Rabbit and Pe Pan (Gibraltar) and Harry Potter (Isle of Man), b France, which last year produced a coloured co featuring Gavroche from *Les Miserables*, has nc released a series of three coins with images European childhood, cleverly combining the ther of a united Europe with pictures of Cindere Pinocchio and Snow White, likewise picked out colour against the silver or gold background.

Pobjoy, always one jump ahead of the re have already produced coins for Niue featuri the characters from Pokemon, and have now add a series of seven from Sierra Leone which, in f colour, depict scenes and characters from Ast Boy. One is left with the feeling that coins ha come a long way from the convenient medium small change, via a numismatic collectable, something completely different, in which t coinage element is purely incidental. Who bu such coins? Probably not numismatists in t accepted sense, but clearly there is a big mar out there, somewhere, consisting of people w will buy these chunks of metal because of th subject matter and not because they emanate fro a particular country. Well, numismatics is a bro church and there is still ample material f collectors of coins per se.

Niue silver $10 featuring characters from Pokemon

Gibraltar's 1 Crown centenary of Peter Rabbit and Peter Pan

EVERYTHING FOR THE COIN COLLECTOR!
ALL UNDER ONE ROOF!

Fast Mail Order Service - post free over £50! (UK only - at cost overseas)
For orders under £50, postage 10% of order value, minimum £2.00
VISA, Mastercard, Switch and Delta accepted. Minimum order £10 please.

Send for our FREE ILLUSTRATED CATALOGUE or order online

www.collectors-gallery.co.uk

Collectors Gallery

24 The Parade, St.Mary s Place, Shrewsbury SY1 1DL
Tel: 01743 272140 Fax: 01743 366041
e.mail:enquiries@collectors-gallery.co.uk

Books
of the year

very coin collector knows that knowledge is the key to forming a good collection and each ear new books or new editions of older works, as well as standard reference works, are upated by dedicated specialists. Here we list the most important numismatic titles that have ppeared during the past year. Most have been reviewed in COIN NEWS.

BRITISH ART MEDALS, 1982-2002, by Philip Attwood. 56 pages, laminated card covers. Illustrated in mono and colour throughout. British Art Medal Society, £10.

is volume celebrates the 20th anniversary of the itish Art Medal Society and chronicles the medals hich have been produced under its auspices. On erage, the Society commissions eight medals a ar, in editions that range from two or three to a aximum of 100. In addition to the catalogue of all e medals since 1982 the book outlines the history the Society and provides a useful introduction the history of the art medal in general from the naissance to the present day.

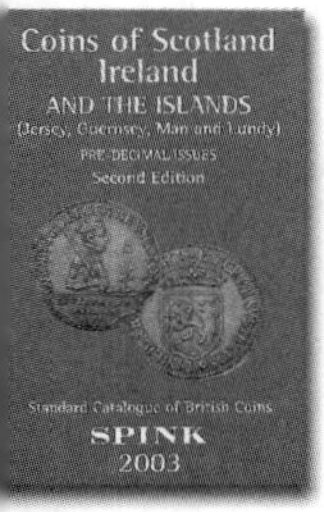

COINS OF SCOTLAND, IRELAND AND THE ISLANDS. 219 pages, casebound, Mono illustrations throughout. Spink, £25.

This is the companion volume to Spink's *Standard Catalogue British Coins*. As the first edition of this volume as published in 1984 the new edition ha been gerly awaited, especially in view of the radical velopment of coinage in Guernsey, Jersey and pecially the Isle of Man in the intervening years. the Irish section new varieties of Gunmoney are ted, while proofs and the issues of the Irish Free ate and Republic are now included in the main dy of the catalogue.

THE COUNTERFEIT COIN STORY, by Ken Peters. 218 A4 pages. Softbound. Mono illustrations throughout. Envoy Publicity, £25.

The forging of coins is one of the oldest professions, and goes back to the very beginning of coinage itself. Counterfeiting was well established in ancient Greece and contemporary forgeries provide an insight into the currency of the classical world. Some are great works of art in their own right while others are crude copies. Most were produced to defraud the revenue but some were created as curios. In Britain, the highpoint of counterfeiting came in the reigns of George II and George III when the Royal Mint could not cope with the demand for coinage and as a result countless counterfeiters were tempted to try their hand, despite the fact that they faced death at the end of a rope if caught and convicted. As well as the coins themselves, the author delves into the background of the forgers and the gruesome tortures and methods of execution meted out by various countries in their desperate attempts to stamp out the practice.

THE DASSIERS OF GENEVA: 18TH CENTURY EUROPEAN MEDALLISTS, by William Eisler. 304 pages, card covers, 183 plates. Musee d'art et d'historie, Geneva.

This is the first volume dealing with the remarkable Dassier family and is devoted to Jean Dassier (1700–33), the medal engraver who worked in Paris and London as well as his native Geneva. A second volume discussing the work of other members of the family will be published in due course. Dassier's reputation rests largely on the amazing series of medals which he produced from 1711 onwards, culminating in the magnificent series devoted to the Kings and Queens of England produced in 1731–32 and the equally interesting series of British Worthies portraying Shakespeare, Milton, Bacon and others.

THE DURHAM MINT, by Martin Allen. 222 pages, casebound with dust jacket. Spink, for the British Numismatic Society, £45.

The fourth volume in the British Numismatic Society's Special Publications Series, it deals exhaustively with the history of the ecclesiastical mint which functioned under the auspices of the Bishops of Durham from the 11th century till the middle of the 16th century. Extraordinary as it may seem, this is the first book on the subject since 1780, and was developed from a doctoral thesis under the aegis of Durham University's Department of Archaeology. It gives a detailed account of the mint, its origins and operations, as well as the coins it produced, placed in the wider context of late-medieval England and the diocese of Durham in particular.

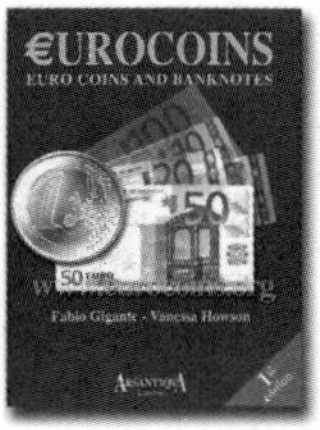

EUROCOINS, by Fabio Gigante and Vanessa Howson. 200 pages, paperback. Colour illustrations throughout. Arsantiqva, £10.

This is the first catalogue devoted to the Euro currency, both coins and banknotes. It begins with a historical summary of the events leading up to the adoption of the European single currency and includes details of the countries in the Eurozone and others in which the Euro is recognised as legal tender. As well as all the coins the catalogue lists starter kits prior to the launch, and includes presentation sets and commemoratives. The book was published simultaneously in five different language editions, the English edition being produced in conjunction with Spink.

THE FACE OF THE REALM, TWENTIETH-CENTURY COINS OF THE UNITED KIMGDOM, THEIR HISTORY AND DESIGN, by John Wall. 150 pages, laminated card covers. Mono illustrations throughout. Spink, £19.95.

This is the first book whi deals exclusively with t designs of British coins the course of the 20 century, although it begi with the Diamond Jubilee Queen Victoria in 1897 a runs right through to 20(The author describes t various technical features the coins, but the core of t book deals with t portraiture and emblems as well as the occasio foray into pictorialism in modern British coina He discusses the aesthetics as well as the meani of the symbolism of the 125-odd coins produced the period. Most people take coins for granted a seldom give them a second glance, but this bo will go a long way to making coin collectors at a rate more aware of coin production and desig

INDIAN PEACE MEDALS AND RELATED ITEMS, by Rita Laws. 161 A4 pages, soft covers. Mono illustrations throughout. Published by the author at PO Box 25, Harrah Oklahoma 73045, USA, $28.75 plus postage.

The sub-title "Collecting the symbols of peace a friendship" gives a clue to the scope of this stu which arose out of a doctoral thesis. It is surprisi to learn that the presentation of medals to Indi chiefs is a tradition that continues to this day, B Clinton giving replicas of the original Jeffers peace medals to a gathering of tribal chiefs at t White House in 1994, while three years la Congressman Frank Lucas of Oklahoma present medals to the leaders of the Cheyenne-Arapa tribe. Peace medals originated in the early 17 century and the manner in which they we awarded, as well as the details of the med themselves, makes for fascinating reading.

ITALIAN MEDALS, c1530-1600, by Philip Attwood. Volume I: 576 pages with 200 mono illustrations in the text. Volume II: 264 pages of which 258 are plates. British Museum, £25

Written by the British Museum Curator of Coi and Medals who is also Editor of *The Medal*, journ of the Art Medal Society, this is a stupendo achievement, covering the period in which t portrait medal had attained its peak. This volu follows on from Sir George Hill's classic work 1930 which dealt with the early period of Itali medals. The new book features more than 1,2 medals with copious background notes a technical details, as well as several introducto apters discussing the centres of medal oduction, techniques, purposes and styles of edals during the period under review.

MEDALS OF BRITISH INDIA, by Robert P. Puddester. 562 pages, casebound with 500 illustrations in the text. Spink, £45.

This is an extraordinary book, a labour of love by someone who has collected and studied these medals for ıny years, as well as researched them in the :hives of the Bombay and Calcutta Mints. This in fact, only the first in a projected series of four lumes, and deals with the commemorative and storical medals from 1750 to 1947. As well as tailed background and historical notes to each edal, the book provides indications of rarity and lue. Further volumes will cover shooting medals, lers, campaign medals and decorations, tokens d the medals of the princely states.

SANELLO, PAINTER TO THE NAISSANCE COURT, by Luke Syon and llian Gordon. 264 pages, casebound with ket. Profusely illustrated in mono and lour throughout. National Gallery, £35.

though the title of this book concentrates on anello as a portrait painter, he is also of major portance to numismatics as the father of the rtrait medal. The book actually reproduces the ges from the artist's sketch-pad as he watched the spectacular cavalcade of the Byzantine Emperor John VIII Palaeologus which inspired his first essay as a medallist in 1438. It seems extraordinary that an entirely new art form should have been born fully-fledged, but here we have the preliminary sketches to prove it. It is not hard to imagine the impact which this medal had on the contemporary world, for its vivid imagery and extremely realistic portraiture have the stamp of genius all over it. The book places Pisanello's work as a medallist in the context of his other artistic endeavours, but also provides a fascinating account of his life and times.

ROMAN COINS AND THEIR VALUES, Volume II, by David R. Sear. 696 pages, mono illustrations throughout, casebound with coloured laminated jacket. Spink. Price £65.

The latest in a prodigious series of publications on Roman coinage by David Sear over four decades, this follows on from the first volume (published in 2001). This now carries the chronicle forward, covering the period from the accession of Nerva in AD 96 to the overthrow of the Severan Dynasty in 225. It lists over 5,000 coins—which demonstrates dramatically how knowledge of Roman coinage has gone ahead by leaps and bounds in recent years. The 1988 edition of this work, for example, dealt with the entire period of Roman coinage from 280 BC to AD 518 in just 388 pages and featured 4,500 coins in all. It is expected that a third volume will cover the remaining period in the same depth. Although it may seem expensive, this volume is an absolute necessity for anyone collecting Roman coins.

All Shapes and sizes

interesting and inexpensive way for the beginner to approach the formation of a coin lection might well be that known as thematic collecting. Natural history (flora and fauna), nous buildings and other landmarks, transport, sporting events, etc., have all been de- ted on coins and tokens, but a more basic idea, as DENZIL WEBB explains, is not so cerned with what is depicted on the piece, but its shape.

It has been suggested that the only reason vast majority of coins are round is because t in ancient times it was found that a globule hot metal struck with a hammer flattened o a roughly circular shape.

na from India and the 12-sided Canada 5 cents.

One of the most fascinating innovations of ancient world was the production of omed" or saucer-shaped coins from a pair dies, one convex, the other concave. Such ns were minted by the Byzantines in the 11th tury. The only modern production of such ces, which are known as scyphates, are in- re 1/2d and 1d checks issued by many desmen in the 1920s and 1930s, designed to vent their improper use in vending and ning machines. In passing, it is worth noting t coins which could only be used at the mises of the issuer are frequently referred as tokens, but should rightly be called cks. True tokens, issued during times of a onic shortage of small change, were minted e used anywhere.

It is often said that necessity is the mother nvention, and the underlying reason for the oduction of coins in varying formats was nable coins to be produced that contrasted h existing circulating coinage. If, for example, the 50p piece, introduced in the autumn of 1969, was not to be confused with florins (two shillings) or halfcrowns (two shillings and sixpence), the ideal solution was to design a piece of a different shape. The only alternative would have been to introduce a much larger coin. When considering the possible formats that the new coin might adopt, it was also necessary to take into account the requirements of the vending and gaming industries. Thankfully, the 50p and 20p coins have not caused any problems. There was also a sound economic reason for the introduction of the 50p coin rather than a banknote of the same value. Paper money has a life of only six months, and the cost of distribution and withdrawal is high. On the other hand, although the initial costs of coin production are much higher, a life-span of some fifty years ensures that in the medium to longer terms, substantial savings would be made. The technical name for the world's first seven-sided coin is "equilateral curve heptagon".

Apart from a few high value issues, such as the eight-sided (octagon) $50 commemorative of 1915 issued in the United States, the majority of unusual-shaped issues are of low face value, and are easily obtained from dealers' oddments trays for a very modest outlay. They are also frequently available at flea-markets and car boot sales. There is ample scope to form a substantial collection, especially so if tradesmens' checks are taken into consideration. Surprisingly triangular-shaped coins are quite hard to find, although a pair of checks in this format were issued by Newcastle-upon-Tyne Co-operative Society. These are pre-payment checks for doorstep

One cent, Straits Settlements.

milk delivery, and are valued at one third and one half pint respectively. As far as checks are concerned, perhaps the most unusual shape is a half-circle or pieces that are somewhat over half.

Collectors should bear in mind that monarchs and heads of state change over the years. For example, the Iraqi ten fils with a scalloped edge occurs in five types—kings Faisal I, Ghazi I, Faisal II young head, Faisal II old head, and the Republic. Scalloped edged coins are in fact more common than one might suspect. Another four may be obtained from Paraguay, namely 10, 15, 25 and 50 cents.

It is interesting to note that the majority of these off-beat coins are from countries of the former British Empire (now Commonwealth), the Middle-East and Africa. The only item from Europe that comes to mind is a square 5 ce in zinc from Holland, which circulated duri World War II.

The beginner can get off to a good start obtaining specimens of all the available Uni Kingdom issues. There are two sizes of the 5 piece, and some special issues, i.e. t centenary of public libraries, the EEC and NI There are two types of the twelve-sided br threepence piece, namely that depicting a th plant, and the portcullis issue. And don't for the 20p!

Prior to commencing this article, I di rough check of known "shaped" issues, a found that the greatest number are scallop edge types—27 from 17 countries. The n highest score was square types—14 from ei countries. Six, eight, ten and twelve-sid pieces occur to a lesser extent. I must stre however, that this is only a rough guide, a should not therefore be regarded as in any w complete. India may be compared to Ir "shaped" coins often occurring in every re from Edward VII till the establishment of Republic. Looking for specimens from sm island communities such as Fiji, Seychell Maldive Islands and Surinam, is m rewarding.

LONDON COINS
Dealers and Auctioneers
What we need:
English Milled Coins
Hammered Gold Coins
Roman and Ancient Coins
British Tokens
English Sets and Proof Items
Sovereigns and Krugerrands
Coin Collections
USA Coins
Foreign Coins
Bank Notes
What we offer:
A friendly and professional service
Expertise in all areas of numismatics.
Highest prices.
Free appraisals
A choice of selling by auction, or immediate cash offer.
Free home visits (anywhere in the world) for worthwhile collections.
Our Experience:
Auctioneers since 1994.
Dealers since 1982
LONDON COINS
BNTA
12 Redhill Wood • New Ash Green • Kent • DA3 8QH Tel: 01474 871464
Email: info@londoncoins.co.uk Website: www.londoncoins.co.uk

The first English Penny

AYMOND PALERMO traces the history of that most familiar of English coins

ior to the mid-8th century, England's coinage as comprised of "sceattas". These were small, ımpy pieces that had had their origins in ude imitations of late Roman coins or coins om Gaul. Many sceattas had decorative and pressive designs, such as a pecking bird and whorl of four wolf heads. Over the years, owever, the artistic standards of the designs adually deteriorated.

On the Continent, the Frankish king, Pepin e Short, had instituted a massive reform of s kingdom's coinage in 755. He introduced a w silver denomination called the *denier,* after e latin *denarius*. These coins had broader and inner flans than their predecessors. The verse had the king's name or onogram, and the reverse re the name of the mint. evious issues had borne the ıme of the moneyer rather an the mint. Thus Pepin re- serted royal authority over e issue of the coinage.

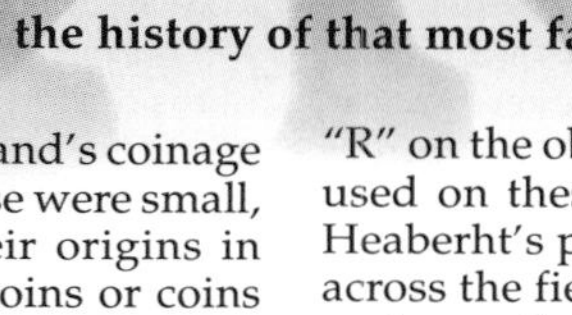

Mercia, Offa (757–796) Penny

In England, reforms of the inage also took place. Instead of being called leniers" the new coins came to be known as ennies". However, the abbreviation "d" from e word "denier" or "denarius" was retained denote "penny" or "pennies" under the unds, shillings and pence system that was ly replaced with the advent of decimalisation 1971.

At Canterbury, Heaberht, king of Kent (*fl.* 5), followed Pepin's lead and issued coins ith a "REX" monogram on the obverse. The verse had five annulets, with a pellet in each, ranged to form a cross and the moneyer's me, "EOBA", in the angles. These coins are tremely rare.

Another Kentish king, Ecgberht (*fl.* 780), ruck pennies with his name around the letter "R" on the obverse. A number of reverses were used on these coins including one similar to Heaberht's penny, one with the letters "VDD" across the field, with a cross above and below, and another with the moneyer's name "BABBA" in the angles of a cross-crosslet design. Like Heaberht's pieces, these coins are extremely rare.

Offa, the powerful king of Mercia (757–796), conquered Kent in 783–784. During his reign he established diplomatic links with Pepin's son and successor, the great Charlemagne. In keeping with the Frankish currency reforms, Offa undertook a massive reform of the coinage of his realm.

Most coins bearing Offa's name were struck at Canterbury. The pennies from his reign can be divided into two broad groups. The first group do not have portraits. Instead, they usually have a cross with "OFFA"—sometimes with the word "REX" in the angles. Other legends include "OFAR" or OFRM" standing for "Offa Rex Mercior" (Offa, King of Mercia). Many types of crosses are used to subdivide the group. Designs found on the obverse include plain crosses, cross-crosslets with a lozenge centre, Celtic crosses, crosses made up of lobes and devices that incorporate saltires. The reverses of these pennies have the moneyer's name in the angles of crosses of various styles. Another type of non-portrait penny has the words "OFFA" and "REX" inscribed in two lines, with a line of pellets in the middle. The reverse styles of these pieces vary from being similar to the obverse to having the moneyer's name inserted in the angles of a cross made up of lobes. A third kind of obverse without a portrait includes an annulet with a pellet in the design.

Between around 787 and 792, Offa issued pennies bearing his portrait as well as continuing with those without. His portrait pennies are some of the most famous coins struck during this period. These show his profile image facing right. There is much variation in the style of his drapery, if this is present. The reverses also vary considerably. They usually have the moneyer's name in the angles of one of many types of cross, which may be floriated, Celtic, plain, lobed or in the form of crosslets. Sometimes the moneyer's name has been omitted in favour of the letters "OFRM". Offa's portrait-type pennies are very desirable, with their profile effigies and attention to detail on the reverse.

Later non-portrait examples of Offa's pennies (around 792 to 796) were struck on larger flans. Offa honoured his wife, Cynethryth, by striking pennies bearing her name. One of these types has her portrait and the moneyer's name "EOBA" on the obverse with a small central circle containing the letter "M" on the reverse, with the legend "CYNETHRYTH REGINA". Another type does not have Cynethryth's portrait but a similar design to the "M" in circle design described above. The reverse consists of Eoba's name on the leaves of a quatrefoil.

Offa also struck two intriguing gold issues, both of which are known by only one example. One was a copy of an Arabic dinar of Caliph Al Mansur. This coin had Arabic inscriptions on both sides, and the Muslim calendar's date—AH 157, corresponding to AD 774. In the middle of the flan on the reverse are the words "OFFA REX", written upside down in relation to the main legend. It has been suggested that this coin was minted as part of a gift from Offa to Pope Adrian I (the coin was found near Rome), to whom the mighty king had promised to pay 365 gold "mancuses" (equal to thi silver pennies) annually. The other coin wa gold penny, complete with a portrait of O on the obverse, and a standing figure on t reverse.

Regional varieties of Offa's pennies we minted in East Anglia, a region that Offa h annexed and whose king he had merciles executed. These sometimes have runic lette and can be crudely struck.

It is likely that Offa himself took an acti interest in the design of his coins. The quali of his designs would not be surpassed until t advent of the Renaissance some eight hundr years later. The superb workmanship of pennies was admired on t Continent, a contemporary imitatio have been found far afield as Luc in Italy.

In Englan Offa's coina was quick imitate over most Englan except Northumbr wher sceatt continued be minted close anothe century. Ov this period, th were first stru from debased silv and later from copper a brass.

Offa's reform of the coinage w economically important because it broug much of the English southern region into li with the monetary changes that were sweepi across Europe at the time. It also facilitat trade with European countries such as t mighty Frankish Empire.

The most significant legacy of the penny that it has survived in one form or another over 1,200 years. The humble penny, introduc in the 8th century, has thus been retained as integral part of English, and indeed, Briti culture.

Talking *Tokens*

Strictly speaking, a token is any piece of money whose intrinsic value is less than its face value. In that sense, therefore, all modern coins are mere tokens, because their metallic worth is invariably less than their nominal, legal tender value. Until the 19th century, however, most countries issued coins which contained metal up to the value which they circulated. This applied mainly to gold and silver coins, but it should be noted that Britain's first copper penny and twopence (1797) were so cumbersome because they contained one and two ounces of metal respectively, copper being then valued at a penny an ounce.

The desire for parity between intrinsic and nominal value led to copper coins containing a small plug of silver to bring them up to their full value. The UK abandoned full value in 1816; as a result of the recoinage of that year the gold sovereign became the absolute standard and all silver and copper coins became mere tokens. The difference between real and nominal value widened in subsequent years with the debasement of silver coins and finally the replacement of silver altogether by cupro-nickel and other base alloys. Oddly enough, there have been many instances of small copper or bronze coins in recent years which had a greater intrinsic value than their face value and actually cost twice as much to produce as they were worth in circulation.

A token is an outward sign or pledge, something given or shown as a guarantee of authority or good faith. The word comes from German *zeichen* and Old English *tacen*, meaning a sign or mark. From this developed the notion of a promise, symbol or keepsake. In the numismatic sense, however, the term is restricted to any coinlike object, either issued by a body other than a government, or something which is used in place of money and can be exchanged for specified goods and services. Broadly speaking, tokens include any unofficial coins supplied by local bodies or occasionally even private individuals and tolerated in general circulation at times of shortage of government issues of small change.

Tokens go back a surprisingly long way. The earliest issues in base metal with limited local validity were produced by Sicily in the middle of the fifth century BC, the bronze litra being easi to handle than its tiny silver counterpart. Hime was one of the first towns to issue such toke but by the end of the century many Sicilian tow had adopted small bronze pieces as tok currency, the intrinsic value of which w considerably below the circulating value plac on them by the issuing authorities.

This concept gradually spread to all other pa of the Greek world. Under the Roman Empi base-metal tokens were issued from the time Augustus to the late third century AD. Sometim referred to quasi-autonomous coinage, the pieces were struck mostly in bronze with t nominal value of drachmae or sestertii, and ha portraits of local deities instead of the Rom emperor and members of his family. These toke were struck by every town and city and their ran and variety is enormous.

This concept survived the fall of the Rom Empire and many towns in medieval Euro continued to strike small base-metal pieces for u as local currency. They were usually accorded measure of legality because they were authoris by the royal or imperial government, even if th actual design and metal content were decided the municipal authorities. In addition to the toke which served as small change there are oth categories of coinlike material which deser comment.

Jetons (from French *jeter*, to throw) originat in medieval France as counters used on t chequerboard by merchants and bankers as w as royal treasurers to do their moneta lculations. These pieces spread rapidly all over ırope, but found their greatest expression at uremberg where, in the hands of Hans rauwinckel (flourished 1580–1620), they attained e status of an art form and were often produced thematic sets.

While many jetons were struck in gold or silver ıd were eventually used (especially in France) a form of New Year bonus to servants, the vast ajority of them were struck in debased silver loys (billon) or in copper, bronze, brass or ewter. Base-metal Nuremberg jetons, in fact, ten circulated as small change in countries here there was a shortage of total lack of ›vernment issues of small change. This situation ·ose in England early in the 14th century, uremberg jetons circulating freely until 1335 hen they were banned by statute.

nglish tokens

The first indigenous tokens in England were ıst or struck in lead and have been recorded as rculating in 1404. For many years these local rthings and half-farthings were tolerated but ad no official sanction. They were certainly well-stablished in Tudor times and it was not until 598 that any attempt was made to regulate them. ueen Elizabeth then licensed Bristol to issue lead ›kens, to be valid within a ten-mile radius of the ty. At the same time, private tokens were xpressly forbidden, so that the municipal tokens ere given a monopoly. By the end of the Civil ar (1649) there was an acute shortage of small ıange, and illicit tokens, mainly in lead and ıcluding pewter, brass, copper or even leather ieces, were revived in England and Wales.

Almost 4,000 types of token were issued in ondon alone, by tradesmen and shopkeepers of ll kinds, and often circulating no farther than the nd of the street. As the vast majority were roduced before the Great Fire of 1666 they form n invaluable record of London streets and their ccupants from this period. Following the ıtroduction of regal copper farthings and alfpence in 1672 these tradesmen's tokens were anned, but they continued in some parts of ngland until 1674, and survived in Ireland until 679. By contrast there was virtually no need for ›kens in 17th century Scotland because of an bundant supply of copper coinage, and only two cottish tokens (c. 1668) have so far been recorded.

In many ways tokens benefited the poor, who vere no longer compelled to purchase more than ıey actually required because the smallest coin vailable was a penny. Tokens were also used as lms, as people would gladly give a farthing but vould think twice about giving a halfpenny or

17th century tokens come in a variety of shapes and sizes.

penny. For this reason many tokens of the 17th century were inscribed "Remember the Poore", "For the Poore's Advantage" or "For Change & Charitie" or some other pious slogan.

There were even tokens inscribed in verse: "To supply the poore's need is charitie indeed". Other poetic inscriptions include "When you please, I'll change thee", "Although but brass, yet let me pass", "Welcome you be to trade with me" or "Take these that will, I'll change them still".

Eighteenth century tokens

Tokens were revived in the British Isles in 1787 to fill a gap in the regal coinage. Silver pennies for general circulation were only sporadically produced in the reign of George III and none at all were minted after 1786. The dearth of copper halfpence and farthings was even greater as none was minted after 1775. On this occasion the way was led by the Angelsey Copper Mining Company which began striking pennies with the effigy of a Druid on the obverse. This triggered off an immense deluge of token pennies, halfpennies and farthings. The range was not as great as it had been in the 17th century as fewer individual shopkeepers now issued them.

There was a greater concentration of tokens issued by municipal authorities and the more important merchant companies. On the other hand, the quality of design and execution improved beyond all recognition and latterly they were aimed at the contemporary collector market,

The prolific issues of 18th century tokens such as this one were banned on the introduction of the "Cartwheel" coinage in 1797.

with emphasis on heraldry, landmarks, scenery, historic events and portraits of local and national celebrities. These tokens enjoyed a decade of use before they were banned following the introduction of the "Cartwheel" coinage in 1797.

Nineteenth century tokens

Silver tokens were issued between 1804 and 1816 as a result of a continuing shortage of silver coins. At first countermarked Spanish dollars and half-dollars were issued but in 1811–12 the Bank of England released silver pieces inscribed BANK TOKEN on the reverse, with the value and date below. The obverse portrayed George III and had his name and titles round the circumference like the proper silver coins. Denominations of 1s6d and 3s were issued; though 9d pieces exist they were only patterns. The Bank of Ireland had silver tokens in the same period, but denominated in a decimal system of 5, 10 and 30 pence, as well as 6 shillings. Many private silver tokens were issued in 1811–12 in denominations from 3d to 5s, mainly by private banks, local authorities and large companies.

Copper or bronze tokens were again issued in the British Isles from 1811 to the 1830s. As no copper subsidiary coins were issued between 1807 and 1821 (no halfpence or pennies until 1825–26) the range of tokens in this period was far greater than ever. Significantly a high proportion of these tokens were now issued by banks rather than by private individuals.

Other types of tokens

Tokens have been produced in most countri at some time or another. Very extensive series, f example, were produced in Canada and Austra before these countries introduced subsidia coinage. They were also produced on a numb of occasions in the USA, from the revolutiona period onwards, and notably during the Ha Times (1834–44) during a shortage of copper cer and half-cents. There was a further spate of loc tokens during the Civil War (1861–65), often wi patriotic motifs and having a propagan purpose as well as filling the gap in the coinag Many countries issued tokens during and aft the First World War, every type of material fro pasteboard and wood to leather and even rubb being pressed into service. A special catego consists of trade dollars issued all over Canad These are often commemorative or intended tourist mementoes, but they have a nomin value, redeemable for cash within a certain ar and over a fixed period, usually twelve month They are immensely popular and now have wide following in North America.

In Britain from the 18th century onwar tokens were often issued by textile mills, collierie iron foundries and other industrial undertakin in exchange for a day's work. These tokens cou only be used to obtain goods from the compar stores, and were eventually outlawed by the Tru Act in 1844. Nevertheless they survived in vario parts of Britain, often in specific forms of labou A very prolific series, for example, consists of ho pickers' tokens, associated mainly with th

The Parys Mines of Anglesey produced vast number of "Druid's Head" tokens.

Hop pickers were usually paid in tokens which are highly collected today.

opfields of Kent and Sussex. In Scotland, owever, fruit-pickers' tokens were also issued by any of the farms in the Clyde Valley and the uit-growing areas of Perthshire and Angus.

Another vast area consists of the checks and kens issued by co-operative societies, often in roportion to the money spent by the member in e societies' stores, as a form of dividend. When certain quantity of checks had been accumulated ey could be exchanged for goods or services. The ame concept underlay the discount schemes, remium giveaways and trading stamps of more cent items.

Tokens of metal, pasteboard or even plastic ave been used as a method of controlling the use f public transport by employees of companies, e Post Office or local authorities, being given ut whenever it was necessary for an employee travel on official business. Such tokens were roduced by local authorities or the private ompanies operating buses, ferries, trams and ther services. At the other end of the spectrum re the tokens and passes, often in silver or even old, or ivory, which were issued to directors of e railway companies to enable them to travel ee of charge. Tokens in the same materials, and or the same purpose, were produced for the use f the directors and shareholders of theatres and ther places of entertainment, and were often ighly ornate in design.

Gaming tokens

This is another vast field, ranging from the brass halfpenny and penny tokens issued by many pubs and taverns in the 19th century for use in games of chance, to the modern tokens, often in cupro-nickel, bronze or aluminium-bronze, used in one-armed bandits and fruit machines. These tokens range from the fairly utilitarian designs showing perhaps a company name and a unit of value only, to the very elaborate tokens used by casinos and gaming clubs, often with special security features built into their design and composition. Many of the gaming tokens of more recent years have a quasi-commemorative or publicity character.

Richard Orchard's Sawbridgeworth token sold for the world record price of £24,400 in 1998.

Dates
on coin

The vast majority of modern coins bear the date prominently on one side. In most cases dates are expressed in modified Arabic numerals according to the Christian calendar and present no problem in identification. There have been a few notable exceptions to this general rule, however. Morocco, for example, has used European numerals to express dates according to the Moslem calendar, so that a coin dated 1321 actually signifies 1903. Dates are almost invariably written from left to right—even in Arabic script which writes words from right to left. An exception, however, occurred i the Philippines quarto of 1822 where the date appeared as 2281, and the "2s" back to front for good measure.

	ARABIC-TURKISH	CHINESE, JAPANESE KOREAN, ANNAMESE (ORDINARY)	CHINESE, JAPANESE KOREAN, ANNAMESE (OFFICIAL)	INDIAN	SIAMESE	BURMESE
1	١	一	壹	१	๑	၁
2	٢	二	貳	२	๒	၂
3	٣	三	叁	३	๓	၃
4	٤	四	肆	४	๔	၄
5	٥	五	伍	५	๕	၅
6	٦	六	陸	६	๖	၆
7	٧	七	柒	७	๗	၇
8	٨	八	捌	८	๘	၈
9	٩	九	玖	९	๙	၉
0	٠			०	๐	၀
10	١٠	十	拾		๑๐	
100	١٠٠	百			๑๐๐	
1000	١٠٠٠	千				

Dates in Roman numerals have been used sin 1234 when this practice was adopted by the Danis town of Roskilde. Such Roman numerals we used sporadically throughout the Middle Ag and in later centuries and survive fitfully to th day. This was the system used in England for th first dated coins, the gold half-sovereigns Edward VI struck at Durham House in 154 (MDXLVIII). This continued till 1550 (MDL) b thereafter Arabic numerals were used, beginnin with the half-crown of 1551. Notable exceptions more recent times include the Gothic coinage Queen Victoria (1847–87).

The first coin with the date in Europea numerals was a plappart of St Gallen, Switzerlan dated 1424, but this was an isolated case. In 147 Maria of Burgundy issued a guldiner which bor a date on the reverse, in the form of two pairs digits flanking the crown at the top. The numera in this instance were true Gothic, an interestin transition between true Arabic numerals and th modified Arabic figures now used in Europe. Th Tyrolese guldengroschen of 1484–6 were the fir coins to be regularly dated in European numera and thereafter this custom spread rapidly.

For the numismatist, the problem arises whe coins bear a date in the numerals of a differer alphabet or computed according to a different er Opposite is a table showing the basic numera used in different scripts. The various eras whic may be found in coin dates are as listed an explained opposite.

ijra

The era used on Moslem coins dates from the ght of Mohammed from Mecca to Medina on ly 15, 622 and is often expressed as digits followed AH (*Anno Hegirae*). Moslems employ a lunar lendar of twelve months comprising 354 11/30 ys. Tipu Sultan of Mysore in 1201 AH (the fifth ar of his reign)introduced a new era dating from e birth of Mohammed in AD 570 and using a ni-solar system. Tipu also adopted the Hindu cle of sixty years (the Tamil Brihaspate Cycle), it changed this two or three years later, from ijra to Muludi.

Afghan coins used the lunar calendar until 20 and during 1929–31, but at other times have ed the solar calendar. Thus the Democratic public began issuing its coins in SH 1358 (1979).

To convert an AH date to the Christian calendar u must translate the Arabic into European imerals. Taking an Arabic coin dated 1320, for ample, first deduct 3% (to convert from the oslem lunar year to our solar year). This gives .6 which, rounded up to the nearest whole imber, is 40. Deduct 40 from 1320 (1280), then ld 622. The answer is 1902.

There have been a few notable exceptions. Thus e Khanian era of Ilkhan Ghazan Mahmud began 1 1st Rajab 701 AH (1301). This era used a solar lendar, but was shortlived, being confined to ins of Mahmud and his nephew Abu Said down year 34 (1333).

The era of Tarikh Ilahi was adopted by the ughal emperor Akbar in the thirteenth year of s reign (922 AH). This era dated from his cession on 5th Rabi al-Sani 963 AH (February , 1556). The calendar had solar months and days it no weeks, so each day of the month had a fferent name. This system was used by Akbar, hangir and Shah Jahan, often with a Hijra date as ell.

aphar

The era of the Caesars began on January 1, 38 C and dated from the conquest of Spain by ugustus. Its use on coinage, however, seems to ave been confined to the marabotins of Alfonso III of Castile and was expressed in both Latin nd Arabic.

amvat

The era of Vikramaditya began in 57 BC and as a luni-solar system used in some Indian states. oins may be found with both Samvat and Hijra ates. Conversion to the Christian date is simple; erely subtract 57 from the Samvat to arrive at the D date.

Saka

This originated in the southwestern district of Northern India and began in AD 78. As it used the luni-solar system it converts easily by adding 78 to the Saka date.

Nepal

Nepalese coins have used four different date systems. All coins of the Malla kings were dated in Nepal Samvat (NS) era, year 1 beginning in 881. This system was also used briefly by the state of Cooch Behar. Until 1888 all coins of the Gurkha dynasty were dated in the Saka era (SE) which began in AD 78. After 1888 most copper coins were dated in the Vikram Samvat (VS) era from 57 BC. With the exception of some gold coins struck in 1890 and 1892, silver and gold coins only changed to the VS era in 1911, but now this system is used for all coins struck in Nepal. Finally, dates in the Christian era have appeared on some commemorative coins of recent years.

Ethiopian

This era dates from August AD 7, so that EE 1885 is AD 1892. Ethiopian dates are expressed in five digits using Amharic numerals. The first two are the digits of the centuries, the third is the character for 100, while the fourth and fifth are the digits representing the decade and year. On modern coins dates are rendered in Amharic numerals using the Christian era.

Thailand

Thai coins mainly use the Buddhist era (BE) which dates from 543 BC, but some coins have used dates from the Chula-Sakarat calendar (CS) which began in AD 638, while others use a Ratanakosind Sok (RS) date from the foundation of the Chakri dynasty in AD 1781.

Hebrew

The coins of Israel use the Jewish calendar dating from the beginning of the world (Adam and Eve in the Garden of Eden) in 3760 BC. Thus the year 1993 is rendered as 5753. The five millennia are assumed in dates, so that only the last three digits are expressed. 735 therefore equates with AD 1975. Dates are written in Hebrew letters, reading from right to left. The first two characters signify 400 and 300 respectively, totalling 700. The third letter denotes the decades (*lamedh* = 30) and the fourth letter, following the separation mark (") represents the final digit (*heh* = 5). The Jewish year runs from September or October in the Christian calendar.

Dates from the creation of the world

This system was also used in Russia under Ivan IV. The dating system *Anno Mundi* (AM) was established by the Council of Constantinople in AD 680 which determined that the birth of Christ had occurred in 5508 AM. Ivan's coins expressed the date as 7055 (1447).

Dynastic dates

The system of dating coinage according to regnal years is a feature of Chinese and Japanese coins. Chinese coins normally have an inscription stating that they are coins of such and such a reign period (not the emperor's name), and during the Southern Sung dynasty this was joined by the numeral of the year of the reign. This system was continued under the republic and survives in Taiwan to this day, although the coins of the Chinese Peoples Republic are dated in western numerals using the Christian calendar.

Early Japanese coins bore a reference to the era (the title assumed by each emperor on his accession) but, like Chinese coins, could not be dated accurately. From the beginning of the Meiji era (1867), however, coins have included a regnal number. The Showa era, beginning in 1926 with the accession of Hirohito, eventually ran to sixty-three (expressed in western numerals on some denominations, in Japanese ideograms on others) to denote 1988, although the rest of the inscription was in Japanese characters.

Dynastic dates were used on Korean milled coins introduced in 1888. These bore two characters at the top *Kae Kuk* (founding of the dynasty) followed by quantitative numerals. The system dated from the founding of the Yi dynasty in 1392. Curiously enough, some Korean banknotes ha borne dates from the foundation of the first dyna in 2333 BC.

Iran adopted a similar system in 19 celebrating the 15th anniversary of the Pahl regime by harking back to the glories of Dari The new calendar dated from the foundation the Persian Empire 2535 years earlier, but w abolished only three years later when the Sh was overthrown.

Political eras

France adopted a republican calendar in 17 when the monarchy was abolished. Coins we then inscribed L'AN (the year) followed by Rom numerals, but later Arabic numerals we substituted. This continued to the year 14 (18 but in that year the Emperor Napoleon restor the Christian calendar.

The French system was emulated by Ha whose coins dated from the revolution of 18 The date appeared as AN followed by a numb until AN 31 (1834) on some coins; others had bo the evolutionary year and the Christian date fro 1828 until 1850 (AN 47). Coins with a date in t Christian calendar appeared only in 1807–9 a then from 1850 onwards.

Mussolini introduced the Fascist calendar Italy, dating from the seizure of power in Octob 1922. This system was widely employed documents and memorials, but was first used silver 20 lire coins of 1927 and then only in additi to the Christian date and appearing discreetly Roman numerals. Subsequently it was extend to gold 50 lire and 100 lire coins in 1931 and t subsidiary coinage in 1936, being last used in t year XXI (1943).

Around the World

Listed here are the names of all the coins of the world, many of which have been around for hundreds of years, others are no longer in use. Some of the denominations have been introduced only recently, whilst others are familiar household words. A number of the names are shared by different countries and a few have even been used by different civilisations.

Abazi Caucusus
Abbasi, Abbassi Afghanistan, Georgia, Persia
Ackey Gold Coast
Adli Altin Ottoman Empire
Afghani Afghanistan
Agnel France
Agora (ot) Israel
Ahmadi Mysore, Yemen
Akce Turkey
Akcheh Turkestan
Albertusdaler Denmark
Albus German States, Swiss Cantons
Altin, Altun Egypt, Turkey
Altinlik Turkey
Altyn, Altynnik Russia
Amani Afghanistan
Amman Cash Mewar Udaipur, Pudukota, India
Angel England, Scotland, Isle of Man

Angel

Angelet France
Angelot France
Angster Lucerne
Anna Burma, India, Pakistan, Kenya, Muscat & Oman
Antoninianus Rome
Ardite Navarre
Argentino Argentina
Ariary Malagasy Republic
As Rome
Asarfi Nepal
Ashrafi Afghanistan, Awadh, Bahawalpur, Egypt, Hyderabad
Asper Algeria, Egypt, Libya, Trebizond, Tunisia, Turkey
Asses Luxembourg
At Laos
Atia Portuguese India
Atribuo Frankfurt
Att Cambodia, Laos, Siam (Thailand)
August d'Or Saxony
Augustale Sicily
Aurar (plural **Eyrir**) Iceland
Austral Argentina
Avo Macau, Timor
Bagarone Bologna
Bagattino Venice
Baggliangster Lucerne
Baht Thailand
Baiocco (plural **Baiocchi**) Papal States
Baisa Oman
Baiza Kuwait
Baizah Muscat & Oman
Balboa Panama
Ban (plural **Bani** or **Banu**) Roumania
Banica Croatia
Barbarina Mantua
Barbonaccio Lucca
Barbone Lucca
Barbuda Portugal
Barilla Philippines
Batzen German States, Swiss Cantons
Bawbee Scotland
Bazaruco Portuguese India
Bazaruk Dutch Settlements in India
Belga Belgium
Benduqi Morocco
Besa (plural Bese) Ethiopia, Somalia
Beshlik Soviet Central Asia
Bezant Byzantine Empire, Cyprus, Jerusalem
Bezzo Italian States

anco (plural **Bianchi**) Bologna, Papal States
che French Indian Settlements
nio Roman Empire
pkwele Equatorial Guinea
r (r) Ethiopia
sti Caucasia
t Guyana, West Indies
tt Danish Virgin Islands
ack Dog Nevis
affert Switzerland
anc France
odsklipping Sweden
uzger Swiss Cantons
odle Scotland
ogach Yemen
olivar Venezuela
oliviano Bolivia
olognino Papal States
onk Ceylon, Dutch East Indies
onnet Scotland
oo Japan
raspenning Flanders
road England
u Japan
udju Algeria
uqsha Yemen Arab Republic
urbe(ns) Tunisia
utut Gambia
ache French Indian Settlements
agliareso Italian States
alderilla Spain
andareen China
arbovanetz Ukraine
arlin Sicily
arlino Papal States
arolin Austria,German States, Sweden
ash China, Hong Kong, India, Mysore, Travancore, Turkestan, Vietnam
assathaler German States
auri Guinea
eitil Portugal
ent Australia, Bahamas, Barbados, Belize, Bermuda, Botswana, British East Caribbean Territories, British Honduras, British North Borneo, British Virgin Islands, Brunei, Canada, Cayman Island, Ceylon, China, Cochin China, Cocos (Keeling) Islands, Cook Islands, Curacao, Cyprus, Danish West Indies, East Africa, Ethiopia, Fiji, French Indochina, Gilbert and Ellice Islands, Guyana, Hawaii, Hong Kong, Indonesia, Jamaica, Kenya, Kiao Chau (Kiatschau), Kiribati, Laos, Liberia, Malaya, Malaysia, Malta, Mauritius, Netherlands, Netherlands Antilles, Netherlands Indies, New Zealand, Nova Scotia, Panama, Prince Edward Island, Sarawak, Seychelles, Sierra Leone, Singapore, Solomon Islands, South Africa, Sri Lanka, Straits Settlements, Suriname, Swaziland, Tanzania, Trinidad and Tobago, Tuvalu, Uganda, United States of America, Virgin Islands, Zanzibar, Zimbabwe

Centas (plural **Centa, Centu**) Lithuania
Centavo Angola, Argentina, Bolivia, Brazil, Cape Verde Islands, Chile, Colombia, Costa Rica, Cuba, Dominican Republic, Ecuador, El Salvador, Guatemala, Guinea-Bissau, Honduras, Mexico, Mozambique, Nicaragua, Paraguay, Peru, Philippines, Portugal, Portuguese Guinea, Portuguese India, Puerto Rico, St Thomas and Prince Islands, Timor, Venezuela
Centecimo Bolivia
Ccntentionalis Roman Empire
Centesimo Bolivia, Chile, Dominican Republic, Ethiopia, Italian East Africa, Italy, Panama, Paraguay, San Marino, Somalia, Uruguay, Vatican
Centime Algeria, Antwerp, Belgian Congo, Belgium, Cambodia, Cameroon, Cochin China, Comoro Islands, Djibouti, France, French Equatorial Africa, French Guiana, French Indochina, French Oceania, French Polynesia, French Somali Coast, French West Africa, Guadeloupe, Guinea, Haiti, Laos, Monaco, Morocco, New Caledonia, Reunion, Senegal, Switzerland, Togo, Tunisia, Vietnam, Westphalia, Yugoslavia, Zaire
Centimo Costa Rica, Mozambique, Paraguay, Peru, Philippines, Puerto Rico, St Thomas and Prince Islands, Spain, Venezuela
Centu Lithuania
Chaise Antwerp, Bavaria, France
Chervonetz (plural **Chervontzy**) Russia
Chetrum Bhutan
Cheun South Korea
Chiao China, Formosa, Manchukuo
Chi'en China
Chio China
Cho-gin Japan

Chomseh Yemen
Chon Korea
Christian d'Or Denmark
Chuckram Travancore
Colon Costa Rica, El Salvador
Condor Chile, Colombia, Ecuador
Cordoba Nicaragua
Cornado Spain
Cornuto Savoy
Coroa de Prata Portugal
Coroin Eire
Corona Austrian provinces of Italy, Naples
Coronato Castile, Naples
Couronne d'Or France
Crocione Italian States
Crossazzo Genoa
Crown Ascension, Australia, Bermuda, England, Ghana, Gibraltar, Ireland, Isle of Man, Jamaica, Jersey, Malawi, New Zealand, Nigeria, Rhodesia, Rhodesia and Nyasaland, St Helena, Scotland, Southern Rhodesia, Tristan da Cunha, Turks and Caicos Islands

Cruzadinho Brazil, Portugal
Cruzado Brazil, Portugal
Cruzeiro Brazil
Cuartillo, Cuartino Mexico
Cuarto Bolivia, Spain
Daalder Netherlands
DakBler Danish West Indies, Denmark, Sweden
Dam Afghanistan, India, Nepal
Daric Persia
Dauphin France
Decime France
Decimo Argentina, Chile, Colombia, Ecuador, Galapagos
Decussis Roman Republic
Dekadrachm Syracuse, Hellenistic kingdoms
Dekanummion Byzantine Empire
Dekobolon Greece
Demareteion Syracuse
Demer France
Demy Scotland
Denar Hungary
Denarius Rome
Denaro Italian States
Denga Russia
Dengi Roumania
Denier France and colonies, Haiti, Swiss Cantons
Denning Denmark
Deut Rhineland, Westphalia
Deutschemark Germany
Dhofari Riyal Yemen
Diamante Ferrara
Diamantino Ferrara
Dicken Swiss Cantons
Didrachm Greece
Dime Canada, Hawaii, USA
Dinar Afghanistan, Algeria, Bahrain, Hejaz, Iraq, Kuwait, Morocco, Persia, Saudi Arabia, Serbia, Tunisia, Turkey, Yugoslavia
Diner Andorra
Dinero Peru, Spain
Diobol Greece
Dirham Jordan, Libya, Morocco, United Arab Emirates
Dirhem Dubai, Iraq, Morocco, Qatar
Dio, Diu Portuguese India
Disme USA
Dobla Genoa, Naples and Sicily
Doblado Spanish colonies
Doblenca, Doblenga Aragon, Barcelona
Dobler Mallorca
Doblon Chile, Spain, Urugay
Dobra St Thomas and Prince
Dodekadrachm Carthage
Doit Netherlands, Netherlands Indies, Indonesia
Dokdo Junagadh, Kutch, Nawanagar (Indian States)
Dollar Anguilla, Antigua and Barbuda, Australia, Bahamas, Belize, Bermuda, Canad Cayman Islands, China, Cocos (Keeling) Islands, Cook Islands, East Caribbean Territories, Fiji, Great Britain, Grenada, Guyana, Hawaii, Hong Kong, Indonesia, Jamaica, Japan, Kiribati, Liberia, Malaysia, Mauritius, Montserrat, Newfoundland, New Zealand, Panama, St Kitts-Nevis, St Lucia, St Vincent, Scotland, Sierra Leone, Singapore, Solomin Islands, Straits Settlements, Trinidad and Tobago, Tuvalu, USA, Virgin Islands, Western Samoa, Zimbabwe
Dolya Russia
Dong Annam, Vietnam
Doppia Italian States
Doppietta Sardinia
Double Guernsey

ou Dou French Indochina
ouzain France
rachma Crete, Greece
ram Armenia
reibatzner Austria, German States
reigroscher Lithuania, Prussia
reiling German States
ub Hyderabad, India
ubbeltje Holland
ucat Austria, Austrian States, Courland, Czechoslovakia, Denmark, German States, Hungary, Italian States, Liechtenstein, Liege, Netherlands,Poland, Roumania, Sweden, Swiss Cantons, Russia, Yugoslavia
ucaton Belgium, Netherlands
ucatone Italian States
udu India
uetto Italian States
uit Ceylon, German States, Netherlands, Netherlands Indies
ukat Czechoslovakia, German States, Hungary, Poland, Sweden, Yugoslavia
uplone Swiss Cantons
uro Spain
yak Nepal
:u Belgium, Bosnia, France, Gibraltar
kuele Equatorial Guinea
isabeth d'Or Russia
nalangeni Swaziland
scalin Belgium, Guadeloupe, Haiti, Liege, Martinique
scudillo Spain
scudo Angola, Argentina, Azores, Bolivia, Cape Verde Islands, Central American Republic, Chile, Colombia, Costa Rica, Ecuador, Guadeloupe, Guatemala, Guinea-Bissau, Madeira, Mexico, Mozambique, Peru, Portugal, Portuguese Guinea/India, St Thomas and Prince Islands, Spain, Timor
spadin Portugal
sphera Goa
uro Austria, Belgium, Finland, France, Germany, Greece, Ireland, Italy, Luxembourg, Monaco, The Netherlands, Portugal, San Marino, Spain, The Vatican
xcelente Spain
yrir (singular **Aurar**) Iceland
als Iraq
aluce Ceylon
alus Afghanistan, China, India, Iran, Morocco, Turkestan
anam Ceylon, Dutch East Indies, Travancore
ano Tranquebar (Danish Indian Settlements)
anon French Indian Settlements
arthing Antigua, Ceylon, Great Britain, Isle of Man, Jamaica, Malta, Scotland, South Africa
els Algeria

Fen People's Republic of China, Manchukuo
Fenig (ow) Poland
Feoirling Eire
Ferding Courland, Livonia
Filiberto Savoy
Filippo Italian States
Filler Hungary
Fils Bahrain, Iraq, Jordan, Kuwait, South Arabia, United Arab Emirates, Yemen
Fiorino Italian States
Flitter South German States
Floirin Eire
Florin Australia, Austria, East Africa, Fiji, Great Britain, Hungary, Ireland, Malawi, New Zealand, Rhodesia and Nyasaland, South Africa, Swiss Cantons
Follis Rome, Byzantine Empire
Forint Hungary

Franc Algeria, Belgian Congo, Belgium, Burundi, Cambodia, Cameroon, Central African Republic, Chad, Comoro Islands, Congo, Danish West Indies, Djibouti, Dominican Republic, Ecuador, France, French colonies, Gabon, Guadeloupe, Guinea, Ivory Coast, Katanga, Luxembourg, Madagascar, Malagasy Republic, Mali, Martinique, Mauretania, Monaco, Morocco, New Caledonia, New Hebrides, Reunion, Ruanda-Urundi, Rwanda, St Pierre and Miquelon, Senegal, Switzerland, Togo, Tunisia, West African States
Francescone Italian States
Franchi Switzerland
Franco Dominican Republic, Ecuador, Italian States, Swiss Cantons
Frang Luxembourg
Frank(en) Belgium, Liechtenstein, Saar, Switzerland, Westphalia
Franka Ara Albania
Frederik d'Or Denmark
Friedrich d'Or German States
Fyrk Sweden
Gabellone Papal States

Gayah Sumatra
Gazetta Venice
Genovino Genoa, Florence, Venice
Genevoise Geneva
George Noble England
Georgstaler German States
Gersh Ethiopia
Gigliato Hungary, Naples, Rhodes
Gigot Brabant, Flanders
Gin Japan
Giorgino Ferrara, Modena
Giovannino Genoa
Girsh Hejaz, Nejd, Saudi Arabia, Sudan
Giulio Italian States
Golde Sierra Leone
Goldgulden German States, Swiss Cantons
Goldpfennig German States
Goryoban Japan
Gourde Haiti
Gourmier Morocco
Gram Afghanistan
Gramme Burma
Gramo Bolivia, Tierra del Fuego
Grana Italian States
Grano Italian States, Mexico, Sovereign Order of Malta
Grenadino Colombia, New Granada
Greschl Roumania, Transylvania
Grivenka Russia
Grivennik Russia
Grivna (plural **Grivny**) Ukraine
Groat Great Britain
Groeschl Bohemia
Groot Netherlands
Gros France
Groschel German States
Groschen Austria, German States, Poland, Swiss Cantons
Groshen Austria, German States
Grossetto Dalmatia, Illyria, Venice
Grosso Italian States
Grossone Italian States
Grosspfennig Pomerania, Rhineland
Grossus Courland, Poland
Grosz (plural **Grosze** or **Groszy**) Poland
Grote German States
Grush Albania
Guarani Paraguay
Guerche Egypt, Saudi Arabia
Guinea Great Britain, Saudi Arabia
Gulden Austria, Curacao, German States, Netherlands, Netherlands Indies, Swiss Cantons
Guldiner Austria, South German States, Swiss Cantons
Gutegroschen North and Central German States
Guterpfennig German States
Habibi Afghanistan
Halala Saudi Arabia, Yemen
Halbag Frankfurt
Haler (plural **Halere, Haleru**) Czechoslovakia, Czech Republic
Halierov Slovakia
Haller Swiss Cantons
Hao China, Vietnam
Hapalua Hawaii
Hardhead Scotland
Hardi France, Turin
Hau Tonga
Hayrir Altin Iraq, Turkey
Hekte Lesbos, Mytilene
Heller Austria, German States, German East Africa
Helm England
Henri d'Or France
Hryvnia Ukraine
Hsien China
Hvid Denmark
Hwan Korea
Hyperpyron Byzantine Empire
Ichibu-gin Japan
Ikilik Russia
Imadi Yemen
Imami Mysore
Imperial Russia
Isabella Spain
Ischal Russia
Ishu Gin Japan
Jacondale France
Jawa Nepal
Jeon Korea
Jerome d'Or Westphalia
Jiao People's Republic of China
Jedid Egypt
Jefimok (plural **Jefimki**) Russia
Joachimico Italy
Joachimik Poland
Joachimstaler Bohemia
Joao Portugal
Johanna Portugal
Johannes Portugal
Jokoh Kelantan, Malaysia
Judenpfennig Frankfurt
Justo Portugal
Kapang Sarawak
Kapeikas Latvia, Belarus
Karolin German States
Kas Danish Indian Settlements
Kasu Mysore
Kazbeg Caucasia, Safavid Persia
Khayriya Egypt
Khoum Mauretania
Kin Japan

na Papua New Guinea
p Laos
ban Japan
bo Nigeria
pec Poland
pejek Outer Mongolia (Tannu Tuva)
pek Russia
ri Kutch**Korona** Bohemia and Moravia, Hungary, Slovakia
rtling German States
run(a) (plural **Koruny** or **Koruncic**) Czechoslo-vakia
ula Tonga
ajczar Hungary
an Iran, Persia
eu(t)zer Austria, Austrian States, Czechoslovakia, German States, Hungary, Liechtenstein, Poland, Roumania, Swiss Cantons
ona (plural **Kronor** or **Kronur**) Iceland, Sweden
ona (plural **Kroner** or **Kronen**) Austria, Denmark, German States, Greenland, Liechtenstein, Norway
oon(i) Estonia
ugerrand South Africa
na (plural **Kune**) Croatia
pang Malaysia, Thailand
rus Turkey
ta Congo-Kinshasa, Zaire
vacha Malawi, Zambia
vanza Angola
vartnik Poland
at Burma, Myanmar
rmis Russia
ng Annam
ree, Lari, Lariat or Larin Maldive Islands
ti, Lats Latvia
urel England
i Roumania
k (plural **Leke** or **Leku**) Albania
mpira Honduras
one Sierra Leone
opard England
pton (plural **Lepta**) Crete, Greece, Ionian Islands
u (plural **Lei**) Roumania
v(a) Bulgaria
Manchukuo
ang China, Laos
ard Belgium, France, Luxembourg
bra Peru
cente Lesotho
kuta Zaire
langeni Swaziland
on Scotland
on d'Or Austrian Netherlands
Lira (plural **Lire**) Eritrea, Italian East Africa, Italy, San Marino, Syria, Turkey, Vatican
Lira (plural **Lirot**) Israel
Lisente Lesotho
Litas (plural **Litai** or **Litu**) Lithuania

Litra Sicily, Syracuse
Livre France, Guadeloupe, Lebanon, Martinique, Mauritius, Reunion
Louis d'Argent France
Louis d'Or France
Luhlanga Swaziland
Lumma Armenia
Lweis Angola
Mace China
Macuta Angola
Magdalon d'Or Aix-en-Provence, Tarascon
Mahalek Ethiopia
Mahallak Harar
Mahbub Egypt, Ottoman Empire
Mahmudi Saudi Arabia
Makuta Zaire
Maloti Lesotho
Manat Azerbaijan
Manghir Crimea
Marabotin Moorish kingdoms, Southern Spain
Maravedi Spain
Marchetto Italian States
Marck German States
Marengo France
Mariengroschen German States
Mark Germany, German States, German New Guinea, Norway, Poland, Sweden
Marka Estonia
Markka(a) Finland
Mas Malaysia
Masriya Egypt
Masson Lorraine and Bar
Mat Burma
Matapan Venice
Mathbu Morocco
Maticaes Mozambique
Matona Ethiopia
Mattier German States
Maximilian d'Or German States

Mazuna Morocco
Medin Egypt
Mehmudiye Altin Ottoman Empire
Meinhard Austria, German States
Melgarejo Bosnia
Merk Scotland
Metica Mozambique
Meung Japan
Mil Cyprus, Hong Kong, Israel, Malta, Palestine
Milan d'Or Serbia
Miliarense Byzantine Empire
Milesima Spain
Millieme Egypt, Libya
Millime Tunisia
Milreis Brazil
Miscals China
Mohar Nepal
Mohur Afghanistan, Bikanir, Cooch Behar, Gwalior, Hyderabad, India (Mughal Empire), Maldive Islands, Netherlands Indies, Rajkot
Moidore (Moeda de ouro) Portugal
Momme Japan
Mon Japan, Ryukyu Islands
Mongo Mongolia
Mouton d'Or France
Mu Burma
Mun Korea
Mung Mongolia
Munzgulden Swiss Cantons
Muzuna Algeria
Naira Nigeria
Nami-sen Japan
Napoleon France
Naya Paisa Bhutan, India
Negotiepenning Netherlands
Neugroschen German States
New Pence Gibraltar, Great Britain, Guernsey, Isle of Man, Jersey
Ngultrum Bhutan
Ngwee Zambia
Nisar Afghanistan, India
Nisfiya Egypt
Noble Austria,England, Scotland, Isle of Man
Nomisma Byzantine Empire
Nonsunt Scotland
Nummion (plural **Nummia**) Byzantine Empire
Oban Japan
Obol Greece, Ionian Islands
Ochavo Spain
Octavo Mexico, Philippines
Omani Oman
Onca Mozambique
Oncia Italian States
Onlik Crimea
Onluk Turkey
Onza Bolivia, Chile, Costa Rica, Mexico
Or Sweden
Ore Denmark, Faroe Islands, Greenland, Norway, Sweden
Ort(e) Poland, Prussia
Ortug (plural **Ortugar**) Sweden
Ouguiya Mauretania
Pa'anga Tonga
Pagoda India (Madras)
Pahlavi Iran
Pai India, Siam (Thailand)
Paisa Afghanistan, Bhutan, India, Nepal, Pakistan
Panchia India
Pano Portuguese Africa
Paoli Italian States
Papetto Papal States
Para (plural **Paras** or **Parades**) Crimea, Egypt, Greece, Iraq, Libya, Nejd, Roumania, Saud[i] Arabia, Serbia, Sudan, Syria, Turkey, Walachia, Yugoslavia
Pardao Portuguese India
Parisis d'Or France
Pataca Macau
Pataco Portugal
Patagon Belgium
Patrick Ireland
Pavillon d'Or France
Pe Burma, Cambodia
Peca Portugal
Pengo Hungary
Penni(a) Finland
Penning(ar) Denmark, Sweden
Penny (plural **Pence**) Australia, Bahamas, Barbados, Bermuda, Biafra, British Guiana, British East Africa British West Africa, Canad[a], Ceylon, Falkland Islands, Fiji, Gambia, Ghan[a], Gibraltar, Gold Coast, Great Britain, Guernse[y], Ireland, Isle of Man, Jamaica, Jersey, Malawi, Montserrat, New Guinea, New Zealand, Nigeria, Rhodesia and Nyasaland, St Helena St Kitts-Nevis, South Africa, Southern Rhodesia, Trinidad & Tobago, Tristan da Cunha, Zambia
Pentekontalitron Sicily
Pentekontedrachm Hellenistic kingdoms
Pentenummion Byzantine Empire
Perper(a) Montenegro
Pesa German East Africa
Peseta Andorra, Equatorial Guinea, Peru, Spa[in]
Pesewa Ghana
Peso Argentina, Bolivia, Cambodia, Chile, Colombia, Costa Rica, Cuba, Dominican Republic, El Salvador, Guatemala, Guinea-Bissau, Honduras, Mexico, Netherlands Antilles, Nicaragua, Paraguay, Peru, Philippines, Puerto Rico, Uruguay, Venezue[la]
Pessa Yemen (Lahej), Zanzibar
Petermannchen Trier

ennig(e) Austria, Bohemia, Germany, German States, Poland, Swiss Cantons
enning Austrian States, German States
ilippeioi Macedon
oenix Greece
astra Italian States
astre Annam, Cambodia, Cochin China, Cyprus, Denmark, Egypt, French Indochina, Hejaz, Iraq, Khmer, Lebanon, Libya, Nejd, Saudi Arabia, Syria, Sudan, Tonkin, Tunisia, Turkey, Vietnam, Yemen
ataltynny Russia
ciolo Sovereign Order of Malta
ccolo Italian States
e Bhutan, Ceylon, East Africa, India, Kenya, Malaysia
nto Portugal
so Philippines
stole France, German States, Ireland, Scotland, Swiss Cantons
is Brunei, Java, Sumatra, Siam
ack Scotland
appart Switzerland
isha Bangladesh
ltina Russia
ltura Hungary, Roumania
ludenga Russia
lupoltinnik Russia
lushka Russia
nd Transvaal
und Ascension, Australia, Biafra, Cyprus, Egypt, Falkland Islands, Ghana, Gibraltar, Great Britain, Guernsey, Iran, Isle of Man, Israel, Jersey, Malta, Nigeria, Rhodesia, St Helena, South Arabia, South Africa, Sudan, Syria
otea South Africa
uta(ot) Israel
ffin Lundy
l Afghanistan, China, Turkestan
la Botswana
li Caucasia
ltorak Poland
a(t) Burma
sa Zanzibar
ndar(ka) Albania
ran Afghanistan
rsh Egypt
adrans Roman Republic
an Annam
art Gibraltar, Swiss Cantons
art d'Ecu France
artenses Silesia
artillo Spain
artinho Portugal
arto Ecuador, Mexico, Philippines, Spain
artuncia Rome
aternio Rome
Quattrino Italian States
Qepiq Azerbaijan
Quetzal Guatemala
Quinarius Rome
Quint USA
Quinto di Scudo Papal States
Rand South Africa
Rappen Switzerland
Rasi Netherlands Indies
Reaal Curacao
Real(es) Argentina, Bolivia, Central American Republic, Chile, Colombia, Costa Rica, Dominican Republic, Ecuador, El Salvador, Venezuela
Real Batu Indonesia
Reichsmark Germany
Reichspfennig Germany
Reichsthaler Germany
Reis Angola, Azores, Brazil, Madeira, Mozambique, Portugal, Portuguese India
Reisedaler Denmark
Rentenmark Germany
Rentenpfennig Germany
Reul Eire
Rial Iran, Morocco, Muscat and Oman, Oman, Persia, Yemen Arab Republic
Rider Scotland
Riel Kampuchea
Rigsbankdaler Denmark
Rigsbankskilling Denmark
Rigsdaler, Denmark, Norway
Rigsmontskilling Denmark
Rijder Friesland, Guelderland, United Provinces
Rijksdaalder Netherlands
Riksdaler Sweden
Riksdaler Riksmynt Sweden
Riksdaler Specie Sweden
Rin Japan
Ringgit Malaysia
Rio Japan
Rixdollar Ceylon
Riyal Iran, Iraq, Saudi Arabia, United Arab Emirates, Yemen Arab Republic
Rose Noble England
Rouble Russia, USSR
Royal d'Or France
Royalin(er) Tranquebar, Danish Indian Settlements
Rub Ethiopia
Rubel German occupation of Russia
Rubiya Egypt
Ruble Poland, Transnistria
Rublis Latvia
Rufiyaa Maldive Islands
Rumi Altin Ottoman Empire
Rupee Afghanistan, Andaman Islands, Bhutan, Burma, China, Cocos Keeling Islands, India,

Iran, Kenya, Mauritius, Nepal, Pakistan, Saudi Arabia, Seychelles, Sri Lanka, Tanzania, Tibet, United Arab Emirates, Yemen

Rupia Portuguese India, Somalia

Rupiah Indonesia

Rupie German East Africa

Ruspone Italian States

Ryal England, Hejaz, Iran, Muscat and Oman, Nejd, Oman, Persia, Quaiti State, Saudi Arabia, Yemen, Zanzibar

Ryo Japan

Rytterpenning Denmark, Hanseatic League

Saidi Oman

Saiga Merovingian Empire

Salung Siam (Thailand)

Salut d'Or France

Sampietrino Papal States

Sanar Afghanistan

Sanese Siena

Santa Croce Italian States

Santim(at) Morocco

Santims (plural **Santimi** or **Santimu**) Latvia

Sapeque Annam, Cochin China, French Indochina

Sar Sinkiang

Sarrazzino Crusader kingdoms

Satang Siam (Thailand)

Sceat Anglo-Saxon England

Scellino Somalia

Schilling Austria, German States, Poland, Swiss Cantons

Schoter Breslau, Silesia

Schwaren German States

Scilling Eire

Scudo Bolivia, Italian States, Mexico, Malta, Papal States, Peru, San Marino

Sechsling German States

Semis Rome

Semuncia Rome

Sen Brunei, Cambodia, Indonesia, Irian Barat, Japan, Kampuchea, Malaysia, Riau Lingga, West New Guinea

Sene Samoa

Sengi Zaire

Seniti Tonga

Sent Estonia

Sente Lesotho

Senti Estonia, Somalia, Tanzania

Sentimo Philippines

Serebrnik Bulgaria

Sertum Bhutan

Sesena Spain

Sesino Italian States

Sestertius Rome

Sestino Italian States

Shahi Afghanistan, Iran, Turkestan

Sheqal(im) Israel

Shilingi Tanzania

Shilling Australia, Biafra, British West Africa Canada, Cyprus, East Africa, Fiji, Gambia, Ghana, Great Britain, Grenada, Guernsey, Ireland, Isle of Man, Jamaica, Jersey, Kenya, Malawi, Malta, New Guinea, New Zealand, Nigeria, Scotland, Somalia, South Africa, Trinidad and Tobago, Uganda, Zambia

Sho Nepal, Tibet

Shokang Tibet

Shu Japan

Siglos Achaemenid Empire

Sik Siam (Thailand)

Silbergroschen German States,Luxembourg

Silbergulden South Germany

Sizain France

Skar Tibet

Skilling Danish West Indies, Denmark, Norway, Sweden

Skillingrigsmont Denmark

Skot Prussia, Silesia

Sol(es) Argentina, Belgium, Bolivia, France, Haiti, Luxembourg, Mauritius, Peru, Reuni Switzerland, Windward Islands

Soldo (plural **Soldi**) Italian States, Swiss Cantons, Papal States, Yugoslavia

Solidus Argentina, Bolivia, Peru, Rome

Solot Siam

Som Kyrgyzstan

Somalo Somalia

Sosling Denmark

Sou Canada, French colonies, Guadeloupe, Mauritius, Reunion, Spain

Souverain d'Or Austrian Netherlands

Sovereign Australia, Canada, England, Falkland Islands, India, Isle of Man, Saudi Arabia, South Africa, United Kingdom

Sovrano Italian States

Speciedaler Denmark, Norway

Species Ducat Denmark

Srang Tibet

Stater Greece

Stella USA

Stiver British Guiana, Ceylon, Demerara and Essequibo, Dutch East Indies, Netherlands

Stotinka Bulgaria

Stuber German States

Stuiver Curacao, Dutch East Indies, Netherlands, Netherlands Antilles

rca Northumbria
ver Sweden
South Vietnam
cre Ecuador, Galapagos
eldo Bolivia, Spain
kus Indonesia
ltani Algeria, Libya, Tunisia
rre Altin Ottoman Empire
li Guinea
ckoe Gold Coast
el China, Laos
ka Bangladesh
la Samoa, Tokelau
lar(a) Poland
laro Ethiopia
ler German States, Poland, Swiss Cantons
lirion Greece
llero Ethiopia, Italian States, Ragusa
mbac-tron Annam
mbala Malawi
mlung Siam
nga Portuguese India
ngka Tibet
nka Nepal
nkah Burma
rin Naples, Sicily
ro (plural **Tari**) Italian States, Malta
k Altin Ottoman Empire
nga China, Bokhara, Turkestan
rnar Poland
ster England
stern British East Indies
stone Italian States
stoon England
tartemorion Greece
tarteron Byzantine Empire
tradrachm Greece
trobol Greece
aler Austria, Austrian States, Courland, Czechoslovakia, German States, Hungary, Liechtenstein, Poland, Roumania, Switzerland
ebe Botswana
eler Frankfurt
istle Crown England
istle Merk Scotland
istle Noble Scotland
rymsa Anglo-Saxon England
cal Cambodia, Thailand
en Annam, Vietnam
lla Afghanistan, Sinkiang, Turkestan
masha Afghanistan
stao Portugal
ea Papua New Guinea
la India, Nepal

Tolar Slovenia
Toman Iran, Persia, Azerbaijan
Tornese Italian States
Tournois France
Trade Dollar Great Britain, Japan, USA
Trah Malaysia
Tremissis Rome, Byzantine Empire, Franks, Lombards, Visigoths
Tressis Rome
Triens Rome
Trihemiobol Greece
Triobol Greece
Tritartemorion Greece
Tughrik Mongolia
Turner Scotland
Tympf Poland
Tyyn Kyrgyzstan
Unghero Italian States
Unicorn Scotland
Unit Scotland, French West Africa
Unite England
Van Vietnam
Vatu Vanuatu
Veld Pond South African Republic
Venezolano Venezuela
Vereinstaler Austria-Hungary, German States
Victoriate Rome
Vierer Swiss Cantons
Vintem Portugal
Wan Korea
Wark Ethiopia
Warn Korean
Wen China
Whan Korea
Won South Korea
Xerafim Portuguese India
Xu Vietnam
Yang Korea
Yarim Turkey
Yen Japan
Yirmilik Ottoman Empire
Yuan China
Yuzluk Ottoman Empire
Zaire Zaire
Zalat Yemen Arab Republic
Zecchino Italian States, Malta
Zelagh Morocco
Zeri Mahbub Egypt, Libya, Turkey
Zloty (plural **Zlote** or **Zlotych**) Poland
Zolota Turkey
Zolotnik Russia
Zolotoj Russia
Zweidritteltaler German States
Zyfert East Friesland

Glossary of coin terms

this section we list all the terms commonly encountered in numismatics or in the oduction of coins.

bey Coins Medieval coins struck in the abbeys, convents and other great religious houses which were granted coinage rights. These coins were often used also by pilgrims journeying from one monastery to another.

schlag (German for "discount") A *restrike* from an original die.

colated Synonym for *conjoined* or *jugate* and signifying two or more profiles overlapping.

monital Acronym from *Aciaio Monetario Italiano*, a stainless steel alloy used for Italian coins since 1939.

djustment Reduction of metal in a *flan* or *blank* to the specified weight prior to striking, accomplished by filing down the face. Such file marks often survived the coining process and are occasionally met with in coins, especially of the 18th century.

e Abbreviation for the Latin *Aes* (bronze), used for coins made of brass, bronze or other copper alloys.

es Grave (Latin for heavy bronze) Heavy circular coins first minted at Rome in 269 BC.

es Rude (Latin for rough bronze) Irregular lumps of bronze which gradually developed into ingots of uniform shape and were the precursors of coins in Rome.

es Signatum (Latin for signed bronze) Bronze ingots of regular size and weight, bearing marks of authority to guarantee their weight (289–269 BC).

gonistic (Greek) Term for coins issued to commemorate, or pertaining to, sporting events.

lliance Coinage struck by two or more states acting together and having common features of design or inscription.

lloy Coinage metal composed of two or more metallic elements.

ltered Deliberately changed, usually unofficially, with the aim of increasing the numismatic value of a coin, medal or note. This applies particularly to dates, where a common date may be altered to a rare date by filing or re-engraving one of the digits.

Aluminium (American *Aluminum*) Silvery lightweight metal, developed commercially in the late 19th century for commemorative medals, but used for tokens and emergency money during the First World War and since 1940 widely used in subsidiary coinage.

Aluminium-bronze Alloy of aluminium and copper. Hard-wearing and gold-coloured, it is now widely used in tokens and subsidiary coinage.

Amulet Coin or medal believed to have talismanic qualities, such as warding off disease and bad luck. Many Chinese and Korean pieces come into this category. See also *Touchpiece*.

Androcephalous Heraldic term for creatures with a human head.

Anepigraphic Coins or medals without a legend.

Annealing Process of heating and cooling applied to metal to relieve stresses and prepare it for striking into coins.

Annulet Small circle often used as an ornament or spacing device in coin inscriptions.

Antimony Brittle white metal, chemical symbol *Sb*, virtually impractical as a coinage metal but used for the Chinese 10 cents of Kweichow, 1931. Alloyed with tin, copper or lead, it produces the white metal popular as a medallic medium.

Antoniniani Silver coins minted in Imperial Rome. The name derives from the Emperor Caracalla (Marcus Aurelius Antoninus) in whose reign they were first struck. The silver content was progressively reduced and by the last issue (AD 295) they were reduced to *billon*.

Ar Abbreviation for Latin *Argentum* (silver), used for coins struck in this metal.

Assay Mark Mark applied to a medal struck in precious metal by an assayer or assay office as a guarantee of the fineness of the metal.

Assignat Type of paper money used in France

1789–96, representing the land assigned to the holders.

Attribution Identification of a coin by characteristics such as issuing authority, date or reign, mint, denomination, metal, and by a standard reference.

Au Abbreviation for *aurum* (Latin for gold), denoting coins of this metal.

AU Abbreviation for "About Uncirculated", often found in catalogues and dealers' lists to describe the condition of a numismatic piece.

Autodollar Name given to the silver yuan issued by Kweichow, 1928, and having a contemporary motor car as the obverse motif.

Auxiliary Payment Certificate Form of paper money intended for use by American military personnel stationed in overseas countries. See also *Baf* and *Scrip*.

Babel Note Nickname given to the paper money of the Russian Socialist Federated Soviet Republic (1919) because it bore the slogan "workers of the world unite" in seven languages, a reference to the biblical tower of Babel.

Baf Acronym from British Armed Forces, the popular name for the vouchers which could only be exchanged for goods in service canteens from 1945 onwards.

Bag Mark Minor scratch or abrasion on an otherwise uncirculated coin, caused by coins in mint bags knocking together.

Banknote Form of paper money issued by banks and usually promising to pay the bearer on demand in coin of the realm.

Barbarous Imitation of Greek or Roman coins by the Celtic and Germanic tribes who lived beyond the frontiers of the civilised world.

Base Non-precious metals or alloys.

Bath Metal Inferior bronze alloy, named after the English city where it was used for casting cannon. Used by William Wood of Bristol for Irish and American tokens and by Amos Topping for Manx coins of 1733/4.

Beading Ornamental border found on the raised rim of a coin.

Behalfszahlungsmittel German term for auxiliary payment certificates used in occupied Europe from 1939 to 1945.

Bell Metal Alloy of copper and tin normally used for casting bells, but employed for the subsidiary coinage of the French Revolutionary period.

Billon Silver alloy containing less than 50 per cent fine silver, usually mixed with copper. In Spain this alloy was known as *vellon*.

Bi-metallic Coins struck in two separate metals or alloys. Patterns for such coins exist from the 19th century but actual coins with a centre of one metal surrounded by a ring of another not appear till 1982 (Italy, San Marino a Vatican). Canada introduced coins with a t plaque inset in a second metal (1990). See a *Clad*, *Plugged* and *Sandwich*.

Bi-metallism Monetary system in which t metals are in simultaneous use and equa available as legal tender, implying a defir ratio between the two. A double standard gold and silver, with a ratio of 16:1, existed the mid-19th century.

Bingle American term for a trade token, m specifically the US government issue of tok for the Matacuska, Alaska colonization proj 1935.

Birthday Coins Coins celebrating the birthc of a ruler originated in Roman Imperial tim notably the reigns of Maximianus (286–3 and Constantinus I (307–37). Birthday tal were issued by many German states, and amc recent examples may be cited coins marki the 70th, 80th and 90th birthdays of Gus Adolf VI of Sweden, 80th and 90th birthc coins from the British Commonwealth for Queen Mother, and coins honouring Qu Elizabeth, the Duke of Edinburgh and the Pri of Wales.

Bit Term denoting fragments of large silver coi cut up and circulating as fractional valu Spanish dollars were frequently broken up circulation in the American colonies and West indies. Long bits and short bits circula at 15 and 10 cents respectively, but the te came to be equated with the Spanish real eighth peso, hence the American colloquiali "two-bit" signifying a quarter dollar.

Black Money English term for the debased sil deniers minted in France which circulated fre in England until they were banned government decree in 1351.

Blank Piece of metal, cut or punched out o roller bar or strip, and prepared for striking produce coins. Alternate terms are *flan* a *planchet*.

"Breeches" money, so-called from the reverse design!

"Cartwheel" penny, so called because of its
·nbersome size.

undered Inscription Legend in which the lettering is jumbled or meaningless, indicating the illiteracy of the tribes who copied Greek and Roman coins.

nnet Piece Scottish gold coin, minted in 1539–40. The name is derived from the obverse portraying King James V in a large, flat bonnet.

n Pour French for "good for", inscribed on Chamber of Commerce brass tokens issued in 1920–7 during a shortage of legal tender coinage.

uquet Sou Canadian copper token halfpenny of 1837 deriving its name from the nosegay of heraldic flowers on the obverse.

x Coin Small container formed by *obverse* and *reverse* of two coins, hollowed out and screwed together.

acteate (Latin *bractea*, a thin piece of metal) Coins struck on blanks so thin that the image applied to one side appears in reverse on the other. First minted in Erfurt and Thuringia in the 12th century, and later produced elsewhere in Germany, Switzerland and Poland till the 14th century.

ass Alloy of copper and zinc, widely used for subsidiary coinage. The term was also formerly used for bronze Roman coins, known numismatically as first, second or third brass.

eeches Money Derisive term given by the Royalists to the coinage of the Commonwealth, 1651, the conjoined elongated oval shields on the reverse resembling a pair of breeches.

ockage Mis-struck coin with only one design, normal on one side and *incuse* on the other. This occurs when a coin previously struck adheres to the die and strikes the next blank to pass through the press.

oken Bank-note Note issued by a bank which has failed, but often applied more generally to banknotes which have been demonetised.

Bronze Alloy of copper and tin, first used as a coinage metal by the Chinese c. 1000 BC. Often used synonymously with copper, though it should be noted that bronze only superseded copper as the constituent of the base metal British coins in 1860.

Bull Neck Popular term for the coins of King George III, 1816–17.

Bullet Money Pieces of silver, *globular* in shape, bearing various *countermarks* and used as coins in Siam (Thailand) in the 18th and 19th centuries.

Bullion Precious metal in bars, ingots, strip or scrap (i.e. broken jewellery mounts, watch-cases and plate), its weight reckoned solely by weight and fineness, before being converted into coin.

Bullion Coin A coin struck in platinum, gold or silver, whose value is determined solely by the prevailing market price for the metal as a commodity. Such coins do not generally have a nominal face value, but include in their inscriptions their weight and fineness. Good examples of recent times include the Krugerrand (South Africa), the Britannia (UK), the Maple Leaf (Canada), Libertad (Mexico), the Nugget (Australia) and the Eagle (USA).

Bun Coinage British coins of 1860–94 showing Queen Victoria with her hair in a bun.

Bungtown Coppers Derisive term (from Anglo-American slang *bung*, to swindle or bribe) for halfpence of English or Irish origin, often counterfeit, which circulated in North America towards the end of the colonial period.

Carat (American *Karat*) Originally a unit of weight for precious stones, based on carob seeds (ceratia), it also denotes the fineness or purity of gold, being 1/24th part of the whole. Thus 9 carat gold is .375 fine and 22 carat, the English sovereign standard, is .916 fine. Abbreviated as ct or kt.

Cartwheel Popular term for the large and cumbersome penny and twopenny pieces of 1797 weighing one and two ounces, struck by Matthew Boulton at the Soho Mint, Birmingham.

Cased Set Set of coins in mint condition, housed in the official case issued by the mint. Formerly leather cases with blue plush or velvet lining were used, but nowadays many sets are encapsulated in plastic to facilitate handling.

Cash (from Portuguese *caixa*, Hindi *kasu*). Round piece of bronze or brass with a square hole in the centre, used as subsidiary coinage in China for almost 2000 years, till the early 12th century. In Chinese these pieces were known as *Ch'ien* or *Li* and strung together in groups of 1000 were equivalent to a silver tael.

Cast Coins Coins cast from molten metals in moulds. This technique, widespread in the case of early commemorative medals, has been used infrequently in coins, the vast majority of which are struck from *dies*. Examples of cast coins include the Chinese cash and the Manx coins of 1709.

Check A form of *token* given as a means of identification, or issued for small amounts of money or for services of a specific nature.

Cheque (American *Check*) A written order directing a bank to pay money.

Chop (Hindi, to seal). Countermark, usually consisting of a single character, applied by Chinese merchants to precious metal coins and ingots as a guarantee of their weight and fineness. Coins may be found with a wide variety of chop marks and the presence of several different marks on the same coin considerably enhances its interest and value. See also *Shroff mark*.

Christmas Coins issued as Christmas gifts date from the Middle Ages when the Venetian Doges struck *Osselle* as presents for their courtiers. In modern times, however, the custom has developed only since the late 1970s, several countries having issued attractive coins at Christmas since then.

Cistophori (Greek for chest bearing) a generic term for the coins of Pergamum with an obverse motif of a chest showing a serpent crawling out of the half-opened lid. Cistophori became very popular all over Asia Minor in the 3rd and 2nd centuries BC and were struck also at mints in Ionia, Phrygia, Lydia and Mysia.

Clad Coins Coins with a core of one alloy, covered with a layer or coating of another. US half dollars from 1965 to 1970, for example, had a core of 21 per cent silver and 79 per cent copper, bonded to outer layers of 80 per cent silver and 20 per cent copper. More recently, however, coins usually have a body in a cheap alloy, with only a thin cladding of a more expensive material, such as the British 1p and 2p coins of stainless steel with a copper cladding, introduced late in 1992.

Clash Marks Mirror image traces found on a coin which has been struck from a pair of dies, themselves damaged by having been struck together without a blank between.

Clipped Coins Precious metal coins from which small amounts have been removed by clipping the edges. It was to prevent this that *graining* and *edge inscriptions* were adopted.

Cob Crude, irregularly shaped silver piece, often with little more than a vestige of die impressions, produced in the Spanish American mints in the 16th–18th centuries.

Coin Piece of metal, marked with a device, issu by government authority and intended for u as money.

Collar Retaining ring within which the *dies* the *obverse* and *reverse* operate. When the *bl* is struck under high pressure between the d the metal flows sideways and is formed by collar, taking up the impression of *reeding* *edge inscription* from it.

Commemorative Coin, medal, token or pa note issued to celebrate a current event or anniversary of a historic event or personali

Communion Token Token, cast in lead, but la struck in pewter, brass, bronze or white me issued to members of a congregation to per them to partake of the annual communi service in the Calvinist and Presbyteri churches. John Calvin himself is said to ha invented the communion token in 1561 b they were actually referred to in the minutes the Scottish General Assembly in 1560. La they were adopted by the Reformed churc in many parts of Europe. They survived Scotland till the early years of this centu Each parish had its own tokens, often beari the names or initials of individual ministe with dates, symbols and biblical texts.

Conjoined Term denoting overlapped profi of two or more rulers (e.g. William and Mar

Contorniate (from Italian *contorno*, edge). L 4th and 5th century Roman bronze piece who name alludes to the characteristic grooving the edges.

Contribution Coins Coins struck by Bambe Eichstatt, Fulda and other German cities in 1790s during the First Coalition War agai the French Republic. The name alludes to fact that the bullion used to produce the co necessary to pay troops was raised contribution from the Church and the publ

Convention Money Any system of coina agreed by neighbouring countries for mut acceptance and interchange. Examples inclu the Amphictyonic coins of ancient Greece, a

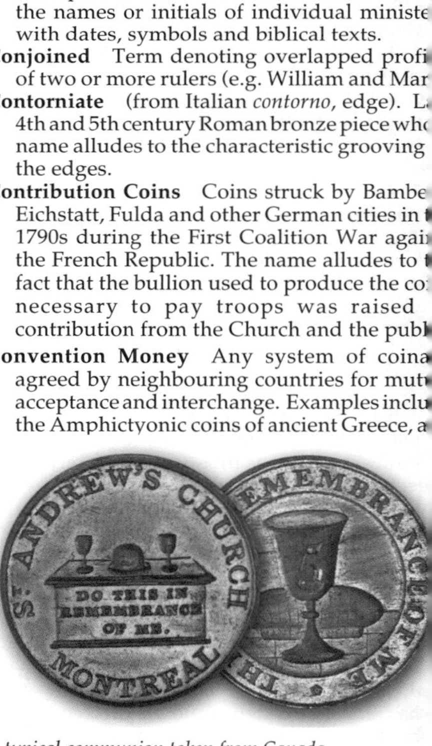

A typical communion token from Canada.

the Austrian and Bavarian talers and gulden of 1753–1857 which were copied by other south German states and paved the way for the German Monetary union.

pper Metallic element, chemical symbol *Cu*, widely used as a coinage medium for 2,500 years. Pure or almost pure copper was used for subsidiary coinage in many countries till the mid-19th century, but has since been superseded by copper alloys which are cheaper and more durable: *bronze* (copper and tin), *brass* (copper and zinc), *Bath metal* or *bell metal* (low-grade copper and tin), *aluminium-bronze* (copper and aluminium), *potin* (copper, tin, lead and silver) or *cupro-nickel* (copper and nickel). Copper is also alloyed with gold to give it its reddish hue, and is normally alloyed with silver in coinage metals. When the copper exceeds the silver content the alloy is known as *billon*.

pperhead Popular term for a copper *token* about the size and weight of an American cent which circulated in the USA during the Civil War (1861–65) during a shortage of subsidiary coinage. Many different types were produced, often of a political or patriotic nature.

ppernose Popular name for the debased silver shillings of Henry VIII. Many of them were struck in copper with little more than a silver wash which tended to wear off at the highest point of the obverse, the nose on the full-face portrait of the king.

unter A piece resembling a coin but intended for use on a medieval accountancy board or in gambling. See also *jeton*.

unterfeit Imitation of a coin, token or banknote intended for circulation to deceive the public and defraud the state.

untermark Punch mark applied to a coin some time after its original issue, either to alter its nominal value, or to authorise its circulation in some other country.

wrie Small shell (*Cypraea moneta*) circulating as a form of primitive currency from 1000 BC (China) to the present century (East and West Africa) and also used in the islands of the Indian and Pacific Oceans.

ockard Debased silver imitation of English pennies produced in the Netherlands and imported into England in the late 13th century. Edward I tried to prevent their import then, in 1299, allowed them to pass current as halfpennies. As they contained more than a halfpennyworth of silver this encouraged their trading in to be melted down and they disappeared from circulation within a year. Sometimes known as *pollards*. See also *Lushbourne*.

Crown Gold Gold of 22 carat (.916) fineness, so called on account of its adoption in 1526 for the English gold crown. It has remained the British standard gold fineness ever since.

Cumberland Jack Popular name for a counter or medalet of sovereign size, struck unofficially in 1837 in brass. The figure of St George was replaced by the Duke of Cumberland on horseback with the inscription "To Hanover" a reference to the unpopular Duke of Cumberland, uncle of Queen Victoria, who succeeded to the Hanoverian throne since Victoria, as a female, was debarred by Salic law from inheritance.

Cupellation (Latin *cupella*, a little cup). Process by which gold and silver were separated from lead and other impurities in their ores. A cupel is a shallow cup of bone-ash or other absorbent material which, when hot, absorbs any molten material that wets its surface. Lead melts and oxidises with impurities into the cupel, whereas gold and silver remain on the cupel. Cupellation is also used in assaying the fineness of these precious metals.

Cupro-nickel Coinage alloy of 75 per cent copper and 25 per cent nickel, now widely used as a base metal substitute for silver. A small amount of zinc is added to the alloy in modern Russian coins.

Currency Coins, tokens, paper notes and other articles intended to pass current in general circulation as money.

Current Coins and paper money still in circulation.

Cut Money Coins cut into smaller pieces to provide correspondingly smaller denominations. The cross on many medieval coins assisted the division of silver pennies into halfpence and farthings. Spanish dollars were frequently divided into *bits* which themselves became units of currency in America and the West Indies.

Darlehnskassen (German for "state loan notes"). Paper money issued during the First World War in an abortive bid to fill the shortage of coinage in circulation. These low-denomination notes failed to meet demand and were superseded by local issues of small *Notgeld* in 1916.

Debasement The reduction in the precious metal content of the coinage, widely practised since time immemorial by governments for economic reasons. British coins, for example, were debased from sterling (.925 fine) silver to .500 in 1920 and from silver to cupro-nickel in 1947.

Decimalisation A currency system in which the principal unit is subdivided into ten, a hundred, or a thousand fractions. Russia was the first country to decimalise, in 1534 when the rouble of 100 kopeks was introduced, but it was not till 1792 that France adopted the franc of 100 centimes and 1793 when the USA introduced the dollar of 100 cents. Most European countries decimalised their currency in the 19th century. Britain toyed with the idea, introducing the florin or tenth of a pound in 1849 as the first step, but did not complete the process till 1971. The last countries to decimalise were Malta and Nigeria, in 1972 and 1973 respectively.

Demidiated Heraldic term to describe the junction of two armorial devices, in which only half of each is shown.

Demonetisation The withdrawal of coins or paper money from circulation and declaring them to be worthless.

Device Heraldic term for the pattern or emblem on coins or paper notes.

Die Hardened piece of metal bearing a mirror image of the device to be struck on one side of a coin or medal.

Die Proof An impression, usually pulled on soft carton or India paper, of an *intaglio* engraving of a banknote, usually taken during the progress of the engraving to check the detail. Banknote proofs of this nature usually consist of the portrait or some detail of the design, such as the border, rather than the complete motif.

Dodecagonal Twelve-sided, a term applied to the nickel-brass threepence of Great Britain, 1937–67.

Dump Any primitive coin struck on a very thick *flan*, but more specifically applied to the circular pieces cut from the centre of Spanish dollars, countermarked with the name of the colony, a crown and the value, and circulated in New South Wales at 15 pence in 1813. See *Holey Dollar*.

Duodecimal Currency system based on units of twelve, i.e. medieval money of account (12 denarii = 1 soldo) which survived in Britain as 12 pence to the shilling as late as 1971.

Ecclesiastical Coins Coins struck by a religious authority, such as an archbishop, bishop, abbot, prior or the canons of a religious order. Such coins were common in medieval times but survived as late as the early 19th century, the bishops of Breslau (1817) and Gurk (1823) being the last prelates to exercise coinage rights. Coins were struck by authority of the Pope at Rome till 1870 but since 1929 coinage has been struck at the Italian state mint on behalf of the Vatican.

Edge Inscription Lettering on the edge of a coin or medal to prevent clipping. Alluding to this, the Latin motto *Decus et Tutamen* (an ornament and a safeguard) was applied to the edge of English milled coins in the reign of Charles II.

Edge Ornament An elaboration of the *grain* found on many milled coins to prevent clippi taking the form of tiny leaves, flore interlocking rings, pellets and zigzag patter In some cases the ornament appears betw layers of more conventional reeding.

EF Abbreviation for Extremely Fine.

Effigy An image or representation of a pers normally the head of state, a histori personage, or an allegorical figure, usually the *obverse* or "heads" side of a coin or med

Electrotype A reproduction of a coin or me made by an electrolytic process.

Electrum Alloy of gold and silver, sometin called white gold, used for minting the stat of Lydia, 7th century BC, and other ea European coins.

Elongated Coin An oval *medalet* created passing a coin, such as an American ce between rollers under pressure with the eff of squeezing it out and impressing on i souvenir or commemorative motif.

Emergency Money Any form of money us intimes of economic and political upheav when traditional kinds of currency are available. Examples include the comparativ crude silver coins issued by the Royalists duri the *Civil War* (1642–49), *obsidional* money, issu in time of siege, from Tyre (1122) to Mafeki (1900), the *Notgeld* issued by many Germ towns (1916–23), *encased money, fractio currency, guerrilla notes, invasion, liberation* a *occupation money* from the two World Wars a minor campaigns. Among the more rec examples may be cited the use of sweets a cheques in Italy (1976–77) and the issue coupons and vouchers in many of the countr of the former Soviet Union pending introduction of their own distinctive coins a notes.

Enamelled Coins Coins decorated enamelling the obverse and reverse motifs contrasting colours was an art practised many jewellers in Birmingham and Paris in 19th century, and revived in Europe a America in the 1970s.

Encased Money Postage and revenue stam enclosed in small metal and mica-faced dis circulated as small change in times emergency. The practice was invented by Jo Gault, a Boston sewing-machine salesm during the American Civil War (1862). T face of the stamp was visible through transparent window, while the back of the d was embossed with firms' advertisements. T practice was revived during and after the Fi World War when there was again a shortage small coins. Encased stamps have also be recorded from France, Austria, Norway, Germany and Monaco. See also under *Stamp Money*.

grailing Technical term for the close serrations or vertical bars round the edge of a coin, applied as a security device.

graving The art of cutting lines or grooves in plates, blocks or dies. Numismatically this takes the form of engraving images into the face of the dies used in striking coins, a process which has now been almost completely superseded by *hubbing* and the use of *reducing machinery*. In the production of paper money, *intaglio* engraving is still commonly practised. In this process the engraver cuts the design into a steel die and the printing ink lies in the grooves. The paper is forced under great pressure into the grooves and picks up the ink, and this gives banknotes their characteristic ridged feeling to the touch. Nowadays many banknotes combine traditional intaglio engraving with multicolour lithography or photogravure to defeat the would-be counterfeiter.

igraphy The study of inscriptions, involving the classification and interpretation of coin legends, an invaluable adjunct to the study of a coin series, particularly the classical and medieval coins which, in the absence of dates and mintmarks, would otherwise be difficult to arrange in chronological sequence.

sion The removal of the title or effigy of a ruler from the coinage issued after his or her death. This process was practised in imperial Rome, and applied to the coins of Caligula, Nero and Geta, as part of the more general practice of *damnatio memoriae* (damnation of the memory) ordered by the Senate.

or Mistakes on coins and paper money may be either caused at the design or engraving stage, or as a result of a fault in the production processes. In the first category come misspellings in legends causing, in extreme cases, *blundered inscriptions*, or anachronisms or inaccuracies in details of the design. In the second, the most glaring error is the mule caused by marrying the wrong dies. Faulty alignment of dies can cause obverse and reverse to be out of true. Although many coins are issued with obverse and reverse upside down in relation to each other, this can also occur as an error in coins where both sides should normally be facing the same way up. Other errors caused at the production stage include striking coins in the wrong metal or with the wrong *collar* thus creating a different edge from the normal (e.g. British 10p with scalloped Hong Kong edge).

Essay (From the French *essai*, a trial piece). The term is applied to any piece struck for the purposes of examination, by parliamentary or financial bodies, prior to the authorisation of an issue of coins or paper money. The official nature of these items distinguishes them from *patterns*, which denote trial pieces often produced by mints or even private individuals bidding for coinage contracts.

Evasion Close copy or imitation of a coin, with sufficient deliberate differences in the design or inscription to avoid infringing counterfeit legislation. A good example is the imitation of Sumatran coins by European merchants, inscribed SULTANA instead of SUMATRA.

Exergue Lower segment of a coin or medal, usually divided from the rest of the *field* by a horizontal line, and often containing the date, value, ornament or identification symbols.

Exonumia Generic term for numismatic items not authorised by a government, e.g. *patterns*, *tokens*, *medalets* or *model coins*.

Face The surface of a coin, medal or token, referred to as the *obverse* or the *reverse*. The corresponding faces of a paper note are more correctly termed *verso* and *recto*, but the coin terms are often used instead.

An example of a "Facing" portrait on the obverse of a medallion of Henry Simms, 1901. Actual size 360mm.

Facing Term for the portrait, usually on the obverse, which faces to the front instead of to the side (profile).

Fantasy Piece of metal purporting to be the coinage of a country which does not exist. Recent examples include the money of Atlantis and the Hutt River Province which declared its independence of Western Australia.

FDC Abbreviation for *Fleur de Coin*, a term denoting the finest possible condition of a coin.

Fiat Money Paper notes issued by a government but not redeemable in coin or bullion.

Field Flat part of the surface of a coin or medal, between the *legend*, the *effigy* and other raised parts of the design.

Fillet Heraldic term for the ribbon or headband on the effigy of a ruler or allegorical figure.

Find Term applied to an archaeological discovery of one or more coins. A large quantity of such material is described as a *hoard*.

Flan Alternative name for *blank* or *planchet*, the piece of metal struck between dies to produce a coin or medal.

Forgery An unauthorised copy or imitation, made with the intention of deceiving collectors. Forgeries intended to pass current for real coins or notes are more properly called *counterfeits*.

Fractional Currency Emergency issue of small-denomonation notes by the USA in 1863–5, following a shortage of coins caused by the Civil War. This issue superseded the *Postage Currency* notes, but bore the inscription "Receivable for all US stamps", alluding to the most popular medium of small change at that time. Denominations ranged from 3c to 50c.

Franklinium Cupro-nickel alloy developed by the Franklin Mint of Philadelphia and used for coins, medals and gaming tokens since 1967.

Freak An *error* or *variety* of a non-recurring type, usually caused accidentally during production.

Frosting Matt surface used for the high relief areas of many proof coins and medals, for greater contrast with the mirrored surface of the field.

Funeral Money Imitations of banknotes, used in China and Latin America in funeral ceremonies.

Geat (Git) Channel through which molten metal is ducted to the mould. Cast coins and medals often show tiny protrusions known as geat marks.

Ghost Faint image of the design on one side of a coin visible on the other. Good examples were the British penny and halfpenny of George V, 1911–27, the ghosting being eliminated by the introduction of a smaller effigy in 1928.

Globular Coins struck on very thick *dumps* with convex faces. The term is applied to some Byzantine coins, and also the *bullet money* of Siam (Thailand).

Godless (or *Graceless*) Epithet applied to any coin which omits the traditional reference to the deity, e.g. the British florin of 1849 which omitted D.G. (*Dei Gratia*, "by the Grace of God").

Gold Precious metal, atomic symbol and numismatic abbreviation *Au*, from the *Latin Aurum*, used as a coinage medium from the 7th century BC till the present day. The purit gold is reckoned in *carats* or a decimal syst Thus British gold sovereigns are 22 carat .916 fine. Medieval coins were 23.5 carat or . fine, and some modern bullion coins virtually pure gold, denoted by the inscript .999. Canadian maple leaves are now struck "four nines" gold and bear the inscription .9

Goodfor Popular name for token coins *emergency money* made of paper or card, fr the inscription "Good for" or its equivalen other languages (e.g. French *Bon pour* or Du *Goed voor*) followed by a monetary value. T have been recorded from Europe, Africa America during times of economic crises shortage of more traditional coinage.

Gothic Crown Popular name for the silver cro issued by the United Kingdom (1847–53), called on account of its script (more prope Old English, rather than Gothic).

Grain The weight of a single grain of wheat taken as the smallest unit of weight in Engla The troy grain was 1/5760 of a pound, w the avoirdupois grain was 1/7000 pound, former being used in the weighing of preci metals and thus employed by numismatist weighing coins. A grain is 1/480 troy ounc 0.066 gram in the metric system.

Graining Term sometimes used as a synon for the *reeding* on the edge of milled coins.

Gripped Edge Pattern of indentations found the majority of American cents of 1797, cau by the milling process. Coins of the same d with a plain edge are rather scarcer.

Guerrilla Money Money issued in areas un the control of guerrillas and partisans dur wartime range from the *veld ponds* of the Bo (1900–2) to the notes issued by the Garib Brigade in Italy and the anti-fascist notes Tito's forces in Yugoslavia. The most pro issues were those produced in Luz Mindanao and Negros Occidental by Filipino resistance during the Japan occupation (1942–5).

Guilloche French term signifying the intric pattern of curved lines produced by the r engine and used as a security feature in production of banknote, cheques, stocks a share certificates.

Gun Money Emergency coinage of Ireland (16 –91) minted from gunmetal, a type of bro used in the casting of cannon. denominations of James II, from the sixpe to the crown, normally struck in silver, w produced in this base metal.

Gutschein German word for voucher or coup denoting the paper money used aboard sh of the Imperial Navy during the First Wo

War. The last issue was made at Scapa Flow, 1918–19, during the internment of the High Seas Fleet.

mmered Term denoting coins produce by the traditional method of striking a *flan* laid on an anvil with a hammer. A characteristic of hammered coins is their uneven shape which tended to encourage *clipping*. This abuse was gradually eliminated by the introduction of the screw press in the 15th century and the mechanisation of coining processes in the course of the 16th and 17th centuries.

rd Times" tokens issued by the New York and lem Railroad Company.

rd Times Token Copper piece the size of the large cent, issued in the USA, 1834–44, during a shortage of coins caused by the collapse of the Bank of the United States, the panic of 1837 and the economic crisis of 1839, the landmarks in the period known as the Hard Times. Banks suspended *specie* payments and the shortage of coinage was filled by tradesmen's tokens. Many of these were more in the nature of satirical *medalets* than circulating pieces.

t Piece Alternative name for the *bonnet piece* of James VI of Scotland, 1591.

ll Notes Imitation paper money used in Chinese funeral ceremonies and buried with the dead to pay for services in the next world.

ard Accumulation of coins concealed in times of economic or political upheaval and discovered, often centuries later. Under English common law, such hoards are subject to th law of *treasure trove* if they contain precious metal.

g Money Popular name for the early coinage of Bermuda, issued about 1616. The coins were minted in brass with a silver wash and circulated at various values from twopence to a shilling. They derived their name from the hog depicted on the obverse, an allusion to the pigs introduced to the island in 1515 by Juan Bermudez.

led Term denoting two different categories: (a) coins which have been pierced for suspension as a form of jewellery or talisman, and (b) coins which have a hole as part of their design. In the latter category come the Chinese *cash* with a square hole, and numerous issues of the 19th and 20th centuries from many countries, with the object of reducing weight and metal without sacrificing overall diameter.

Holey Dollar Spanish silver peso of 8 reales with the centre removed. The resultant ring was counter-marked "New South Wales" and dated 1813, with "Five Shillings" on the reverse, and placed into circulation during a shortage of British coin. The centre, known as a *dump*, was circulated at 15 pence.

Hub Heavy circular piece of steel on which the *die* for a coin or medal is engraved. The process of cutting the die and transferring the master die, by means of intermediary *punches*, to the die from which the coins will be struck, is known as hubbing. Soft steel is used in the preliminary process, and after the design has been transferred, the hub is hardened by chemical action.

Hybrid Alternative name for a *mule*.

Imitation Money Also known as play money or toy money, it consists of coins and notes produced for games of chance (like Monopoly), children's toy shops and post offices, as tourist souvenirs, or for political satire (e.g. the shrinking pound or dollar). See also *funeral money, hell notes, model coins* and *skit notes*.

Imprint Inscription on a paper note giving the name of the printer.

Incuse Impression which cuts into the surface of a coin or medal, as opposed to the more usual raised relief. Many of the earliest coins, especially those with a device on one side only, bear an incuse impression often in a geometric pattern. An incuse impression appears on one side of the coins, reflecting the image on the other side. Few modern coins have had an incuse design, notable examples being the American half and quarter eagle gold coins of 1908–29 designed by Bela Pratt. Incuse inscriptions on a raised rim, however, are more common, and include the British *Cartwheel* coins of 1797 and the 20p coins since 1982.

Inflation Money Coins produced as a result of inflation date back to Roman times when bronze minimi, little bigger than a pinhead, circulated as denarii. Nearer the present day inflation has had devastating effects on the coinge and banknotes of Germany (1921–3), Austria (1923), Poland (1923), Hungary (1945–6), Greece (1946) and many Latin American countries since the 1980s. Hungary holds the record for the highest value of any note ever issued — one thousand million adopengos, which is written as 20,000,000,000,000,000,000,000,000,000 pengos.

Ingot Piece of precious metal, usually cast in a mould, and stamped with the weight and fineness. though mainly used as a convenient method of storing bullion, ingots have been used as currency in many countries, notably Russia and Japan.

Inlay Insertion into the surface of a coin or medal of another substance for decorative effect. e.g. Poland Amber Trade Routes 20zl (amber), Isle of Man Queen Mother centenery (pearl) and various coins incorporating rubies or diamonds.

Intaglio Form of *engraving* in which lines are cut into a steel die for the recess-printing of banknotes.

Intrinsic The net metallic value of a coin, as distinguished from the nominal or face value.

Iron Metal, chemical symbol *Fe* (from Latin *Ferrum*), used as a primitive form of currency from classical times onwards. Iron spits (obeliskoi) preceded the obol as the lowest unit of Greek coinage, a handful of six spits being worth a drachma (from *drassomai*, "I grasp"). Cast iron coins were issued in China as a substitute for copper *cash*. Many of the emergency token issues of Germany during the First World War were struck in iron. Iron coins were issued by Bulgaria in 1943. See also *Steel*.

Ithyphallic (Greek for "erect penis"). Term descriptive of coins of classical Greece showing a satyr.

Janiform Double profiles back to back, after the Roman god Janus.

Jeton (From French *jeter*, to throw). Alternative term for *counter*, and used originally on the chequerboard employed by medieval accountants. Nuremberg was the most important centre for the production of medieval jetons, often issued in lengthy portrait series. In modern parlance the term is often synonymous with *token*, though more specifically confined to pieces used in vending equipment, parking meters, laundromats, telephones and urban transport systems in many European countries. Apart from security, removing the temptation of vandals to break into the receptacles, the main advantage of such pieces is that they can be retariffed as charges increase, without any alteration in their design or composition, a method that is far cheaper than altering costly equipment to take larger coins.

Jugate (From Latin *jugum*, a yoke). Alternative to *accolated* or *conjoined* to denote overlapping profiles of rulers.

Key Date Term describing the rarest in a long-running series of coins with the dates changed at annual intervals.

Kipperzeit German term meaning the time of clipped money, denoting the period during and after the Thirty Years War (1618–48) in which debased and clipped money was in circulation.

Klippe Rectangular or square pieces of me bearing the impression of a coin. Coins of t type were first struck in Sweden in the 1 century and were subsequently produced many of the German states. The idea has be revived in recent years as a medium for strik commemorative pieces.

Knife Money Cast bronze pieces, with elongated blade and a ring at one end facilitate stringing together in bunches, w used as currency in China from the 9th cent BC until the 19th century.

Kreditivsedlar (Swedish for "credit notes"). T name given to the first issue of paper mo made in the western world. Paper money this type was the brainchild of Johan Palmstr at Riga in 1652, but nine years elapsed befor was implemented by the Stockholm Bank. T notes were redeemable in copper *platmynt*.

Laureate Heraldic term for a laurel wreath, of framing a state emblem or shown, in the Ron fashion, as a crown on the ruler's forehead

Leather Money Pieces of leather embossed w an official device have been used as money various occasions, including the sieges Faenza and Leiden and in the Isle of Man in 15th and 16th centuries. Several towns Austria and Germany produced leather tok during and after the First World War.

Legal Tender Coins or paper money which declared by law to be current money and wh tradesmen and shopkeers are obliged to acc in payment for goods or services. (See *Mo and the Law*).

Legend The inscription on a coin or medal.

Liberation Money Paper money prepared use in parts of Europe and Asia, formerly un Axis occupation. Liberation notes were us in France, Belgium and the Netherlands 1944–5, while various Japanese and Chin notes were overprinted for use in Hong Kc when it was liberated in 1945. Indian no overprinted for use in Burma were issued 1945–6 when that country was freed fr Japanese occupation.

Ligature (From Latin *ligatus*, bound togeth Term denoting the linking of two letters i *legend*, e.g. Æ and Œ.

Long Cross Coinage Type of coinage introdu by King Henry III in 1247, deriving its na from the reverse which bore a cross wh arms extended right to the edge to h safeguard the coins against *clipping*. T remained the style of the silver penny, fractions and multiples, till the reign of He VII, and vestiges of the long cross theme can seen in the silver coins throughout t remaining years of the Tudor period.

ve Token A coin which has been altered by smoothing one or both surfaces and engraving initials, dates, scenes, symbols of affection and messages thereon.

shbourne English word for base pennies of inferior silver, said to have emanated from Luxembourg, from which the name derived. These coins were first minted under John the Blind who adopted the curious spelling of his name EIWANES in the hope that illiterate English merchants might confuse it with EDWARDVS and thus be accepted as coin issued in the name of Edward III. Lushbournes were also minted by Robert of Bethune, William I of Namur and the bishops of Toul during the mid-14th century.

stre The sheen or bloom on the surface of an uncirculated coin resulting from the centrifugal flow of metal caused by striking.

gnimat Trade name used by VDM (*Verein Deutscher Metallwerke*) for a high-security alloy containing copper, nickel and magnetised steel. First used for the 5 deutschemark coin of 1975, it has since been adopted for other high-value coins in Germany and other countries.

anilla Copper, bronze or brass rings, sometimes shaped like horseshoes and sometimes open, with flattened terminals, used as currency in West Africa until recent years.

atrix Secondary die for a coin or medal, produced from the master die by means of an intermediate punch. In this way dies can be duplicated from the original cut on the reducing machine.

att or Matte Finely granulated surface or overall satin finish to proof coins, a style which was briefly fashionable at the turn of the century. The Edward VII proof set of 1902 is a notable example. In more recent years many issues of the Franklin Mint have been issued in this finish.

aundy Money Set of small silver coins, in denominations of 1, 2, 3 and 4 pence, distributed by the reigning British monarch to the poor and needy on Maundy Thursday. The custom dates back to the Middle Ages, but in its present form, of distributing pence to as many men and women as the years in the monarch's age, it dates from 1666. At first ordinary silver pennies and multiples were used but after they went out of everyday use distinctive silver coins were produced specifically for the purpose from the reign of George II (1727–60) onwards. For centuries the ceremony took place in Westminster Abbey but since 1955 other venues have been used in alternate years.

edal (French *medaille*, Italian *medaglia*, from Latin *metallum*). A piece of metal bearing devices and legends commemorating an event or person, or given as an award. Military medals date from the 16th and 17th centuries, but were not generally awarded to all ranks till the 19th century. Commemorative medals can be traced back to Roman times, but in their present form they date from the Italian Renaissance when there was a fashion for large cast portrait medals.

Medalet A small medal, generally 25mm or less in diameter.

Medallion Synonym for medal, but usually confined to those with a diameter of 50mm or more.

Milling Process denoting the mechanical production of coins, as opposed to the handmade technique implied in *hammering*. It alludes to the use of watermills to drive the machinery of the screw presses and blank rollers developed in the 16th century. As the even thickness and diameter of milled coins permitted a security edge, the term milling is popularly, though erroneously, used as a synonym for *graining* or *reeding*.

Mint The place in which coins and medals are produced. Mint condition is a term sometimes used to denote pieces in an uncirculated state.

Mint Set A set of coins or medals in the package or case issued by the mint. See also *year set*.

Mintmark A device appearing on a coin to denote the place of minting. Athenian coins of classical times have been recorded with up to 40 different marks, denoting individual workshops. In the 4th century AD the Romans adopted this system to identify coins struck in provincial mints. This system was widely used in the Middle Ages and survives in France and Germany to this day. Initials and symbols are also used to identify mints, especially where the production of a coin is shared between several different mints. From 1351 onwards symbols were adopted in England to denote periods between trials of the *Pyx*, and thus assist the proper chronological sequence of coins, in an era prior to the adoption of dating. These mintmarks continued into the 17th century, but gradually died out as the use of dates became more widespread. See also *countermark* and *privy mark*.

Mionnet Scale Scale of nineteen diameters covering all sizes of coins belonging to the classical period, devised by the French numismatist, Theodore-Edme Mionnet (1770–1842) during the compilation of his fifteen-volume catalogue of the numismatic collection in the Bibliotheque Nationale in Paris.

Mirror Finish The highly polished surface of proof coins.

Misstrike A coin or medal on which the impression has been struck off-centre.

Model Coin Tiny pieces of metal, either reproducing the designs of existing coins (used as play money by children) or, more specifically, denoting patterns produced by Joseph Moore and Hyam Hyams in their attempts to promote an improved subsidiary coinage in 19th century Britain. These small coins were struck in bronze with a brass or silver centre and were designed to reduce the size of the existing cumbersome range of pence, halfpence and farthings.

Modified Effigy Any coin in which the profile on the obverse has been subtly altered. Examples include minor changes in the Victorian Young Head and Old Head effigies and the George V profile by Sir Bertram Mackennal.

Money Order Certificate for a specified amount of money, which may be transmitted by post and encashed at a money order office or post office. This system was pioneered by Britain and the United States in the early 19th century and is now virtually worldwide. The term is now confined to certificates above a certain value, the terms *postal order* and *postal note* being used for similar certificates covering small amounts.

Mule Coin whose obverse is not matched with its official or regular reverse. Mules include the erroneous combination of dies from different reigns, but in recent years such hybrids have arisen in mints where coins for several countries are struck. Examples include the Coronation Anniversary crowns combining Ascension and Isle of Man dies and the 2 cent coins with Bahamas and New Zealand dies. *Restrikes* of rare American coins have been detected in which the dated die has been paired with the wrong reverse die, e.g. the 1860 restrike of the rare 1804 large cent.

Mute An *anepigraphic* coin, identifiable only by the devices struck on it.

Nail Mark Small indentation on ancient coins. The earliest coins of Asia Minor developed from the electrum *dumps* which merchants marked with a broken nail as their personal guarantee of value, the ancient counterpart of the *chop* marks used in China and Japan.

NCLT Coins Abbreviation for "Non Circulating Legal Tender", a term devised by modern coin catalogues to denote coins which, though declared *legal tender*, are not intended for general circulation on account of their precious metal content or superior finish.

Nicked Coin Coin bearing a tiny cut or nick in its edge. Silver coins were tested by this method, especially in the reign of Henry I (1100–35) when so many base silver pennies were circulation. Eventually people refused to acc these nicked coins a problem which was o overcome when the state decreed that all cc should have a nick in them.

Nickel Metallic element, chemical symbol N hard white metal relatively resistant to tarni and extensively used as a cheap substitute silver. It was first used for the American 5 c coin in 1866, hence its popular name which stuck ever since, although nowadays the hig denominations are minted in an alloy of cop and nickel. Although best known as a sil substitute, nickel was widely used in Jama (1869–1969) for halfpence and pennies and British West Africa for the tiny 1/10th penr (1908–57). Pure nickel is used for French fra and German marks, but usually it is alloy with copper or zinc to produce *cupro-nicke* nickel brass.

Notaphily Hybrid word from Latin *nota* (nc and Greek philos (love), coined about 197(denote the branch of numismatics devoted the study of paper money.

Notgeld German word meaning emerge money, applied to the *tokens*, in metals, wo leather and even ceramic materials, issu during the First World War when coina disappeared from circulation. These tok were soon superseded by low-denominat paper money issued by shops and businessm in denominations from 10 to 50 pfennige a known as *kleine Notgeld* (small emerge money). These notes were prohibited September 1922 but by that time some 50,(varieties are thought to have been issu Inflation raced out of control and t government permitted a second issue of lo notes, known as *large Notgeld*, as the deno nations were in thousands, and latterly millio of marks. Some 3,600 types appeared in 1 and over 60,000 in 1923 alone. These mement of the German hyperinflation ceased to circul in 1924 when the currency was reformed.

Numismatics The study of coins, medals a other related fields, a term derived from Latin *numisma* and Greek *nomisma* (money)

Obsidional Currency (From Latin *obsidium* siege). Term for *emergency money* produced the defenders of besieged towns and cities. Th usually took the form of pieces of silver pla commandeered for the purpose, crudely mark with an official device and the value. Instance such seige coinage have been recorded from 12th to the 19th centuries. Paper money w issued in Venice during the Austrian siege 1848, and by Mafeking during the Boer War.

Obverse The "heads" side of a coin or med

generally bearing the effigy of the head of state or an allegorical figure (e.g. Liberty—Argentina, USA; Helvetia or William Tell—Switzerland; or La Semeuse—France).

f Metal Term denoting a piece struck in a metal other than the officially authorisied or issued alloy. This originally applied to *patterns* which were often struck in lead or copper instead of gold and silver as trial pieces or to test the dies; but in recent years it has applied to collectors' versions, e.g. proofs in platinum, gold or silver of coins normally issued in bronze or cupro-nickel.

'erdate One or more digits in a date altered by superimposing another figure. Alterations of this kind, by means of small hand punches, were made to dated dies so that they could be used in years other than that of the original manufacture. Coins with overdates invariably show traces of the original digit.

'erstrike Coin, token or medal produced by using a previously struck pieces as a flan. The Bank of England dollar of 1804 was overstruck on Spanish pieces of eight, and examples showing traces of the original coins are worth a good premium.

duan Name given to imitations of medals and bogus coins produced in Italy in the 16th century, and deriving from the city of Padua where forgeries of bronze sculpture were produced for the antique market.

tina Oxidation forming on the surface of metallic objects. So far as coins and medals are concerned, this applies mainly to silver, brass, bronze and copper pieces which may acquire oxidation from the atmosphere, or spectacular patination from salts in the ground in which they have been buried. In extreme forms patina leads to verdigris and other forms of rust which corrode the surface, but in uncirculated coins it may be little more than a mellowing of the original *lustre*. Coins preserved in blue velvet presentation cases often acquire a subtle toning from the dyes in the material.

ttern Piece resembling a coin or medal, prepared by the mint to the specifications or on the authorisation of the coin-issuing authority, but also applied to pieces produced by mints when tendering for coinage or medal contracts. Patterns may differ from the final coins as issued in the type of alloy used (*off metal*) but more often they differ in details of the design.

llet Raised circular ornament used as a spacing device between words and abbreviations in the *legend* of coins and medals. Groups of pellets were also used as ornaments in the angles of the cross on the reverse of English silver pennies.

ece de Plaisir (French for "fancy piece"). Term given to coins struck in a superior precious metal, or to a superior finish, or on a much thicker flan than usual. See *off metal*, *piedfort* and *proof*.

A piedfort £1 coin compared to one of a normal flan.

Piedfort (Piefort) Piece struck with coinage dies on a *flan* of much more than normal thickness. This practice originated in France in the late 16th century and continues to the present day. In recent years it has been adopted by mints in Britain and other countries as a medium for collectors' pieces.

Pile Lower die incorporating the obverse motif, used in striking coins and medals. See also *trussel*.

Planchet French term used as an alternative for *blank* or *flan*.

Plaque or **Plaquette** Terms sometimes used for medals struck on a square or rectangular flan.

Plaster Cast taken from the original model for a coin or medal sculpted by an artist, and used in modern reducing machines in the manufacture of the master *die*.

Plated Coins Coins stuck in base metal but given a wash of silver or some other precious metal. This expedient was adopted in inflationary times, from the Roman Republic (91 BC) till the Tudor period. American cents of 1943 were struck in steel with a zinc coating, and more recently *clad* coins have produced similar results.

Platinum The noblest of all precious metals, platinum has a higher specific gravity than gold and a harder, brighter surface than silver. Until an industrial application was discovered in the mid-19th century, it was regarded as of little value, and was popular with counterfeiters as a cheap substitute for gold in their forgeries which, with a light gold wash, could be passed off as genuine. It was first used for circulating coins in Russia (the chief source of the metal since 1819) and 3, 6 and 12 rouble coins were mined at various times between 1828 and 1845. In recent years platinum has been a popular metal for limited-edition proof coins.

Platmynt (Swedish for "plate money"). Large copper plates bearing royal cyphers and values from half to ten dalers produced in Sweden between 1643 and 1768. They represented laudable attempts by a country rich in copper to produce a coinage in terms of its silver value, but the net result was far too cumbersome to be practical. The weight of the daler plate, for example, ranged from 766 grams to 1.1kg, and special carts had to be devised to transport them!

Plugged Coins Coins struck predominantly in one metal, but containing a small plug of another. This curious practice may be found in the farthings of Charles II (1684–85) and the halfpence or farthings of James II (1685–87), which were struck in tin, with a copper plug, to defeat forgers.

Pollard Alternative name for *crockard*.

Porcelain Money Tokens made of porcelain circulated in Thailand from the late 18th century till 1868. The Meissen pottery struck tokens in 1920–22 as a form of small *Notgeld*, using reddish-brown Bottger stoneware and white *bisque* porcelain. These ceramic tokens circulated in various towns of Saxony.

Postage Currency Small paper notes in denominations of 5, 10, 25 and 50 cents, issued by the US federal government in 1862–63, were thus inscribed and had reproductions of postage stamps engraved on them — five 5c stamps on the 25c and five 10c stamps on the 50c notes. The earliest issue even had perforations in the manner of stamps, but this unnecessary device was soon done away with. See also *stamp money*.

Postal Notes or Orders Low-value notes intended for transmission by post and encashable at post offices. Introduced by Britain in 1883, they were an extension of the earlier *money order* system, and are now issued by virtually every country.

Potin (French for pewter). Alloy of copper, tin, lead and silver used as a coinage metal by the Celtic tribes of eastern Gaul at the beginning of the Christian era.

Privy Mark Secret mark incorporated in the design of a coin or medal to identify the minter, or even the particular die used. The term is also used more loosely to denote any small symbol or initials appearing on a coin other than a *mint mark*, and is sometimes applied to the symbols associated with the trial of the *Pyx* found on English coins.

Prize Coins Coins of large size and value struck primarily as prizes in sporting contests. this principle dates from the late 5th century BC when Syracuse minted decadrachms as prizes in the Demareteian Games. The most notable example in modern times is the lengthy series of talers and five-franc coins issued by the Swiss cantons since 1842 as prizes in the annual shooting festivals, the last of which honoured the Lucerne contest of 1939.

Profile A side view of the human face, widely used as a coinage effigy.

Proof Originally a trial strike testing the d but now denoting a special collectors' vers struck with dies that have been speci polished on *flans* with a mirror finish. Pres operating at a very slow speed, or multi-strik processes, are also used.

Propaganda Notes Paper money containin political slogan or a didactic element. During Second World War forgeries of German a Japanese notes were produced by the Allies a additionally inscribed or overprinted with slog such as "Co-Prosperity Sphere—What is worth?" (a reference to the Japanese occup areas of SE Asia). Forged dollars with a American propaganda were airdropped o Sicily by the Germans in 1943 and counter pounds with Arabic propaganda over Egyp 1942–43. Various anti-communist organisati liberated propaganda forgeries of paper mo by balloon over Eastern Europe during the C War period.

Provenance Mark Form of *privy mark* denot the source of the metal used in coins. Examp include the plumes or roses on English co denoting silver from Welsh or West of Engla mines, and the elephant or elephant and ca on gold coins denoting bullion imported by African Company. Coins inscribed VI (1702–03) or LIMA (1745–46) denote bull seized from the Spaniards by Anglo-Du privateers and Admiral Anson respective Other provenance marks on English co include the letters EIC and SSC, denoti bullion imported by the East India Compa or the South Sea Company.

Pseudo Coins Derisory term coined in rec years to signify pieces of precious metal, of struck in *proof* versions only, aimed at international investment market. Many of th pieces, though bearing a nominal face val are not *legal tender* in the countries purporti to issue them and in many cases they go strai from the overseas mint where they produced to coin dealers in America a western Europe, without ever appearing in so-called country of origin. See also *NC coins*.

Punch or Puncheon Intermediate *die* where working dies can be duplicated from the mas die, prior to the striking of coins and meda

Pyx Box in which a specimen from every pounds troy weight of gold and every 60 pour of silver minted in England is kept for ann trial by weight and assay. Many of *mintmarks* on English coins of the 14th–1 centuries were in use from one trial to the n and still exist today and can therefore be us to date them.

Reducing Machinery Equipment designed the pantographic principle for transferring t image from a *plaster* to a *hub* and reducing it to the size of the actual coin or medal. The image is transferred by means of a stylus operating rather like a gramophone needle, but working from the centre to the outer edge.

eding Security edging on coins, consisting of close vertical ridges. As a rule, this appears all round the edge but some coins, e.g. New Zealand's 50c (1967) and the Isle of Man's £1 (1978) have segments of reeding alternating with a plain edge, to help blind and partially sighted persons to identify these coins.

-issue A coin or note issued again after an extended lapse of time.

lief Raised parts of the *obverse* and *reverse* of coins and medals, the opposite of *incuse*.

mainder A note from a bank or issuing authority which has never been circulated, due to inflation, political changes or bank failure. Such notes, some-times in partial or unfinished state (e.g. missing serial numbers or signatures), are generally unloaded on to the numismatic market at a nominal sum and provide a good source of inexpensive material for the beginner.

strike Coin, medal or token produced from *dies* subsequent to the original use. Usually restrikes are made long after the original and can often be identified by marks caused by damage, pitting or corrosion of the dies after they were taken out of service.

trograde Term describing inscriptions running from right to left, or with the letters in a mirror image, thought to arise from unskilled die-cutters failing to realise that inscriptions have to be engraved in negative form to achieve a positive impression. Retrograde inscriptions are common on ancient Greek coins, but also found on Roman and Byzantine coins.

verse The side of a coin or medal regarded as of lesser importance; in colloquial parlance, the "tails" side.

ltire Heraldic term for a cross in the shape of an X.

ndwich Coin *blank* consisting of thin outer layers in one alloy bonded to a core in another. See *clad coins*.

eat (Anglo-Saxon for "treasure", or German *Schatz*). Money of account in Kent early in the 7th century as the twelfth part of a shilling or Merovingian gold tremissis. As a silver coin, it dates from about AD 680–700 and weighed about 20 grains, putting it on par with the Merovingian denier or penny. Sceats spread to other parts of England in the 8th century but tended to decline in weight and value, but from about 760 it was gradually superseded by the silver penny minted under Offa and his successors.

cissel The clippings of metal left after a *blank* has been cut. Occasionally one of these clippings accidentally adheres to the blank during the striking process, producing characteristic crescent-shaped flaws on the finished coin.

Scrip Paper money of restricted validity or circulation, e.g.*Bafs* and other military scrip used in canteens and post exchanges.

Scyphate (Greek *scypha*, a skiff or small boat). Byzantine coin with a concave *flan*.

Sede Vacante (Latin for "Vacant See"). Coins struck at *ecclesiastical mints* between the death of a prelate and the election of his successor are often thus inscribed. This practice originated at Rome in the 13th century and spread to every part of Europe.

Seignorage or Seigneurage Royalty or percentage paid by persons bringing *bullion* to a mint for conversion into coin, but nowadays synonymous with the royalty paid by mints in respect of the precious metal versions of coins sold direct to collectors. It arises from the medieval right of the king to a small portion of the proceeds of a mint, and amounted to a tax on moneying. It has also been applied to the money accruing to the state when the coinage is re-issued in an alloy of lesser fineness, as, for example, the debased sovereigns of Henry VIII in 20 instead of 23 carat gold, the king's treasury collecting the difference.

Series Term applied to sets of medals of a thematic character, which first became fashionable in the early 18th century. Jean Dassier pioneered the medallic series in the 1720s with his set of 72 medals portraying the rulers of France till Louis XV. The idea was developed by J. Kirk, Sir Edward Thomason, J. Mudie and A. J. Stothard in Britain, and by Moritz Fuerst and Amedee Durand in Europe. The fashion died out in the 19th century, but has been revived in America and Europe since 1964.

Serrated Having a notched or toothed edge, rather like a cogwheel. Coins of this type, struck in *electrum*, an alloy of silver and gold, are known from Carthage in the 2nd century BC, and some silver denarii of Rome in the 2nd century AD also come into this category.

Sexagesimal System Monetary system in which the principal unit is divided into 60 parts. The oldest system in the Western world was based on the gold talent of 60 minae and the mina of 60 shekels. In medieval Europe 60 groschen were worth a fine mark; in England from 1551, the silver coinage was based on the crown of 60 pence, and in the south German states till 1873 the gulden was worth 60 kreuzers.

Shin Plasters Derisory term originally applied to the Continental currency notes issued during the American War of Independence, the fractional currency of the Civil War period and also the low-denomination notes of Canada between 1870 and 1935, but often applied indiscriminately to any other low-denomination, small-format notes.

Short Cross Coinage Term for the silver coinage introduced by Henry II in 1180 and minted till 1247 at which time it was replaced by the *Long Cross* type. The termination of the arms of the cross on the reverse well within the circumference encouraged the dishonest practice of *clipping*.

Shroff Mark A *countermark* applied by Indian bankers or merchants to attest the full weight and purity of coins. See also *chop*.

Siege Money See *Obsidional Currency*

Silver Precious metal, chemical symbol *Ag*, numismatic abbreviation *Ar*, from Latin *Argentum*, widely used as a coinage metal from the 6th century BC to the present day.

Sterling silver denotes an alloy of .925 fine silver with .075 copper. Fine silver alloys used over the past 2,500 years have ranged from .880 to .960 fine, but base silver has also been all too common. British coins from 1920 to 1946 were struck in .500 fine silver, while alloys of lesser fineness are known as *billon* or *vellon*. Silver alloyed with gold produces a metal called *electrum*, used for the earliest coinage of the western world, the staters of Lydia in the 7th century BC. Since 1970 silver as a medium for circulating coinage has almost virtually disappeared, yet the volume of silver coins for sale to collectors has risen considerably in recent years.

Skit Note Piece of paper masquerading as a banknote. It differs from a *counterfeit* in that its design parodies that of a genuine note, often for political, satirical or advertising reasons. Others were produced as April Fools' Day jokes or a form of Valentine (e.g. the Bank of Lovers). In recent years they have been produced as advertising gimmicks, or as coupons permitting a discount off the list price of goods.

Slug Popular name for the $50 gold pieces produced by private mints in California in the mid-19th century. The term is also applied nowadays to *tokens* intended for use in gaming machines.

Spade Guinea Name given to the guineas of George III issued between 1787 and 1799 because the shield on the reverse design resembled the shape of a spade. In Victorian times the spade guinea was extensively copied in brass for gaming counters.

Spade Money Cast bronze pieces resembling miniature spades and other agricultural implements, used as money and derived from the actual implements which had previously been used in barter. Often referred to as *Pu* or *Boo* money.

Specie Financial term denoting money in t form of precious metals (silver and gol usually struck as coin, as opposed to money the form of paper notes and bills of exchan It occurs in the name of some European co (e.g. *speciedaler*, *speciestaler* and *speciesducat*) denote the use of fine silver or gold.

Specimen Generally used to denote a sing piece, but more specifically applying to a co in a special finish, less than *proof* in quality b superior to the general circulating version. also denotes paper notes intended f circulation between banks or for press public and distinguished from the generally issu version by zero serial numbers, punch holes a security endorsement.

Spintriae Metal tokens produced in Rom imperial times, with erotic motifs, thought have been tickets of admission to brothels.

Spit Copper or iron rod used as a primitive fo of currency in the Mediterranean area. T Greek word *belos* meant a spit, dart or bolt, a from this came the word *obolos* used for a co worth a 6th of a drachma.

Stamp Money Both postage and revenue (fisca stamps have circulated as money duri shortages of coins, from the American Ci War onwards. *Encased postage stamps* we used in the USA, 1861–62, before they we superseded by *Postage Currency* notes, but t same expedient was adopted by many countri during and immediately after the First Wor War. Stamps affixed to special cards ha circulated as money in Rhodesia (no Zimbabwe) in 1900, the French colonies an Turkey during the First World War, in Spa during the Civil War (1936–39) and th Philippines during the Second World Wa Stamps printed on thick card, with a inscription on the reverse signifying their pari with silver coins, were issued in Russia (191 18) and also in Armenia, the Crimea and th Ukraine (1918–20). During the Second Wor War Ceylon (now Sri Lanka) and several India states issued small money cards wi contemporary stamps printed on them.

Steel Refined and tempered from *iron*, and use in chromed or stainless versions as a coinag metal in the 20th century. Zinc-coated ste cents were issued by the USA (1943) but in th form known as *acmonital* (nickel steel) it h been extensively used by Italy since 1939. Oth alloys of nickel and steel have been used fo coins of the Philippines (1944–45) an Roumania since 1963. Chrome steel was use by France for 5 centime coins in 1961–6 Copper-clad steel is now extensively used fo subsidiary coins formerly struck in bronze.

Sterling Word of uncertain origin denotin money of a standard weight and fineness, an hence the more general meaning of recognised worth. The traditionally accepted derivation from the Easterlings, north German merchants who settled in London in the 13th century and produced silver pennies of uniform fineness, is unlikely as the term has been found in documents a century earlier. A more plausible explanation is from Old English *steorling* ("little coin with a star"), alluding to Viking pennies with this device, or even as a diminutive of *stater*. Sterling silver denotes silver of .925 fineness.

one Money Primitive currency in the form of large stone discs, used in West Africa in the pre-colonial period, and in the Pacific island of Yap (now Micronesia) as recently as 1940.

riation A pattern of alternate light and dark parallel marks or minute grooves on the surface of a coin or medal. In the latter case it is sometimes done for textural effect, but in coins it may result from faulty *annealing*. Deliberate ridging of the surface, however, was a distinctive feature of Japanese *koban* and *goryoban* coins of 1736–1862.

yca Name given to the debased silver *sceats* of Northumbria in the 8th century.

el Chinese unit of weight corresponding to the European ounce and sometimes referred to as a liang. It was a measure of silver varying between 32 and 39 grams. In the 19th century it served as *money of account*, 100 British or Mexican trade dollars being worth 72 tael. The term has also been loosely applied to the Chinese silver yuan, although this was worth only .72 tael, or 7 mace and 2 candareens (10 candareens = 1 mace; 10 mace = 1 tael).

rymsa Early Anglo-Saxon gold coin based on the Merovingian tremissis or third-solidus, current in Kent, London and York about AD 63–75.

ical Unit of weight in Thailand, first appearing as coins in the form of crudely shaped *bullet money* current from the 14th till the late 19th centuries. When European-style coins were introduced in 1860 the word was retained as a denomination (32 solot = 16 atts = 8 peinung or sio = 4 songpy or sik = 2 fuang= 1 salung or quarter-tical. The currency was decimalised in 1909 (100 satangs = 1 tical), and the tical was superseded by the baht about 1950.

in Metallic element, chemical symbol *St* (from Latin *Stannum*). Because of its unstable nature and tendency to oxidise badly when exposed to the atmosphere, it is unsatisfactory as a coinage metal, but has been used on several occasions, notably in Malaya, Thailand and the East Indies. In was also used for British halfpence and farthings, 1672–92.

oken Any piece of money whose nominal value is greater than its intrinsic value is, strictly speaking, a token or promise. Thus most of the coins issued since 1964 can be regarded in this light, but numismatists reserve the term for a piece of limited validity and circulation, produced by tradesmen, chambers of commerce and other organisations during times of a shortage of government coinage. The term is also loosely applied to metal tickets of admission, such as *communion tokens*, or *jetons* and *counters* intended for games of chance. Tokens with a nominal value may be produced for security reasons to lessen the possibility of theft from milk bottles, vending machines, telephones, parking meters and transport facilities. Tokens exchangeable for goods have been issued by co-operative societies and used in prisons and internment camps in wartime. In addition to the traditional coinage alloys, tokens have been produced in ceramics, plastics, wood, stout card, leather and even rubber, in circular, square or polygonal shapes.

Tombac Type of brass alloy with a high copper content, used in coinage requiring a rich golden colour. It is, in fact, a modern version of the *aurichalcum* used by the Romans. It was used for the Canadian 5-cent coins of 1942–43, while 5- and 10-pfennig coins of Germany have a tombac cladding on a steel core.

Touchpiece Coin kept as a lucky charm, but more specifically the medieval gold angel of England which was worn round the neck as an antidote to scrofula, otherwise known as king's evil, from the belief that the reigning monarch possessed the power of healing by touch. The ceremony of touching for king's evil involved the suspension of an angel round the victim's neck, hence the prevalence of these coins pierced for suspension.

Trade Coins Coins widely used as a medium of international trade, often far beyond the boundaries of the country issuing them. The earliest examples were the Aiginetan turtles and Athenian tetrdrachms of the classical period. In the Middle Ages the English *sterling* was widely prized on account of its silver purity. Arab dinars and Italian florins were popular as gold coins in late-medieval times, while the British gold sovereign has been the preferred gold coin of modern times. The Maria Theresa silver thaler of Austria, with its date frozen at 1782, has been minted widely down to the present time for circulation in the Near and Middle East as a trade coin. Trade dollars were minted by Britain, the USA, the Netherlands and Japan to compete with the Spanish, and later the Mexican, peso or 8-reales coins as a trading medium in the Far East.

Transport Tokens Coin-like pieces of metal, plastic or card, issued by companies and corporations to employees and exchangeable for rides on municipal transport systems, date from the mid-19th century. In more recent times similar tokens have been used in many countries to activate turnstiles in buses, trams and rapid-transit railway systems.

Treasury Note Paper money worth 10 shillings or one pound, issued by the British Treasury on the outbreak of the First World War when *specie* payments were suspended, and continuing till 1928 when the Bank of England took over responsibility for note-issuing.

Treasure Trove Articles of precious metal concealed in times of economic or political upheaval and discovered years (often centuries) later are deemed by law to be treasure trove (from the French word *trouve,* found). For further details see *Money and the Law.*

Trial Plate Plate of the same metal as the current coinage against which the fineness and quality of the coins produced are compared and tested.

Troy Weight System of weights derived from the French town of Troyes whose standard pound was adopted in England in 1526. It continued in Britain till 1879 when it was abolished, with the exception of the troy ounce and its decimal parts and multiples, which were retained for gold, silver, platinum and precious stones. The troy ounce of 480 grains is used by numismatists for weighing coins.

Truncation Stylised cut at the base of a coinage effigy, sometimes containing a die number, engraver's initials or *mintmark.*

Trussel Reverse die in *hammered* coinage, the opposite of the *pile.*

Type Principal motif on a coin or medal, enabling numismatists to identify the issue.

Type Set A set of coins comprising one of each coin in a particular series, regardless of the actual date of issue.

Uncirculated Term used in grading coins to denote specimens in perfect condition, with original mint lustre. In recent years the term "Brilliant Uncirculated" has been adopted (abbreviated as BUnc or BU).

Uniface Coin, medal or token with a device on one side only.

Variety Variation in, or modification of type, effigy, motif or inscription.

Vecture Term (mainly US) for a *transport token.*

Veld Pond (Dutch for "field pound"). Gold coin struck by the Boer guerrillas at Pilgrims Rest in 1902, in imitation of the British sovereign.

Vellon Spanish form of *billon.*

VF Abbreviation for Very Fine, used to describe the state of a coin or medal.

VG Abbreviation for Very Good.

Vignette Strictly speaking the pictorial elem of a paper note shading off into the surround unprinted paper rather than having a clea defined border or frame; but nowadays appl generally to the picture portion of a bankn as opposed to portrait, armorial or nume elements.

Vis-à-Vis (French for "face to face"). Te describing coins with double portraits of rule their profiles or busts facing each other. A go example is the English coinage of Philip a Mary, 1554–58.

Wampum Barter currency of the North Americ Indians, composed of shells of *Venus mercena* strung together to form belts or "fathom worth 5 shillings. Wampum were tariff variously from three to six to the English pen in the American colonies till 1704.

White Gold Alternative term for *electrum.*

Wire Money Primitive currency of the Maldi Islands in the form of lengths of silver w known as lari, from which the modern curren unit *laree* is derived. The term was also appli to English coins of the 18th century in whi the numerals of value were exceptionally th resembling wire.

Wooden Coins Thin pieces of wood used tokens are known from many parts of Chi and Africa, and as small *Notgeld* from Aust and Germany during the First World W Wooden nickels is the somewhat contradicto name given to tokens of a commemorati nature, widely popular in the USA since 19

Year set. A set of coins issued annually by mint. It often contains specimens not genera released for circulation in that year.

Young Head Profile of Queen Victoria sculpt by William Wyon for the Guildhall Medal 1837 and subsequently utilised for British coi struck from 1837 to 1860 (copper) and 18 (silver and gold).

Zinc Metallic element, chemical symbol Z widely used, with copper, as a constituent brass. Alloyed with copper to form *tombac,* was used for Canadian 5-cent coins (1942–4 and, coated on steel, it was used for Americ cents (1943). Zinc was used for *emergency coina* in Austria, Belgium, Luxembourg and Germa (1915–18) and in Germany and Germa occupied countries during the Second Wor War. Since then alloys of copper, nickel ar zinc have been used for coinage in Easte Europe, and an alloy of zinc with titanium h been developed in the 1970s as a potenti substitute for *bronze* in subsidiary coinage.

Mintmarks
of the world

ıe following is a list of the initials and symbols denoting mints. In many cases, ›tably the Royal Mint, no mintmark was used on either British coins or those struck ı behalf of other countries. Conversely many countries have only used one mintmark, at of one or other of the leading private mints.

should be noted that the mintmarks of the main ivate mints have been recorded on the coins of e following countries:

(Heaton, later the Birmingham Mint): Australia, Bolivia, British Honduras, British North Borneo, British West Africa, Bulgaria, Canada, Ceylon, Chile, Colombia, Costa Rica, Cyprus, Dominican Republic, East Africa, Ecuador, Egypt, El Salvador, Finland, French Indochina, Great Britain, Greece, Guatemala, Guernsey, Haiti, Hong Kong, Iran, Israel, Italy, Jamaica, Jersey, Liberia, Malaya and British Borneo, Mauritius, Mombasa, Mozambique, Newfoundland, Nicaragua, Poland, Roumania, Sarawak, Serbia, Siam, Straits Settlements, Uruguay and Venezuela.

ʍ (Franklin Mint, Philadelphia): Bahamas, Belize, British Virgin Islands, Cayman Islands, Cook Islands, Guyana, Jamaica, Liberia, Malaysia, Malta, Panama, Papua New Guinea, Philippines, Solomon Islands, Trinidad and Tobago.

M (Pobjoy Mint, Sutton, Surrey): Ascension, Bosnia, Cook Islands, Gibraltar, Isle of Man, Liberia, Macau, Niue, Philippines, St Helena, Senegal, Seychelles, Tonga and Tristan da Cunha.

LBANIA

	London
	Rome
	Valona

RGENTINA

A	Buenos Aires
s	Buenos Aires
AS	Buenos Aires
'P	Jose Policarpo Patino
I	Mendoza
NP	Pedro Nolasco Pizarro
PP	Pedro Nolasco Pizarro
PTS	Potosi
R	Rioja
RA	Rioja
SE	Santiago del Estero
SoEo	Santiago del Estero
TN	Tucuman

AUSTRALIA

A	Perth
D	Denver
H	Heaton (1912–16)
I	Bombay (1942–43)
I	Calcutta (1916–18)
M	Melbourne
P	Perth
PL	Royal Mint, London
S	Sydney
S	San Francisco (1942–43)
Dot before and after PENNY and I on obverse	Bombay (1942–43)
Dot before and after HALFPENNY and I on obverse	Bombay (1942–43)
Dot before and after PENNY	Bombay (1942–43)
Dot after HALFPENNY	Perth
Dot before SHILLING	Perth (1946)
Dot above scroll on reverse	Sydney (1920)
Dot below scroll on reverse	Melbourne (1919–20)
Dot between designer's initials KG	Perth (1940–41)
Dot after AUSTRALIA	Perth (1952–53)

AUSTRIA

A	Vienna (1765–1872)
AH–AG	Carlsburg, Transylvania (1765–76)
AH–GS	Carlsburg (1776–80)
A–S	Hall, Tyrol (1765–74)
AS–IE	Vienna (1745)
AW	Vienna (1764, 1768)
B	Kremnitz (1765–1857)
B–L	Nagybanya (1765–71)

B–V	Nagybanya (1772–80)
C	Carlsburg (1762–64)
C	Prague (1766–1855)
C–A	Carlsburg (1746–66)
C–A	Vienna (1774–80)
CG–AK	Graz (1767–72)
CG–AR	Graz (1767)
C–K	Vienna (1765–73)
CM	Kremnitz (1779)
CVG–AK	Graz (1767–72)
CVG–AR	Graz (1767)
D	Graz (1765–72), Salzburg (1800–09)
E	Carlsburg (1765–1867)
EC–SK	Vienna (1766)
EvM–D	Kremnitz (1765–74)
EvS–AS	Prague (1765–73)
EvS–IK	Prague (1774–80)
F	Hall (1765–1807)
FH	Hall
G	Graz (1761–63)
G	Gunzburg (1764–79)
G	Nagybanya (1766–1851)
G–K	Graz (1767–72)
G–R	Graz (1746–67)
GTK	Vienna (1761)
H	Hall (1760–80)
H	Gunzburg (1765–1805)
H–A	Hall (1746–65)
H–G	Carlsburg (1765–77)
H–S	Carlsburg (1777–80)
IB–FL	Nagybanya (1765–71)
IB–IV	Nagybanya (1772–80)
IC–FA	Vienna (1774–80)
IC–IA	Vienna (1780)
IC–SK	Vienna (1765–73)
I–K	Graz (1765-67)
I–K	Vienna (1767)
IZV	Vienna (1763–65)
K	Kremnitz (1760–63)
K–B	Kremnitz (1619–1765)
K–D	Kremnitz (1765)
K–M	Kremnitz (1763–65)
M	Milan (1780–1859)
N	Nagybanya (1780)
N–B	Nagybanya (1630–1777, 1849)
O	Oravicza (1783–1816)
P	Prague (1760–63)
P–R	Prague (1746–67)
PS–IK	Prague (1774–80)
S	Hall (1765–80), Schmollnitz (1763–1816)
S–C	Gunzburg (1765–74)
SC–G	Gunzburg (1765)
S–F	Gunzburg (1775–80)
S–G	Gunzburg (1764–65)
S–IE	Vienna (1745)
SK–PD	Kremnitz (1774–80)
TS	Gunzburg (1762–88)
V	Venice (1805–66)
VC–S	Hall (1774–80)
VS–K	Prague (1774–80)
VS–S	Prague (1765–73)
W	Vienna (1748–63)
W–I	Vienna (1746–71)

BAHAMAS

FM	Franklin Mint
JP	John Pinches

BELGIUM

A	Vienna
B	Kremnitz
C	Prague
E	Carlsburg
F	Hall
G	Nagybanya
H	Gunzburg
hand	Antwerp
lion	Bruges

BELIZE (British Honduras)

FM	Franklin Mint
H	Heaton (1912–16)

BOLIVIA

H	Heaton (1892–1953)
P, PTR, PTS	Potosi

BRAZIL

A	Berlin (1913)
B	Bahia (1714–1831)
C	Cuiaba (1823–33)
G	Goias (1823–33)
M	Minas Gerais (1823–28)
P	Pernambuco
R	Rio de Janeiro (1703–1834)
RS	Rio de Janeiro (1869)
SP	Sao Paulo (1825–32)

BRITISH NORTH BORNEO (Sabah)

H	Heaton (1882–1941)

BRITISH WEST AFRICA

G	JR Gaunt, Birmingham
H	Heaton, Birmingham (1911–57)
K	King's Norton
KN	King's Norton
SA	Pretoria

BULGARIA

A	Berlin
BP	Budapest
Heaton	Heaton, Birmingham (1881–1923)
KB	Kormoczbanya
cornucopia	Paris
thunderbolt	Poissy

ANADA

	Ottawa
	Heaton (1871–1907)
ple leaf	Ottawa (on coins struck after the year inscribed on them)

NTRAL AMERICAN REPUBLIC

R	San Jose (Costa Rica)
	Guatemala
G	Guatemala
	Tegucigalpa (Honduras)

YLON

	Heaton (1912)

HILE

	Agustin de Infante y Prado (1768–72)
	The above and Jose Maria de Bobadilla (1800–01)
	Domingo Eizaguirre
A	Domingo Eizaguirre and Agustin de Infante (1772–99)
F	Francisco Rodriguez Brochero
F	Brochero and Jose Maria de Bobadilla (1803–17)
	Heaton (1851)
	Jose Larraneta (1749–67)
	Santiago
A	Val Distra

OLOMBIA

	Paris
	Bogota
A	Bogota
B	Bogota
	Heaton (1912)
	Medellin
R	Nuevo Reino
oRo	Nuevo Reino
	Popayan
N, Pn	Popayan
M	Santa Marta

OSTA RICA

R	San Jose (1825–1947)
BM	Heaton (1889–93)
	San Domingo
D	San Domingo

OURLAND

CS	Justin Carl Schroder
S	Johan Friedrich Schmickert

YPRUS

	Heaton (1881–2)

DENMARK

FF	Altona
KM	Copenhagen Altona (1842)
crown	Copenhagen
heart	Copenhagen
orb	Altona (1839–48)

Other letters are the initials of mintmasters and moneyers

DOMINICAN REPUBLIC

HH	Heaton (1888–1919)

EAST AFRICA

A	Ackroyd & Best, Morley
H	Heaton (1910–64)
I	Bombay
K	Kynoch (IMI)
KN	King's Norton
SA	Pretoria

ECUADOR

BIRM^{M}H	Heaton (1915)
BIRMING-HAM	Heaton (1899–1900, 1928)
D	Denver
H	Heaton (1890, 1909, 1924–5)
HEATON BIRMING-HAM	Heaton (1872–95)
HF	Le Locle
LIMA	Lima
Mo	Mexico
PHILA	Philadelphia
QUITO	Quito
SANTIAGO	Santiago de Chile

EGYPT

H	Heaton (1904–37)

EL SALVADOR

CAM	Central American Mint, San Salvador
H	Heaton (1889–1913)
Mo	Mexico
S	San Francisco

FIJI

S	San Francisco

FINLAND

H	Heaton (1921)
heart	Copenhagen (1922). Since then coins have been struck at Helsinki without a mintmark.

Initials of mintmasters:

S	August Soldan (1864–85)
L	Johan Lihr (1885–1912)
S	Isaac Sundell (1915–47)

L	V. U. Liuhto (1948)
H	Uolevi Helle (1948–58)
S	Allan Soiniemi (1958–75)
SH	Soiniemi & Heikki Halvaoja (1967–71)
K	Timo Koivuranta (1977, 1979)
KN	Koivuranta and Antti Neuvonen (1978)
KT	Koivuranta and Erja Tielinen (1982)
KM	Koivuranta and Pertti Makinen (1983)
N	Reino Nevalainen (1983)

FRANCE

A	Paris (1768)
AA	Metz (1775–98)
B	Rouen (1786–1857)
B	Beaumont le Roger (1943–58)
BB	Strasbourg (1743–1870)
C	Castelsarrasin (1914, 1942–46)
CC	Genoa (1805)
CL	Genoa (1813–14)
D	Lyons (1771–1857)
G	Geneva (1796–1805)
H	La Rochelle (1770–1837)
L	Limoges (1766–1837)
K	Bordeaux (1759–1878)
L	Bayonne (1761–1837)
M	Toulouse (1766–1837)
MA	Marseilles (1787–1857)
N	Montpellier (1766–93)
O	Riom
P	Dijon
Q	Perpignan (1777–1837)
R	Royal Mint, London (1815)
R	Orleans (1780–92)
T	Nantes (1739–1835)
U	Turin (1814)
V	Troyes
W	Lille (1759–1857)
X	Amiens (1740)
&	Aix en Provence (1775)
9	Rennes
cow	Pau (1746–93)
flag	Utrecht (1811–14)
crowned R	Rome (1811–14)
thunderbolt	Poissy (1922-24)
star	Madrid (1916)

In addition, French coins include symbols denoting the privy marks of Engravers General (Chief Engravers since 1880) and Mint Directors.

GERMANY

The first name gives the location of the mint, and the second the name of the country or state issuing the coins.

A	Amberg, Bavaria (1763–94)
A	Berlin (1850)
A	Clausthal, Hannover (1832–49)
AE	Breslau, Silesia (1743–51)
AGP	Cleve, Rhineland (1742–43)
AK	Dusseldorf, Julich-Berg (1749–66)
ALS	Berlin (1749)
B	Bayreuth, Franconia (1796–1804)
B	Breslau, Silesia (1750–1826)
B	Brunswick, Brunswick (1850–60)
B	Brunswick, Westphalia (1809–13)
B	Dresden, Saxony (1861–72)
B	Hannover, Brunswick (1860–71)
B	Hannover, East Friesland (1823–25)
B	Hannover, Hannover (1821–66)
B	Hannover, Germany (1866-78)
B	Regensburg, Regensburg (1809)
B	Vienna, Germany (1938–45)
BH	Frankfurt (1808)
B–H	Regensburg, Rhenish Confederation (1802–12)
C	Cassel, Westphalia (1810–13)
C	Clausthal, Brunswick
C	Clausthal, Westphalia (1810–11)
C	Dresden, Saxony (1779–1804)
C	Frankfurt, Germany (1866–79)
CHI	Berlin (1749–63)
CLS	Dusseldorf, Julich-Berg (1767–70)
D	Aurich, East Friesland (1750–1806)
D	Dusseldorf, Rhineland (1816–48)
D	Munich, Germany (1872)
E	Dresden, Germany (1872–87)
E	Koenigberg, East Prussia (1750–98)
E	Muldenhutte, Germany (1887–1953)
EC	Leipzig, Saxony (1753–63)
EGN	Berlin (1725–49)
F	Dresden, Saxony (1845–58)
F	Magdeburg, Lower Saxony (1740–180
F	Cassel, Hesse-Cassel (1803–07)
F	Stuttgart, Germany (1872)
FW	Dresden, Saxony (1734–63)
G	Dresden, Saxony (1833–44, 1850–54)
G	Glatz, Silesia (1807–09)
G	Karlsruhe, Germany (1872)
G	Stettin, Pomerania (1750–1806)
GK	Cleve (1740–55)
GN	Bamberg, Bamberg
H	Darmstadt, Germany (1872–82)
H	Dresden, Saxony (1804–12)
HK	Rostock, Rostock (1862–64)
I	Hamburg, Germany (1872)
IDB	Dresden, Prussian occupation (1756–5
IEC	Dresden, Saxony (1779–1804)
IF	Leipzig, Saxony (1763–65)
IGG	Leipzig, Saxony (1716–34, 1813–32)
J	Hamburg, Germany (1873)
J	Paris, Westphalia (1808–09)
L	Leipzig, Saxony (1761–62)
MC	Brunswick, Brunswick (1813–14, 1820)
PM	Dusseldorf, Julich-Berg (1771–83)
PR	Dusseldorf, Julich-Berg (1783–1804)

	Dresden, Saxony (1813–32)
	Hannover, Hannover (1839–44)
	Schwabach, Franconia (1792–94)
GH	Dresden, Saxony (1804–12)
T	Strickling, Blomberg (1820–40)

;REAT BRITAIN

	Ashby (1645)
	Nicolas Briot (1631–39)
	Bridgnorth (1646)
	Bristol (1696)
r	Bristol (1643–45)
	Chester (1696)
ARL	Carlisle (1644–45)
C	Corfe Castle (1644)
HST	Chester (1644)
R	Chester (1644)
	Southwark (1547–49)
	Exeter (1696)
	Edinburgh (1707–13)
*	Edinburgh (1707–09)
I	Heaton, Birmingham (1874–1919)
IC	Hartlebury Castle (1646)
	London (1547–49)
N	King's Norton
J	Norwich (1696)
X	Oxford (1644–45)
XON	Oxford (1644)
C	Pontefract (1648–49)
C	Scarborough (1644–45)
OHO	Birmingham (1797–1806)
	Canterbury (1549)
C	Bristol (1549)
VS	Bristol (1547–49)
	Southwark (1551)
oar	Shrewsbury (1643–44)
ook	Aberystwyth (1638–42)
ow	Durham House (1548–49)
astle	Exeter (1644–45)
rown	Aberystwyth Furnace (1648–49)
lume	Shrewsbury (1642)
lume	Oxford (1642–46)
lume	Bristol (1643–46)

)ther symbols and marks on the hammered coins of Great Britain are usually referred to as Initial Marks. Complete listings of these marks appear in a number of specialist publications.

GREECE

A	Paris
3	Vienna
3B	Strasbourg
H	Heaton (1921)
K	Bordeaux
KN	King's Norton
owl	Aegina (1828–32)
owl	Athens (1838-55)
hunderbolt	Poissy

GUATEMALA

CG	Guatemala City (1733-76)
G	Guatemala City (1776)
H	Heaton (1894–1901)
NG	Nueva Guatemala (1777)

GUERNSEY

H	Heaton (1855–1949)

HAITI

A	Paris
HEATON	Heaton (1863)

HONDURAS

A	Paris (1869–71)
T	Tegucigalpa (1825–62)

HONG KONG

H	Heaton (1872–1971)
KN	King's Norton

HUNGARY

A	Vienna
B	Kremnitz
BP	Budapest
CA	Vienna
G	Nagybanya
GN	Nagybanya
GYF	Carlsburg
HA	Hall
K	Kremnitz
KB	Kremnitz
NB	Nagybanya
S	Schmollnitz
WI	Vienna

INDIA

B	Bombay (1835-1947)
C	Calcutta (1835-1947)
I	Bombay (1918)
L	Lahore (1943-45)
M	Madras (1869)
P	Pretoria (1943-44)
diamond	Bombay
dot in diamond	Hyderabad
split diamond	Hyderabad
star	Hyderabad

IRAN

H	Heaton (1928–29)

IRAQ

I	Bombay

ISRAEL

H	Heaton (1951–52)
star of David	Jerusalem

ITALY AND STATES

B	Bologna
B/I	Birmingham (1893–4)
FIRENZE	Florence
H	Heaton (1866–67)
KB	Berlin
M	Milan
N	Naples
OM	Strasbourg
R	Rome
T	Turin
V	Venice
ZV	Venice
anchor	Genoa
eagle head	Turin

JAMAICA

C	Ottawa
FM	Franklin Mint
H	Heaton (1882–1916)

JERSEY

H	Heaton (1877)

KENYA

C/M	Calcutta
H	Heaton (1911–64)

LIBERIA

B	Berne
FM	Franklin Mint
H	Heaton (1896–1906)
PM	Pobjoy Mint

LIECHTENSTEIN

A	Vienna
B	Berne
M	Munich

LUXEMBOURG

A	Paris
H	Gunzburg
anchor	Paris
angel	Brussels
caduceus	Utrecht
double eagle	Brussels
sword	Utrecht

MALAYSIA

B	Bombay
FM	Franklin Mint
H	Heaton (1955–61)
I	Calcutta (1941)
I	Bombay (1945)
KN	King's Norton
W	James Watt, Birmingham

MAURITIUS

H	Heaton (1877–90)
SA	Pretoria

MEXICO

A, As	Alamos
C, CN	Culiacan
CA, CH	Chihuahua
Ce	Real del Catorce
D, Do	Durango
Eo	Tlalpam
GA	Guadalajara
GC	Guadelupe y Calvo
Go	Guanajuato
Ho	Hermosillo
M, Mo	Mexico City
Mo	Morelos
MX	Mexico City
O, OA, OKA	Oaxaca
Pi	San Luis Potosi
SLPi	San Luis Potosi
TC	Tierra Caliente
Z, Zs	Zacatecas

MONACO

A	Paris
M	Monte Carlo
clasped hands	Cabanis
thunderbolt	Poissy

MOZAMBIQUE

H	Heaton (1894)
R	Rio

NETHERLANDS AND COLONIES

Austrian Netherlands (1700-93)

H	Amsterdam
S	Utrecht
W	Vienna
hand	Antwerp
head	Brussels
lion	Bruges

Kingdom of the Netherlands

B	Brussels (1821–30)
D	Denver (1943–45)
P	Philadelphia (1941–45)
S	Utrecht (1816–36)
S	San Francisco (1944–45)
Sa	Surabaya
caduceus	Utrecht

NICARAGUA

H	Heaton (1880–1916)
NR	Leon de Nicaragua

NORWAY

hammers	Kongsberg

ANAMA

HI	Valcambi
M	Franklin Mint

ERU

REQ, AREQUIPA	Arequipa
YACUCHO	Ayacucho
UZCO, Co	Cuzco
, LM, LR	Lima
IMAE	Lima
ASCO	Pasco
az, Po	Pasco
	Lima (1568-70)
	Philadelphia
	San Francisco

HILIPPINES

SP	Bangko Sentral Pilipinas
	Denver (1944–45)
M	Franklin Mint
I, MA	Manila
M	Pobjoy Mint
	San Francisco (1903–47)
point star	Manila

OLAND

P	Warsaw (1772–74)
I	Cracow (1765–68)
B	Warsaw (1774–92)
C	Leipzig (1758–63)
F	Stuttgart (1916–17)
H	Warsaw (1815–27)
S	Warsaw (1765–68)
WoF	Dresden (1734–64)
	Cracow (1765–72)
I	Heaton (1924)
B	Warsaw (1811–27)
GS	Dresden (1716–34)
P	Warsaw (1834–43)
S	Warsaw (1768–74)
GG	Leipzig (1750–53)
S	Warsaw (1810–11)
G	Warsaw (1829–34)
MV, MW	Warsaw
rrow	Warsaw (1925–39)
Dot after late	Royal Mint (1925)
torches	Paris (1924)

OUMANIA

B	Bucharest (1879–85)
C	Bucharest (1886)
H	Heaton (1867–1930)
HUGUENIN	Le Locle
	Hamburg
KN	King's Norton
V	Vienna
W	Watt, Birmingham
thunderbolt	Poissy

RUSSIA

AM	Annensk (1762–96)
BM	Warsaw (1825–55)
bM	St Petersburg (1796)
C–M	Sestroretsk (1762–96)
CM	Souzan (1825–55)
E–M	Ekaterinburg (1762–1810)
KM	Kolpina (1810)
K–M	Kolyvan (1762–1810)
MM, M–M	Moscow (1730–96)
MMD	Moscow (1730–96)
MW	Warsaw (1842–54)
NM	Izhorsk (1811–21)
SP	St Petersburg (1798–1800)
SPB	St Petersburg (1724–1915)
SPM	St Petersburg (1825–55)
T–M	Feodosia (1762–96)

SAN MARINO

M	Milan
R	Rome
SIAM (Thailand)	H Heaton (1898)

SOUTH AFRICA

SA	Pretoria

SPAIN

B	Burgos
B, BA	Barcelona
Bo	Bilbao
C	Catalonia
C	Cuenca
C	Reus
CA	Zaragoza
G	Granada
GNA	Gerona
LD	Lerida
J, JA	Jubia
M, MD	Madrid
P	Palma de Majorca
PpP, PL, PA	Pamplona
S, S/L	Seville
Sr	Santander
T, To, Tole	Toledo
TOR:SA	Tortosa
V, VA, VAL	Valencia
crowned C	Cadiz
crowned M	Madrid
aqueduct	Segovia
crowned shield	Tarragona
pomegranate	Granada
quartered shield	Palma
scallop	Coruna

SPAIN *continued*

stars:	
3 points	Segovia
4 points	Jubia
5 points	Manila
6 points	Madrid
7 points	Seville (1833)
8 points	Barcelona (1838)
wavy lines	Valladolid

SURINAM

P	Philadelphia
S	Sydney
caduceus	Utrecht

SWITZERLAND

A	Paris
AB	Strasbourg
B	Berne
B	Brussels (1874)
BA	Basle
BB	Strasbourg
S	Solothurn

URUGUAY

H	Heaton (1869)

UNITED STATES OF AMERICA

C	Charlotte, North Carolina
Cc	Carson City, Nevada
D	Dahlonega, Georgia (1838–61)
D	Denver, Colorado (1906)
O	New Orleans
P	Philadelphia
S	San Francisco
W	West Point

VENEZUELA

A	Paris
H	Heaton (1852)
HEATON	Heaton (1852–63)

YUGOSLAVIA (including former Serbia)

A	Paris
H	Heaton (1883–84)
KOBHNUA, A.D.	Kovnica
V	Vienna
thunderbolt	Poissy

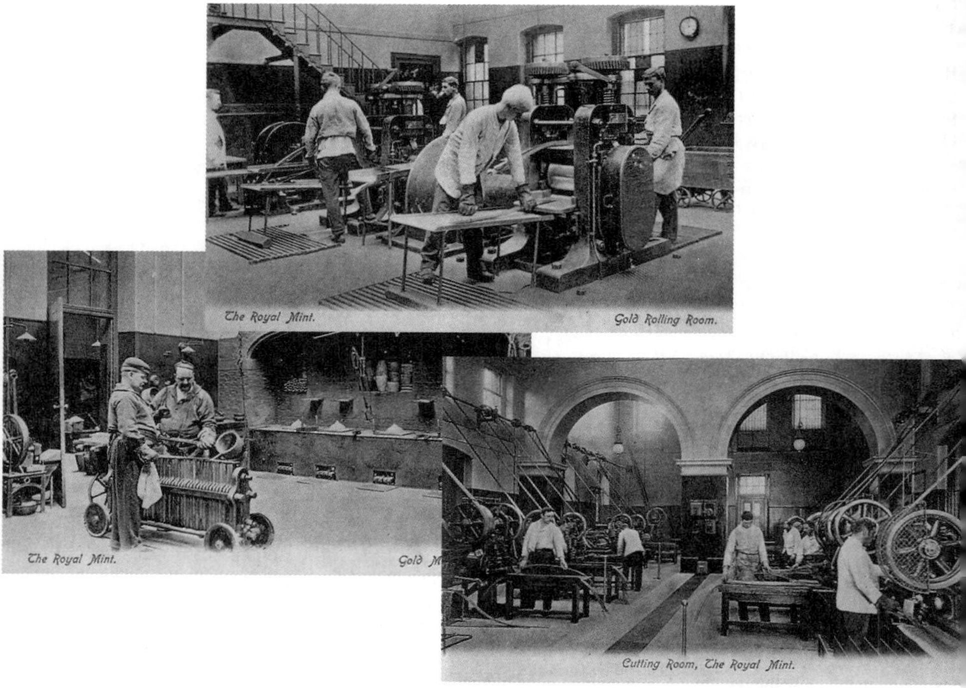

Images from the Royal Mint c. 1900 from a set of contemporary postcards. From left: The gold melting house; the gold rolling room and the cutting room.

Coin inscriptions

This alphabetical listing is confined to inscriptions found on coins, mainly in the form of mottoes or of a commemorative nature. Names of rulers are, for the most part, excluded. Where the inscription is in a language other than English a translation is given, followed by the name of the issuing country or authority in parentheses.

A Deo et Caesare From God and the Emperor (Frankfurt).

A Domino Factum est Istud et est Mirabile in Oculis Nostris This is the Lord's doing and it is marvellous in our eyes (England, Mary).

A Solo Iehova Sapientia From God alone comes true wisdom (Wittgenstein).

Ab Inimicis Meis Libera Me Deus Free me from enemies (Burgundy).

Ad Legem Conventionis According to the law of the Convention (Furstenberg).

Ad Normam Conventionis According to the standard of the Convention (Prussia).

Ad Palmam Pressa Laeturo Resurgo Pressed to the palm I rise more joyfully (Wittgenstein).

Ad Usam Luxemburgi CC Vallati For the use of the besieged Luxembourgers (Luxembourg siege coins).

Adiuva Nos Deus Salutaris Noster Help us, O God, our Saviour (Lorraine).

Adventus Optimi Principis The coming of the noblest prince (Papacy).

Aes Usibus Aptius Auro Bronze in its uses is more suitable than gold (Brazil).

Aeternum Meditans Decus An ornament intended for all time (Alencon).

Aliis Inserviendo Consumor I spend my life devoted to others (Brunswick-Wolfenbuttel).

Alles Mit Bedacht All with reflection (Brunswick).

Amor Populi Praesidium Regis The love of the people is the king's protection (England, Charles I).

Ang Fra Dom Hib & Aquit (King) of England and France, Lord of Ireland and Aquitaine (England, Edward III).

Anno Regni Primo In the first year of the reign (Britain, edge inscription on crowns).

Apres les Tenebres la Lumiere After the shadows, the light (Geneva).

Archangelus Michael Archangel Michael (Italy, Grimoald IV).

Ardua ad Gloriam Via Struggles are the way to glory (Waldeck).

Arte Mea Bis Iustus Moneta Lud Iust By my art I am twice the just coin of King Louis (France, 1641).

Aspera Oblectant Wild places delight (Nassau-Weilburg).

Aspice Pisas Sup Omnes Specio Behold the coin of Pisa, superior to all (Pisa).

Audiatur Altera Pars Let the other part be heard (Stavelot).

Auf Gott Trawe Ich In God I trust (Brunswick).

Ausen Gefaesen der Kirchen und Burger From the vessels of the Church and citizens (Frankfurt siege, 1796).

Auspicio Regis et Senatus Angliae By authority of the king and parliament of England (East India Company).

Auxilio fortissimo Dei With the strongest help of God (Mecklenburg).

Auxilium de Sanctio Aid from the sanctuary (Papacy).

Auxilium Meum a Dno Qui Fecit Celum e Terram My help comes from God who made heaven and earth (Portugal).

Beata Tranquillatis Blessed tranquillity (Rome, Licinius II).

Beatus Qui Speravit in dom Blessed is he who has hoped in the Lord (Mansfeld).

Benedic Haereditati Tuae Blessings on your inheritance (Savoy).

Benedicta Sit Sancta Trinitas Blessed be the Holy Trinity (Albon).

Benedictio Domini Divites Facit The blessing of the Lord makes the rich (Teschen).

Benedictus Qui Venit in Nomine Domini Blessed is he who comes in the name of the Lord (Flanders).

Beschaw das Ziel Sage Nicht Viel Consider the matter but say little (Quedlinburg).
Besser Land und Lud Verloren als ein Falscher Aid Geschworn Better to lose land and wealth than swear a false oath (Hesse).
Bey Gott ist Rath und That With God is counsel and deed (Mansfeld).
Britanniarum Regina Queen of the Britains (Britain, Victoria).
Britt Omn Rex King of all the Britains (i.e. Britain and the overseas dominions) (Britain, 1902–52).
Cal et Car Com de Fugger in Zin et Norn Sen & Adm Fam Cajetan and Carl, Counts of Fugger in Zinnenberg and Nordendorf, Lords and Administrators of the Family (Empire, Fugger).
Candide et Constanter Sincerely and steadfastly (Hesse-Cassel).
Candide sed Provide Clearly but cautiously (Osterwitz).
Candore et Amore With sincerity and love (Fulda).
Candore et Constantia With sincerity and constancy (Bavaria).
Capit Cath Ecclesia Monasteriensis Chapter of the Cathedral Church of Munster (Munster).
Capit Eccle Metropolit Colon Chapter of the Metropolitan Church of Cologne (Cologne).
Capitulum Regnans Sede Vacante Chapter governing, the See being vacant (Eichstadt).
Carola Magna Ducissa Feliciter Regnante Grand Duchess Charlotte, happily reigning (Luxembourg).
Carolus a Carolo Charles (I) to Charles (II) (England).
Cedunt Prementi Fata The fates yield to him who presses (Ploen, Hese-Cassel).
Charitate et Candore With charity and sincerity (East Frisia).
Charta Magna Bavariae The Great Charter of Bavaria (Bavaria).
Christo Auspice Regno I reign under the auspices of Christ (England, Charles I).
Christus Spes Una Salutis Christ is our one hope of salvation (Cleve).
Chur Mainz Electoral Principality of Mainz (Mainz).
Circumeundo Servat et Ornat It serves and decorates by going around (Sweden).
Civibus Quorum Pietas Coniuratione Die III Mai MDCCXCI Obrutam et Deletam Libertate Polona Tueri Conabatur Respublica Resurgens To the citizens whose piety the resurgent commonwealth tried to protect Poland overturned and deprived of liberty by the conspiracy of the third day of May 1791 (Poland).
Civitas Lucemborgiensis Millesimum Ovans Expletannum Completing the celebration of a thousand years of the city of Luxembourg (Luxembourg).
Civium Industria Floret Civitas By the industry of its people the state flourishes (Festival of Britain crown, 1951).
Cluniaco Cenobio Petrus et Paulus Peter and Paul from the Abbey of Cluny (Cluny).
Comes Provincie Fili Regis Francie Court of Provence and son of the King of France (Provence).
Communitas et Senatus Bonon City and senate of Bologna (Bologna).
Concordia Fratrum The harmony of the brothers (Iever).
Concordia Patriae Nutrix Peace, the nurse of the fatherland (Waldeck).
Concordia Res Parvae Crescunt Little things increase through harmony (Batavian Republic)
Concordia Res Parvae Crescunt, Discordia Dilabuntur By harmony little things increase by discord they fall apart (Lowenstein-Wertheim-Virneburg).
Concordia Stabili With lasting peace (Hildesheim).
Confidens Dno Non Movetur He who trusts in God is unmoved (Spanish Netherlands).
Confidentia in Deo et Vigilantia Trust in God and vigilance (Prussian Asiatic Company).
Confoederato Helvetica Swiss Confederation (Switzerland)
Conjuncto Felix Fortunate in his connections (Solms).
Conservator Urbis Suae Saviour of his city (Rome, 4th century).
Consilio et Aequitate With deliberation and justice (Fulda).
Consilio et Virtutis With deliberation and valou (Hesse-Cassel).
Constanter et Sincere Steadfastly and sincerely (Lautern).
Crescite et Multiplicamini Increase and multipl (Maryland).
Cristiana Religio Christian religion (Germany, 11th century).
Crux Benedicat May the cross bless you (Oldenburg).
Cuius Cruore Sanati Sumus By His sacrifice are we healed (Reggio).
Cultores Sui Deus Protegit God protects His followers (England, Charles I).
Cum Deo et Die (Jure) With God and the day (Wurttemberg).
Cum Deo et Jure With God and the law (Wurttemberg).
Cum Deo et Labore With God and work (Wittgenstein).
Cum His Qui Orderant Pacem Eram Pacificus With those who order peace I was peaceful (Zug)
Curie Bonthon to so Doulo Protect his servant, o Lord (Byzantine Empire).
Custos Regni Deus God is the guardian of the kingdom (Naples and Sicily).

a Gloriam Deo et Eius Genitrici Marie Give glory to God and His mother Mary (Wurttemberg).
a Mihi Virtutem Contra Hostes Tuos Give me valour against mine enemies (Netherlands, Charles V).
at Wort is Fleis Gworden The word is made flesh (Muster).
ate Caesaris Caesari et Quae Sunt Dei Deo Render unto Caesar the things that are Caesar's and unto God the things that are God's (Stralsund).
e Oficina . . . From the mint of . . . (France, medieval).
ecreto Reipublicae Nexu Confoederationis Iunctae Die V Xbris MDCCXCII Stanislao Augusto Regnante By decree of the state in conjunction with the joint federation on the fifth day of December 1792, Stanislaus Augustus ruling (Poland).
ecus et Tutamen An ornament and a safeguard (Britain, pound).
educet Nos Mirabiliter Dextera Tua Thy right hand will guide us miraculously (Savoy).
enarium Terrae Mariae Penny of Maryland (Maryland).
eo Conservatori Pacis To God, preserver of peace (Brandenburg-Ansbach).
eo OM Auspice Suaviter et Fortiter sed Luste nec Sibi sed Suis Under the auspices of God, greatest and best, pleasantly and bravely but justly, not for himself but for his people (Speyer).
eo Patriae et Subditio For God, fatherland and neighbourhood (Mainz).
er Recht Glaubt In Ewig Lebt Who believes in right will live in eternity (Linange-Westerburg).
er Rhein ist Deutschlands Strom Nicht Deutschlands Grenze The Rhine is Germany's River not Germany's Frontier.
eum Solum Adorabis You will venerate God alone (Hesse).
eus Constituit Regna God establishes kingdoms (Ni jmegen).
eus Dat Qui Vult God gives to him who wishes (Hanau-Munzenberg).
eus et Dominus God and Lord (Rome, 3rd century).
eus in Adiutorium Meum Intende God stretch out in my assistance (France).
eus Providebit God will provide (Lowenstein-Wertheim-Virneburg).
eus Refugium Meum God is my refuge (Cleve).
eus Solatium Meum God is my comfort (Sweden).
extera Domini Exaltavit Me The right hand of God has raised me up (Modena, Spain).
extra Dei Exalta Me The right hand of God exalts me (Denmark).
ieu et Mon Droit God and my right (Britain, George IV).
Dilexit Dns Andream The Lord delights in St Andrew (Holstein).
Dilexit Dominus Decorem Iustitiae The Lord is pleased with the beauty of justice (Unterwalden).
Dirige Deus Gressus Meos O God, direct my steps (Tuscany, Britain, Una £5).
Discerne Causam Meam Distinguish my cause (Savoy).
Divina Benedictiae et Caesarea Iustitia Sacrifice of blessings and imperial justice (Coblenz).
Dn Ihs Chs Rex Regnantium Lord Jesus Christ, King of Kings (Rome, Justinian II).
Dns Ptetor Ms Z Lib'ator Ms The Lord is my protector and liberator (Scotland, David II).
Dominabitur Gentium et Ipse He himself will also be lord of the nations (Austrian Netherlands).
Domine Conserva Nos in Pace O Lord preserve us in peace (Basle, Mulhausen).
Domine Elegisti Lilium Tibi O Lord Thou hast chosen the lily for Thyself (France, Louis XIV).
Domine ne in Furore Tuo Arguas Me O Lord, rebuke me not in Thine anger (England, Edward III).
Domine Probasti Me et Congnovisti Me O Lord Thou hast tested me and recognised me (Mantua).
Domini est Regnum The Kingdom is the Lord's (Austrian Netherlands).
Dominus Deus Omnipotens Rex Lord God, almighty King (Viking coins).
Dominus Mihi Adiutor The Lord is my helper (Spanish Netherlands).
Dominus Providebit The Lord will provide (Berne).
Dominus Spes Populi Sui The Lord is the hope of his people (Lucerne).
Donum Dei ex Fodinis Vilmariens A gift of God from the Vilmar mines (Coblenz).
Duce Deo Fide et Justicia By faith and justice lead us to God (Ragusa).
Dum Praemor Amplior I increase while I die prematurely (Savoy).
Dum Spiro Spero While I live, I hope (Pontefract siege coins).
Dum Totum Compleat Orbem Until it fills the world (France, Henri II).
Dura Pati Virtus Valour endures hardships (Saxe-Lauenburg).
Durae Necessitatis Through force of necessity (Bommel siege, 1599).
Durum Telum Necessitas Hardship is a weapon of necessity (Minden).
Dux et Gubernatores Reip Genu Duke and governors of the republic of Genoa (Genoa).
E Pluribus Unum One out of more (USA).
Eccl S. Barbarae Patronae Fodin Kuttenbergensium Duo Flor Arg Puri The church of St Barbara, patron of the Kuttensberg mines, two florins of pure silver (Hungary).

Een en Ondelbaer Sterk One and indivisible (Batavian Republic).
Eendracht Mag Macht Unity makes strength (Belgium, South African Republic).
Einigkeit Recht und Freiheit Union, right and freedom (Germany).
Electorus Saxoniae Administrator Elector and administrator of Saxony (Saxony).
Elimosina Alms (France, Pepin).
Ep Fris & Ratisb Ad Prum Pp Coad Aug Bishop of Freising and Regensburg, administrator of Pruem, prince-provost, co-adjutant bishop of Augsburg (Trier).
Equa Libertas Deo Gratia Frat Pax in Virtute Tua et in Domino Confido I believe in equal liberty by the grace of God, brotherly love in Thy valour and in the Lord (Burgundy).
Equitas Iudicia Tua Dom Equity and Thy judgments O Lord (Gelderland).
Espoir Me Conforte Hope comforts me (Mansfeld).
Espreuve Faicto Par Lexpres Commandement du Roy Proof made by the express commandment of the King (France, piedforts).
Et in Minimis Integer Faithful even in the smallest things (Olmutz).
Ex Auro Argentes Resurgit From gold it arises, silver again (Sicily).
Ex Auro Sinico From Chinese gold (Denmark).
Ex Flammis Orior I arise from the flames (Hohenlohe-Neuenstein-Ohringen).
Ex Fodinis Bipontio Seelbergensibus From the Seelberg mines of Zweibrucken (Pfalz-Birkenfeld).
Ex Metallo Novo From new metal (Spain).
Ex Uno Omnis Nostra Salus From one is all our salvation (Eichstadt, Mulhouse).
Ex Vasis Argent Cleri Mogunt Pro Aris et Focis From the silver vessels of the clergy of Mainz for altars and for hearths (Mainz).
Ex Visceribus Fodinse Bieber From the bowels of the Bieber mine (Hanau-Munzenberg).
Exaltabitur in Gloria He shall be exalted in glory (England, quarter nobles).
Exemplum Probati Numismatis An example of a proof coin (France, Louis XIII piedforts).
Exemtae Eccle Passau Episc et SRI Princ Prince Bishop of the freed church of Passau, prince of the Holy Roman Empire (Passau).
Expectate Veni Come, o expected one (Roman Britain, Carausius).
Extremum Subidium Campen Kampen under extreme siege (Kampen, 1578).
Exurgat Deus et Dissipentur Inimici Eius Let God arise and let His enemies be scattered (England, James I).
Faciam Eos in Gentem Unam I will make them one nation (England, unites and laurels).
Faith and Truth I will Bear unto You (UK £5, 1993).
Fata Consiliis Potiora The fates are more powerful than councils (Hesse-Cassel).
Fata Viam Invenient The fates will find a way (Gelderland).
Fecit Potentiam in Brachio Suo He put power in your forearm (Lorraine).
Fecunditas Fertility (Naples and Sicily).
Fel Temp Reparatio The restoration of lucky times (Rome, AD 348).
Felicitas Perpetua Everlasting good fortune (Rome, Constantius II).
Felix coniunctio Happy Union (Brandenburg-Ansbach).
Fiat Misericordia Tua Dne Let Thy mercy be O Lord (Gelderland).
Fiat Voluntas Domini Perpetuo Let the goodwil of the Lord last for ever (Fulda).
Fidei Defensor Defender of the Faith (Britain).
Fidelitate et Fortitudine With fidelity and fortitude (Batthanyi).
Fideliter et Constanter Faithfully and steadfastly (Saxe-Coburg-Gotha).
Fidem Servando Patriam Tuendo By keeping faith and protecting the fatherland (Savoy).
Filius Augustorum Son of emperors (Rome, 4th century).
Fisci Iudaici Calumnia Sublata The false accusation of the Jewish tax lifted (Rome, Nerva).
Florent Concordia Regna Through harmony kingdoms flourish (England, Charles I and II).
Fortitudo et Laus Mea Dominu Fortitude and m praise in the Lord (Sardinia).
Free Trade to Africa by Act of Parliment *(Sic)* (Gold Coast).
Friedt Ernehrt Unfriedt Verzehrt Peace nourishes, unrest wastes (Brunswick).
Fulgent Sic Littora Rheni Thus shine the banks of the Rhine (Mannheim).
Fundator Pacis Founder of peace (Rome, Severus).
Gaudium Populi Romani The joy of the Roman people (Rome, 4th century).
Gen C Mar VI Dim Col USC & RAMAI Cons & S Conf M General field marshal, colonel of the only dragoon regiment, present privy councillo of both their sacred imperial and royal apostoli majesties, and state conference minister (Batthanyi).
Gerecht und Beharrlich Just and steadfast (Bavaria).
Germ Hun Boh Rex AAD Loth Ven Sal King of Germany, Hungary and Bohemia, Archduke of Austria, Duke of Lorraine, Venice and Salzburg (Austria).
Germ Jero Rex Loth Bar Mag Het Dux King of Germany, Jerusalem, Lorraine and Bar, Grand Duke of Tuscany (Austrian Netherlands).
Germania Voti Compos Germany sharing the vows (Brandenburg-Ansbach).

Gloria ex Amore Patriae Glory from love of country (Denmark).

Gloria in Excelsis Deo Glory to God in the highest (France, Sweden).

Gloria Novi Saeculi The glory of a new century (Rome, Gratian).

God With Us (England, Commonwealth).

Godt Met Ons God with us (Oudewater).

Gottes Freundt der Pfaffen Feindt God's friend, the Pope's enemy (Brunswick, Christian).

Gratia Dei Sum Id Quod Sum By the grace of God, I am what I am (Navarre).

Gratia Di Rex By the grace of God, king (France, 8th century).

Gratitudo Concivibus Exemplum Posteritati Gratitude to fellow Citizens, an example to posterity (Poland).

Gud och Folket God and the people (Sweden).

Hac Nitimur Hanc Tuemur With this we strive, this we shall defend (Batavian Republic).

Hac Sub Tutela Under this protection (Eichstadt).

Haec Sunt Munera Minerae S Antony Eremitae These are the rewards of the mine of St Antony the hermit (Hildesheim).

Hanc Deus Dedit God has given this (Pontefract siege coins).

Hanc Tuemur Hac Nitimur This we defend, by this we strive (Batavian Republic).

Has Nisi Periturus Mihi Adimat Nemo Let no one remove these (Letters) from me under penalty of death (Commonwealth, edge inscription).

Henricus Rosas Regna Jacobus Henry (united) the roses, James the kingdoms (England and Scotland, James VI and I).

Herculeo Vincta Nodo Bound by a Herculean fetter (Savoy).

Herr Nach Deinem Willen O Lord Thy will be done (Palatinate, Erbach).

Herre Gott Verleich Uns Gnade Lord God grant us grace (Brunswick).

Hic Est Qui Multum Orat Pro Populo Here is he who prays a lot for the people (Paderborn).

Hir Steid te Biscop Here is represented the bishop (Gittelde).

His Ventis Vela Levantur By these winds the sails are raised up (Hesse-Cassel).

Hispaniarum Infans Infante of Spain and its dominions (Spain).

Hispaniarum et Ind Rex King of Spain and the Indies.

Hispaniarum Rex King of Spain (Spain).

Hoc Signo Victor Eris With this sign you will be victor (Rome, Vetranio).

Honeste et Decenter Honestly and decently (Nassau-Idstein).

Honi Soit Qui Mal y Pense Evil to him who evil thinks (Britain, George III).

Honni Soit Qui Mal y Pense (Hesse-Cassel).

Hospitalis et S Sepul Hierusal Hospital and Holy Sepulchre of Jerusalem (Malta).

Hun Boh Gal Rex AA Lo Wi et in Fr Dux King of Hungary, Bohemia and Galicia, Archduke of Austria, Dalmatia, Lodomeria, Wurzburg and Duke in Franconia (Austria).

Hung Boh Lomb et Ven Gal Lod III Rex Aa King of Hungary, Bohemia, Lombardo-Venezia, Galicia, Lodomeria and Illyria, Archduke of Austria (Austria).

Ich Dien I serve (Aberystwyth 2d, UK 2p).

Ich Getrawe Got in Aller Noth I trust in God in all my needs (Hesse-Marburg).

Ich Habe Nur Ein Vaterland und das Heisst Deutschland I have only one fatherland and that is called Germany (Germany).

Ielithes Penniae Penny of Gittelde (Gittelde, 11th century).

Iesus Autem Transiens Per Medium Illorum Ibat But Jesus, passing through the midst of them, went His way (England, Scotland, Anglo-Gallic).

Iesus Rex Noster et Deus Noster Jesus is our king and our God (Florence).

Ihs Xs Rex Regnantium Jesus Christ, King of Kings (Byzantine Empire).

Ihsus Xristus Basileu Baslie Jesus Christ, King of Kings (Byzantine Empire).

Imago Sanch Regis Illustris Castelle Legionis e Toleto The image of Sancho the illustrious king of Castile, Leon and Toledo.

In Casus Per Vigil Omnes In all seasons through vigil (Wertheim).

In Deo Meo Transgrediar Murum In my God I shall pass through walls (Teschen).

In Deo Spes Mea In God is my hope (Gelderland).

In Domino Fiducia Nostra In the Lord is our trust (Iever).

In Equitate Tua Vivificasti Me In thy equity Thou hast vivified me (Gelderland).

In God We Trust (USA).

In Hoc Signo Vinces In this sign shalt thou conquer (Portugal).

In Honore Sci Mavrici Marti In honour of the martyr St Maurice (St Maurice, 8th century).

In Manibus Domini sortes Meae In the hands of the Lord are my fates (Mainz siege, 1688–9).

In Memor Vindicatae Libere ac Relig In memory of the establishment of freedom and religion (Sweden).

In Memoriam Conjunctionis Utriusque Burgraviatus Norice In memory of the union of both burgraviates in peace (Brandenburg-Ansbach).

In Memorian Connub Feliciaes Inter Princ Her Frider Carol et Dub Sax August Louis Frider Rodas D 28 Nov 1780 Celebrati In memory of the most happy marriage between the hereditary prince Friedrich Karl and the Duchess of Saxony Augusta Louisa Frederika, celebrated on 28 Nov 1780 (Schwarzburg-Rudolstadt).

In Memorian Felicisssimi Matrimonii In memory of the most happy marriage (Wied).
In Memoriam Pacis Teschinensis Commemorating the Treaty of Teschen (Brandenburg-Ansbach).
In Nomine Domini Amen In the name of the Lord amen (Zaltbommel).
In Omnem Terram Sonus Eorum In to all the land their shall go sound (Chateau Renault, Papal States).
In Silencio et Spe Fortitudo Mea In silence and hope is my fortitude (Brandenburg-Kustrin).
In Spe et Silentio Fortitudo Mea In hope and silence is my fortitude (Vianen).
In Te Domine Confido In you O Lord I place my trust (Hesse).
In Te Domine Speravi In You, O Lord, I have hoped (Gurk).
In Terra Pax Peace in the land (Papacy).
In Via Virtuti Nulla Via There is no way for virtue on the way. (Veldenz).
Ind Imp, Indiae Imperator, Imperatrix Emperor (Empress) of India (Britain).
India Tibi Cessit India has yielded to thee (Portuguese India).
Infestus Infestis Hostile to the troublesome (Savoy).
Inimicos Eius Induam Confusione As for his enemies, I shall clothe them in shame (Sardinia, England, Edward VI).
Insignia Capituli Brixensis The badge of the chapter of Brixen (Brixen).
Isti Sunt Patres Tui Verique Pastores These are your fathers and true shepherds (Papacy).
Iudicium Melius Posteritatis Erit Posterity's judgment will be better (Paderborn).
Iure et Tempore By right and time (Groningen).
Iusques a Sa Plenitude As far as your plenitude (France, Henri II).
Iuste et Constanter Justly and constantly (Paderborn).
Iustirt Adjusted (Hesse-Cassel).
Iustitia et Concordia Justice and harmony (Zurich).
Iustitia et Mansuetudine By justice and mildness (Bavaria, Cologne).
Iustitia Regnorum Fundamentum Justice is the foundation of kingdoms (Austria).
Iustitia Thronum Firmat Justice strengthens the throne (England, Charles I).
Iustus Non Derelinquitur The just person is not deserted (Brandenburg-Calenberg).
Iustus Ut Palma Florebit The just will flourish like the palm (Portugal).
L Mun Planco Rauracorum Illustratori Vetustissimo To L Municius Plancus the most ancient and celebrated of the Rauraci (Basle).
Landgr in Cleggov Com in Sulz Dux Crum Landgrave of Klettgau, count of Sulz, duke of Krumlau (Schwarzburg-Sonderhausen).
Latina Emeri Munita Latin money of Merida (Suevi).
Lege et Fide By law and faith (Austria).
Lex Tua Veritas Thy law is the truth (Tuscany).
Liberta Eguaglianza Freedom and equality (Venice)
Libertad en la Ley Freedom within the law (Mexico).
Libertas Carior Auro Freedom is dearer than gold (St Gall).
Libertas Vita Carior Freedom is dearer than life (Kulenberg).
Libertas Xpo Firmata Freedom strengthened by Christ (Genoa).
Liberte, Egalite, Fraternite Liberty, equality, fraternity (France).
Lucerna Pedibus Meis Verbum Est Thy word is lamp unto mine feet (England, Edward VI).
Lumen ad Revelationem Gentium Light to enlighten the nations (Papacy).
L'Union Fait la Force The union makes strength (Belgium)
Macula Non Est in Te There is no sin in Thee (Essen).
Magnus ab Integro Saeculorum Nascitur Ordo The great order of the centuries is born anew (Bavaria).
Mandavit Dominus Palatie hanc Monetam Fiert The lord of the Palatine ordained this coin to be made (Balath).
Manibus Ne Laedar Avaris Lest I be injured by greedy hands (Sweden).
Mar Bran Sac Rom Imp Arcam et Elec Sup Dux Siles Margrave of Brandenburg, archchamberlain of the Holy Roman Empire and elector, senior duke of Silesia (Prussia).
Maria Mater Domini Xpi Mary mother of Christ the Lord (Teutonic Knights).
Maria Unxit Pedes Xpisti Mary washes the feet of Christ (France, Rene d'Anjou).
Mater Castrorum Mother of fortresses (Rome, Marcus Aurelius).
Matrimonio Conjuncti Joined in wedlock (Austria).
Me Coniunctio Servat Dum Scinditur Frangor The relationship serves me while I am being torn to pieces (Lowenstein-Wertheim).
Mediolani Dux Duke of Milan (Milan).
Mediolani et Man Duke of Mantua and Milan (Milan).
Memor Ero Tui Iustina Virgo I shall remember you, o maiden Justina (Venice).
Merces Laborum Wages of work (Wurzburg).
Mirabilia Fecit He wrought marvels (Viking coinage).
Misericordia Di Rex King by the mercy of God (France, Louis II).
Mo Arg Ord Foe Belg D Gel & CZ Silver coin of the order of the Belgian Federation, duchy of Guelder-land, county of Zutphen (Guelderland).

Moneta Abbatis Coin of the abbey (German ecclesiastical coins, 13th–14th centuries).

Moneta Argentiae Ord Foed Belgii Holl Silver coin of the federated union of Belgium and Holland (Batavian Republic).

Mo No Arg Con Foe Belg Pro Hol New silver coin of the Belgian Federation, province of Holland (Holland).

Mo No Arg Pro Confoe Belg Trai Holl New silver coin of the confederated Belgian provinces, Utrecht and Holland (Batavian Republic).

Mon Lib Reip Bremens Coin of the free state of Bremen (Bremen).

Mon Nova Arg Duc Curl Ad Norma Tal Alb New silver coin of the duchy of Courland, according to the standard of the Albert thaler (Courland).

Mon Nov Castri Imp New coin of the Imperial free city of . . . (Friedberg).

Moneta Bipont Coin of Zweibrucken (Pfalz-Birkenfeld-Zweibrucken).

Monet Capit Cathedr Fuld Sede Vacante Coin of the cathedral chapter of Fulda, the see being vacant (Fulda).

Moneta in Obsidione Tornacensi Cusa Coin struck during the siege of Tournai (Tournai, 1709).

Moneta Livosesthonica Coin of Livonia (Estonia).

Moneta Nov Arg Regis Daniae New silver coin of the king of Denmark (Denmark).

Moneta Nova Ad Norman Conventionis New coin according to the Convention standard (Orsini-Rosenberg).

Moneta Nova Domini Imperatoris New coin of the lord emperor (Brunswick, 13th century).

Moneta Nova Lubecensis New coin of Lubeck.

Moneta Nova Reipublicae Halae Suevicae New coin of the republic of Hall in Swabia.

Moneta Reipublicae Ratisbonensis Coin of the republic of Regensburg.

Nach Alt Reichs Schrot und Korn According to the old empire's grits and grain (Hesse).

Nach dem Conventions Fusse According to the Convention's basis (German Conventionsthalers).

Nach dem Frankf Schlus According to the Frankfurt standard (Solms).

Nach dem Schlus der V Staend According to the standard of the union (Hesse).

Navigare Necesse Est It is necessary to navigate (Germany).

Nec Aspera Terrent Nor do difficulties terrify (Brunswick).

Nec Cito Nec Temere Neither hastily nor rashlly (Cambrai).

Nec Numina Desunt Nor is the divine will absent (Savoy).

Nec Temere Nec Timide Neither rashly nor timidly (Danzig, Lippe).

Necessitas Legem Non Habet Necessity has no law (Magdeburg).

Nemo Me Impune Lacessit No one touches me with impunity (UK, Scottish pound edge inscription).

Nihil Restat Reliqui No relic remains (Ypres).

Nil Ultra Aras Nothing beyond the rocks (Franque-mont).

No Nobis Dne Sed Noi Tuo Da Gloriam Not to us, o Lord but to Thy name be glory given (France, Francis I).

Nobilissimum Dom Ac Com in Lipp & St Most noble lord and count in Lippe and Sternberg (Schaumburg-Lippe).

Nomen Domini Turris Fortissima The name of the Lord is the strongest tower (Frankfurt).

Non Aes Sed Fides Not bronze but trust (Malta).

Non Est Mortale Quod Opto What I desire is not mortal. (Mecklenburg).

Non Mihi Sed Populo Not to me but to the people (Bavaria).

Non Relinquam Vos Orphanos I shall not leave you as orphans (Papacy).

Non Surrexit Major None greater has arisen (Genoa, Malta).

Nullum Simulatum Diuturnum Tandem Nothing that is feigned lasts long (Wittgenstein).

Nummorum Famulus The servant of the coinage (England, tin halfpence and farthings).

Nunquam Retrorsum Never backwards (Brunswick-Wolfenbuttel).

O Crux Ave Spes Unica Hail, o Cross, our only hope (England half-angels, France, Rene d'Anjou).

O Maria Ora Pro Me O Mary pray for me (Bavaria).

Ob Cives Servatos On account of the rescued citizens (Rome, Augustus).

Oculi Domini Super Iustos The eyes of the Lord look down on the just (Neuchatel).

Omnia Auxiliante Maria Mary helping everything (Schwyz).

Omnia Cum Deo Everything with God (Reuss-Greiz).

Omnia cum Deo et Nihil Sine Eo Everthing with God and nothing without Him (Erbach).

Omnis Potestas a Deo Est All power comes from God (Sweden).

Opp & Carn Dux Comm Rittb SCM Cons Int & Compi Mareschal Duke of Troppau and Carniola, count of Rietberg, privy councillor of his sacred imperial majesty, field marshal (Liechtenstein).

Opp & Carn . . . Aur Velleris Eques Duke of Troppau . . . knight of the Golden Fleece (Liechtenstein).

Opportune Conveniently (Savoy).

Optimus Princeps Best prince (Rome, Trajan).

Opulentia Salerno Wealthy Salerno (Siculo-Norman kingdom).

Pace et Iustitia With peace and justice (Spanish Netherlands).

Pacator Orbis Pacifier of the world (Rome, Aurelian).

Palma Sub Pondere Crescit The palm grows under its weight (Waldeck).

Pater Noster Our Father (Flanders, 14th century).

Pater Patriae Farther of his country (Rome, Caligula).

Patria Si Dreptul Meu The country and my right (Roumania).

Patrimon Henr Frid Sorte Divisum The heritage of Heinrich Friedrich divided by lot (Hohenlohe-Langenberg).

Patrimonia Beati Petri The inheritance of the blessed Peter (Papacy).

Patrona Franconiae Patron of Franconia (Wurzburg).

Pax Aeterna Eternal peace (Rome, Marcus Aurelius).

Pax et Abundantia Peace and plenty (Burgundy, Gelderland).

Pax Missa Per Orbem Peace sent throughout the world (England, Anne).

Pax Petrus Peace Peter (Trier, 10th century).

Pax Praevalet Armis May peace prevail by force of arms (Mainz).

Pax Quaeritur Bello Peace is sought by war (Commonwealth, Cromwell).

Pecunia Totum Circumit Orbem Money goes round the whole world (Brazil).

Per Aspera Ad Astra Through difficulties to the stars (Mecklenburg-Schwerin).

Per Angusta ad Augusta Through precarious times to the majestic (Solms-Roedelheim, a pun on the name of the ruler Johan August).

Per Crucem Tuam Salva Nos Christe Redemptor By Thy cross save us, O Christ our Redeemer (England, angels).

Per Crucem Tuam Salva Nos Xpe Redemt By Thy cross save us, O Christ our Redeemer (Portugal, 15th century).

Perdam Babillonis Nomen May the name of Babylon perish (Naples).

Perennitati Iustissimi Regis For the duration of the most just king (France, Louis XIII).

Perennitati Principis Galliae Restitutionis For the duration of the restoration of the prince of the Gauls (France, Henri IV).

Perfer et Obdura Bruxella Carry on and stick it out, Brussels (Brussels siege, 1579–80).

Perpetuus in Nemet Vivar Hereditary count in Nemt-Ujvar (Batthanyi).

Pietate et Constantia By piety and constancy (Fulda).

Pietate et Iustitia By piety and justice (Denmark).

Plebei Urbanae Frumento Constituto Free distribu-tion of grain to the urban working-class established (Rome, Nerva).

Pleidio Wyf Im Gwlad True am I to my country (UK, Welsh pound edge inscription).

Plus Ultra Beyond (the Pillars of Hercules) (Spanish America).

Point du Couronne sans Peine Point of the crown without penalty (Coburg).

Pons Civit Castellana The bridge of the town of Castellana (Papacy).

Populus et Senatus Bonon The people and senat of Bologna (Bologna).

Post Mortem Patris Pro Filio For the son after hi father's death (Pontefract siege coins).

Post Tenebras Lux After darkness light (Geneva)

Post Tenebras Spero Lucem After darkness I hope for light (Geneva).

Posui Deum Adiutorem Meum I have made Go my helper (England, Ireland, 1351–1603).

Praesidium et Decus Protection and ornament (Bologna).

Prima Sedes Galliarum First see of the Gauls (Lyon).

Primitiae Fodin Kuttenb ab Aerari Iterum Susceptarum First results dug from the Kuttenberg mines in a renewed undertaking (Austria).

Princps Iuventutis Prince of youth (Roman Empire).

Pro Defensione Urbis et Patriae For the defence of city and country (France, Louis XIV).

Pro Deo et Patria For God and the fatherland (Fulda).

Pro Deo et Populo For God and the people (Bavaria).

Pro Ecclesia et Pro Patria For the church and the fatherland (Constance).

Pro Fausio PP Reitur VS For happy returns of th princes of the Two Sicilies (Naples and Sicily).

Pro Lege et Grege For law and the flock (Fulda).

Pro maximo Dei Gloria et Bono Publico For the greatest glory of God and the good of the people (Wurttemberg).

Pro Patria For the fatherland (Wurzburg).

Propitio Deo Secura Ago With God's favour I lead a secure life. (Saxe-Lauenburg).

Protector Literis Literae Nummis Corona et Salus A protection to the letters (on the face o the coin), the letters (on the edge) are a garland and a safeguard to the coinage (Commonwealth, Cromwell broad).

Protege Virgo Pisas Protect Pisa, O Virgin (Pisa).

Provide et Constanter Wisely and firmly (Wurttem-berg).

Providentia et Pactis Through foresight and pact (Brandenburg-Ansbach).

Providentia Optimi Principis With the foresight of the best prince (Naples and Sicily).

Proxima Fisica Finis Nearest to natural end (Orciano).

Proxima Soli Nearest to the sun (Modena).

Pulcra Virtutis Imago The beautiful image of virtue (Genoa).

Pupillum et Viduam Suscipiat May he support the orphan and the widow (Savoy).

uae Deus Conjunxit Nemo Separet What God hath joined let no man put asunder (England, James I).
uem Quadragesies et Semel Patriae Natum Esse Gratulamur Whom we congratulate for the forty-first time for being born for the fatherland (Lippe-Detmold).
ui Dat Pauperi Non Indigebit Who gives to the poor will never be in need (Munster).
uid Non Cogit Necessitas To what does Necessity not drive. (Ypres).
uin Matrimonii Lustrum Celebrant They celebrate their silver wedding (Austria, 1879).
uocunque Gesseris (Jeceris) Stabit Whichever way you throw it it will stand (Isle of Man).
uod Deus Vult Hoc Semper Fit What God wishes always occurs. (Saxe-Weimar).
econduntur non Retonduntur They are laid up in store, not thundered back (Savoy).
ecta Tueri Defend the right (Austria).
ecte Constanter et Fortiter Rightly, constantly and bravely (Bavaria).
ecte Faciendo Neminem Timeas May you fear no one in doing right. (Solms-Laubach).
ector Orbis Ruler of the world (Rome, Didius Julianus).
ectus et Immotus Right and immovable (Hesse).
edde Cuique Quod Suum Est Render to each that which is his own (England, Henry VIII).
edeunt antiqui Gaudia Moris There return the joys of ancient custom (Regensburg).
eg Pr Pol et Lith Saxon Dux Royal prince of Poland and Lithuania and duke of Saxony (Trier).
egia Boruss Societas Asiat Embdae Royal Prussian Asiatic Society of Emden (Prussia).
egier Mich Her Nach Deinen Wort Govern me here according to Thy word (Palatinate).
egnans Capitulum Ecclesiae Cathedralis Ratisbonensis Sede Vacante Administering the chapter of the cathedral church at Regensburg, the see being vacant (Regensburg).
egni Utr Sic et Hier Of the kingdom of the Two Sicilies and of Jerusalem (Naples and Sicily).
eligio Protestantium Leges Angliae Libertas Parliamenti The religion of the Protestants, the laws of England and the freedom of Parliament (England, Royalists, 1642).
elinquo Vos Liberos ab Utroque Homine I leave you as children of each man (San Marino).
estauracao da Independencia Restoration of inde-pendence (Portugal, 1990).
estitutor Exercitus Restorer of the army (Rome, Aurelian).
estitutor Galliarum Restorer of the Gauls (Rome, Gallienus).
estitutor Generis Humani Restorer of mankind (Rome, Valerian).
estitutor Libertatis Restorer of freedom (Rome, Constantine).
Restitutor Orbis Restorer of the world (Rome, Valerian).
Restitutor Orientis Restorer of the east (Rome, Valerian).
Restitutor Saeculi Restorer of the century (Rome, Valerian).
Restitutor Urbis Restorer of the city (Rome, Severus).
Rosa Americana Utile Dulci The American rose, useful and sweet (American colonies).
Rosa Sine Spina A rose without a thorn (England, Tudor coins).
Rutilans Rosa Sine Spina A dazzling rose without a thorn (England, Tudor gold coins).
S Annae Fundgruben Ausb Tha in N Oe Mining thaler of the St Anne mine in Lower Austria (Austria).
S Ap S Leg Nat Germ Primas Legate of the Holy Apostolic See, born Primate of Germany (Salzburg).
S Carolus Magnus Fundator Charlemagne founder (Munster).
S. Gertrudis Virgo Prudens Niviella St Gertrude the wise virgin of Nivelles (Nivelles).
SI Aul Reg Her & P Ge H Post Mag General hereditary postmaster, supreme of the imperial court of the hereditary kingdom and provinces (Paar).
S. Ian Bapt F. Zachari St John the Baptist, son of Zachary (Florence).
S. Kilianus Cum Sociis Francorum Apostoli St Kilian and his companions, apostles to the Franks (Wurzburg).
S. Lambertus Patronus Leodiensis St Lambert, patron of Liege (Liege).
Sac Nupt Celeb Berol For the holy matrimony celebrated at Berlin (Brandenburg-Ansbach).
Sac Rom Imp Holy Roman Empire (German states).
Sac Rom Imp Provisor Iterum Administrator of the Holy Roman Empire for the second time (Saxony).
Salus Generis Humani Safety of mankind (Rome, Vindex).
Salus Patriae Safety of the fatherland (Italy).
Salus Populi The safety of the people (Spain).
Salus Provinciarum Safety of the provinces (Rome, Postumus).
Salus Publica Salus Mea Public safety is my safety (Sweden).
Salus Reipublicae The safety of the republic (Rome, Theodosius II).
Salus Reipublicae Suprema Lex The safety of the republic is the supreme law (Poland).
Salvam Fac Rempublicam Tuam Make your state safe (San Marino).
Sanctus Iohannes Innoce St John the harmless (Gandersheim).
Sans Changer Without changing (Isle of Man).
Sans Eclat Without pomp (Bouchain siege, 1711).

Sapiente Diffidentia Wise distrust (Teschen).
Scutum Fidei Proteget Eum / Eam The shield of faith shall protect him / her (England, Edward VI and Elizabeth I).
Secundum Voluntatem Tuam Domine Your favourable will o Lord (Hesse).
Securitati Publicae For the public safety (Brandenburg-Ansbach).
Sede Vacante The see being vacant (Papal states, Vatican and ecclesiastical coinage).
Sena Vetus Alpha et W Principum et Finis Old Siena alpha and omega, the beginning and the end (Siena).
Senatus Populus QR Senate and people of Rome (Rome, 1188).
Si Deus Nobiscum Quis Contra Nos If God is with us who can oppose us (Hesse).
Si Deus Pro Nobis Quis Contra Nos If God is for us who can oppose us (Roemhild).
Sieh Deine Seeligkeit Steht Fest Ins Vaters Liebe Behold thy salvation stands surely in thy Father's love (Gotha).
Signis Receptis When the standards had been recovered (Rome, Augustus).
Signum Crucis The sign of the cross (Groningen).
Sincere et Constanter Truthfully and steadfastly (Hesse-Darmstadt).
Sit Nomen Domini Benedictum Blessed be the name of the Lord (Burgundy, Strasbourg).
St T X Adiuto Reg Iste Domba Let it be to you, o Christ, the assistant to the king of Dombes (Dombes).
Sit Tibi Xpe Dat q'tu Regis Iste Ducat May this duchy which Thou rulest be given to Thee, O Christ (Venice, ducat).
Sit Unio Haec Perennis May this union last for ever (Hohenlohe-Langenberg).
Sola Bona Quae Honesta The only good things are those which are honest (Brunswick).
Sola Facta Deum Sequor Through deeds alone I strive to follow God (Milan).
Soli Deo Honor et Gloria To God alone be honour and glory (Nassau).
Soli Reduci To him, the only one restored (Naples and Sicily).
Solius Virtutis Flos Perpetuus The flower of Virtue alone is perpetual (Strasbourg).
Spes Confisa Deo Nunquam Confusa Recedit Hope entrusted in God never retreats in a disorderly fashion (Lippe).
Spes Nr Deus God is our hope (Oudenarde siege, 1582).
Spes Rei Publicae The hope of the republic (Rome, Valens).
Strena ex Argyrocopeo Vallis S Christoph A New Year's gift from the silver-bearing valley of St Christopher (Wurttemberg, 1625).
Sub His Secura Spes Clupeus Omnibus in Te Sperantibus Under these hope is safe, a shield for all who reside hope in Thee (Bavaria).
Sub Pondere Under weight (Fulda).
Sub Protectione Caesarea Under imperial protection (Soragna).
Sub Tuum Praesidium Confug We flee to Thy protection (Salzburg).
Sub Umbra Alarum Tuarum Under the shadow of Thy wings (Iever, Scotland, James V).
Subditorum Salus Felicitas Summa The safety of the subjects is the highest happiness (Lubeck).
Sufficit Mihi Gratia Tua Domine Sufficient to me is Thy grace, o Lord (Ploen).
Supra Firmam Petram Upon a firm rock (Papacy).
Susceptor Noster Deus God is our defence (Tuscany).
Sydera Favent Industriae The stars favour industry (Furstenberg).
Sylvarum Culturae Praemium Prize for the culture of the forest (Brandenburg-Ansbach).
Tali Dicata Signo Mens Fluctuari Nequit Consecrated by such a sign the mind cannot waver (England, Henry VIII George noble).
Tandem Bona Caus Triumphat A good cause eventually triumphs (Dillenburg).
Tandem Fortuna Obstetrice With good luck ultimately as the midwife (Wittgenstein).
Te Stante Virebo With you at my side I shall be strong (Moravia).
Tene Mensuram et Respice Finem Hold the measure and look to the end (Burgundy).
Tert Ducat Secular Tercentenary of the duchy (Wurttemberg).
Thu Recht Schev Niemand Go with right and fear no one (Saxe-Lauenburg).
Tibi Laus et Gloria To Thee be praise and glory (Venice).
Timor Domini Fons Vitae The fear of the Lord is a fountain of life (England, Edward VI shillings).
Tout Avec Dieu Everything with God (Brunswick, 1626).
Traiectum ad Mosam The crossing of the Maas (Maastricht).
Transvolat Nubila Virtus Marriageable virtue soon flies past (Grueyeres).
Travail, Famille, Patrie Work, family, country (Vichy France).
Triumphator Gent Barb Victor over the barbarian people (Byzantine Empire, Arcadius).
Tueatur Unita Deus May God guard these united (Kingdoms) (England, James I; Britain, 1847).
Turck Blegert Wien Vienna besieged by the Turks (Vienna, 1531).
Tut Mar Gab Pr Vid de Lobk Nat Pr Sab Car et Aug Pr de Lobk Regency of Maria Gabriela, widow of the prince of Lobkowitz, born princess of Savoy-Carignan, and August prince of Lobkowitz (Lobkowitz).
Tutela Italiae The guardianship of Italy (Rome, Nerva).

bi Vult Spirat He breathes where he will (Papacy).
bique Pax Peace everywhere (Rome, Gallienus).
nion et Force Union and strength (France).
rbe Obsessa The city under siege (Maastricht).
rbem Virgo Tuam Serva Protects thy city o virgin (Mary) (Strasbourg).
SC & RAM Cons Int Gen C Mar & Nob Praet H Turmae Capit Privy councillor of both their holy imperial and royal apostolic majesties, general field marshal and captain of the noble praetorian Hungarian squadrons (Eszterhazy).
culis Aulae Argenteis Patriae Indigenti Ministravit Auxilia With the silver vessels of the court aid was brought to the needy fatherland (Eichstadt, 1796).
ehiculatione Italiae Remissa Postal tax of Italy remitted (Rome, Nerva).
eni Luumen Cordium Come light of hearts (Vatican).
eni Sancte Spiritus Come Holy Ghost (Vatican).
erbum Domini Manet in Aeternum The word of the Lord abides forever (Hesse-Darmstadt, Veldenz).
eritas Lex Tua The truth is your law (Salzburg).
eritas Temporis Filia Truth is the daughter of time (England and Ireland, Mary Tudor).
eritate et Labore By truth and work (Wittgenstein).
eritate et Iustitia By truth and justice (German states).
ictoria Principum The victory of princes (Ostrogoths).
ideant Pauperes et Laetentur Let the poor see and rejoice (Tuscany).
irgo Maria Protege Civitatem Savonae Virgin Mary Protect the city of Savona (Savona).
iribus Unitis With united strength (Austria).
Virtute et Fidelitate By virtue and faithfulness (Hesse-Cassel).
Virtute et Prudentia With virtue and prudence (Auersperg).
Virtute Viam Dimetiar I shall mark the way with valour (Waldeck).
Virtutis Gloria Merces Glory is the reward of valour (Holstein-Gottorp).
Vis Unita Concordia Fratrum Fortior United power is the stronger harmony of brothers (Mansfeld).
Visitavit Nos Oriens ex Alto He has visited us arising on high (Luneburg).
Vivit Post Funera He lives after death (Bremen).
Von Gottes Gn Iohan Bischof Zu Strasburg Landtgraf in Elsass By God's grace John, Bishop of Strasbourg, Landgrave in Alsace (Strasbourg).
Vota Optata Romae Fel Vows taken for the luck of Rome (Rome, Maxentius).
Vox de Throno A voice from the throne (Papacy).
Was Got Beschert Bleibet Unerwert What God hath endowed leave undisturbed
Wider macht und List Mein Fels Gott Ist Against might and trickery God is my rock (Hesse-Cassel).
Xpc Vincit Xpc Regnat Christ conquers, Christ reigns (Scotland, Spain).
Xpc Vivet Xpc Regnat Xpc Impat Christ lives, Christ reigns, Christ commands (Cambrai).
Xpe Resurescit Christ lives again (Venice).
Xpistiana Religio Christian religion (Carolingian Empire).
Xps Ihs Elegit me Regem Populo Jesus Christ chose me as king to the people (Norway).
Zelator Fidei Usque ad Montem An upholder of the faith through and through (Portugal).
Zum Besten des Vaterlands To the best of the fatherland (Bamberg).

Care
of coins

There is no point in going to a great deal of trouble and expense in selecting the best coins you can afford, only to let them deteriorate in value by neglect and mishandling. Unless you give some thought to the proper care of your coins, your collection is unlikely to make a profit for you if and when you come to sell it. Housing your coins is the biggest problem of all, so it is important to give a lot of attention to this.

orage

The ideal, but admittedly the most expensive, ethod is the coin cabinet, constructed of air-dried ahogany, walnut or rosewood (*never* oak, cedar any highly resinous timber likely to cause emical tarnish). These cabinets have banks of allow drawers containing trays made of the same ood, with half-drilled holes of various sizes to commodate the different denominations of coins. ch cabinets are handsome pieces of furniture but, ing largely handmade, tend to be rather pensive. Occasionally good specimens can be cked up in secondhand furniture shops, or at the spersal of house contents by auction, but the best t is still to purchase a new cabinet, tailored to ur own requirements.

Peter Nichols of 3 Norman Road, St Leonards- -Sea, East Sussex TN37 6NH (telephone 01424 6682) is a specialist manufacturer of display and rage systems who has also been producing coin d medal cabinets to suit every need for more than quarter of a century. He can produce a cabinet to into a wall safe or some other form of security x. He can match existing work, and thus replicate binets which you may already be using, or even oduce designs to suit your specific requirements. e only proviso is that the cabinets are made in ly one timber—Brazilian mahogany, for reason chemical balance. A nice touch is that all the oducts in the Nichols repertoire take their names m Elizabethan mint-marks.

Nichols also offers a custom drilling service for in trays, either all of the same diameter or in xed sizes, depending on what you require. illing templates are also available on request. part from coin cabinets, Peter Nichols anufactures *medal* cabinets in two basic types, the ven-tray Pheon and the fourteen-tray Crozier. The cases for these cabinets are similar in all respects to the coin cabinets, but medal trays are twice the thickness of coin trays. Each tray is made up from solid mahogany mouldings, base and polished mahogany front edges and trimmed with two turned brass knobs. The base of each tray is trimmed with a red felt pad.

The 4-tray Martlet—the smallest in an extensive range from Peter Nichols.

The Crozier—a cabinet for the connoisseur.

The Mini-Porter, smallest of Abafil's plush Diplomat range.

Nichols produces a wide range of cabinets from the seven-tray Pheon all the way up to the massive 40-tray specials designed for the British Museum. All cabinets are fitted with double doors. Nichols also produces the glass-topped Crown display case and the Sceptre display case, fitted with a glazed lid and containing a single tray. The Orb range of display cases are intended for wall mounting and are ideal for a display of campaign medals and decorations.

Prices start at around £30 for a four-tray Martlet coin cabinet and go all the way to the Coronet thirty-tray version at about £300. They are not cheap, but you have the satisfaction of acquiring exquisite examples of the cabinetmaker's craft which would be an elegant addition to any lounge or study.

An excellent compromise is provided by firms such as Abafil of Italy and Lindner of Germany who manufacture coin trays in durable, felt-lined materials with shallow compartments to suit the various sizes of coins. These trays interlock so that they build up into a cabinet of the desired size, and there are also versions designed as carrying cases, which are ideal for transporting coins.

Collectors Gallery of Castle Hall, Castle Gate, Shrewsbury, SY1 2AD (telephone: 01743 272140, fax: 01743 366041) is the UK agent and distributor for the Abafil series manufactured in Milan. These cases are of stout wooden construction covered with simulated leather and lined with red plush. The Diplomat range is designed primarily for secure transportation, but the Mini-diplomat, at around £40, makes a good static cabinet, and can take up to three standard trays holding a maximum of 241 coins, while the Custom case holds 14 de luxe or 20 standard trays and will house up to 1,500 coins. Even cheaper is the Mignon case holding up to 105 coins, ideally suited for carrying in a briefcase or travel bag.

Lindner Publications of 13 Fore Street, Hayle, Cornwall TR27 4DX (telephone 01726 751914) are well-known for their wide range of philatelic a numismatic accessories, but these include a f array of coin boxes, capsules, carrying cases a trays. The basic Lindner coin box is, in fact, shallow tray available in a standard version o smoked glass version. These trays have a crys clear frame, red felt inserts and holes for vario diameters of coins and medals. A novel feature these trays is the rounded insert which facilita the removal of coins from their spaces with t minimum of handling. These boxes are designed such a manner that they interlock and can be bu up into banks of trays, each fitted with a dra handle and sliding in and out easily. Various typ of chemically inert plastic capsules and envelop have been designed for use in combination w plain shallow trays, without holes drilled. Lindr also manufacture a range of luxury cases lined velvet and Atlas silk with padded covers and go embossing on the spines, producing a most taste and elegant appearance.

Safe Albums of 16 Falcon Business Pa Hogwood Lane, Finchampstead, Berkshire RG 4QW (telephone 01734 328976) are the UK age for the German Stapel-Element, a drawer-stacki system with clear plasticiser-free trays that fit in standard bookshelves. The sliding co compartments, lined with blue velvet, can be angl for display to best advantage. Stackable draw cost around £12 each, and can be built up to a height desired. A wide range of drawer sizes available, with compartments suitable for t smallest coins right up to four-compartment tra designed for very large artefacts such as card-ca or cigarette cases. The Mobel-Element cabinet i superb specialised cabinet constructed of the fin timber with a steel frame and steel grip bars whi can be securely locked. It thus combines elegar with security and is the ideal medium for the m valuable coins and medals.

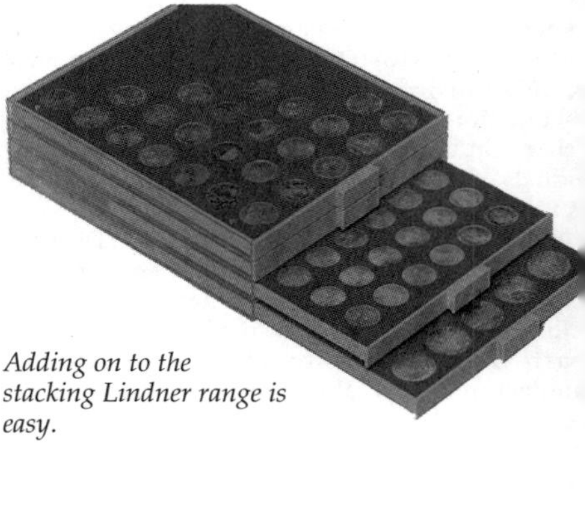

Adding on to the stacking Lindner range is easy.

There are also various storage systems, such as ɔindex, which operate on the principle of narrow ·awers in which the coins are stored in envelopes chemically-inert plastic. A strip across the top ɔlds a little slip giving a brief description, catalogue ımber and the price of each coin.

Kwikseal of the USA produce cards with a plastic indow: these cards are especially suitable for abbing coins. The traditional method used by any collectors was to house coins in small, air-ied manila envelopes that could be stored upright narrow wooden or stout card boxes—knife-boxes ere highly regarded as being the right width and epth. The Sydney Museum in Australia, for ample, keeps its coins in manila envelopes stored plastic lunch-boxes which seemed to do the job retty well!

Safe's cabinet combines elegance with security.

oin Albums

When coin collecting became a popular hobby the 1960s, several firms marketed ranges of coin lbums. They had clear plastic sleeves divided into ny compartments of various sizes and had the erit of being cheap and taking up little room on a ookshelf.

They had several drawbacks, however, not the ast being the tendency of the pages to sag with the eight of the coins, or even, in extreme cases, to ull away from the pegs or rings holding them on the spine. They required very careful handling s the coins could easily fall out of the top row as the ages were turned. The more expensive albums ad little flaps that folded over the top of the coin to vercome this problem.

Arguably the worst aspect of these albums was ıe use of polyvinyl chloride (PVC) in the onstruction of the sleeves. Collectors soon iscovered to their horror that this reacted hemically with their coins, especially those made f silver, causing a rather disgusting yellow slime adhere to the coins' surface. I shudder to think ow many fine collections were ruined as a result, r of the countless coins that required highly expert

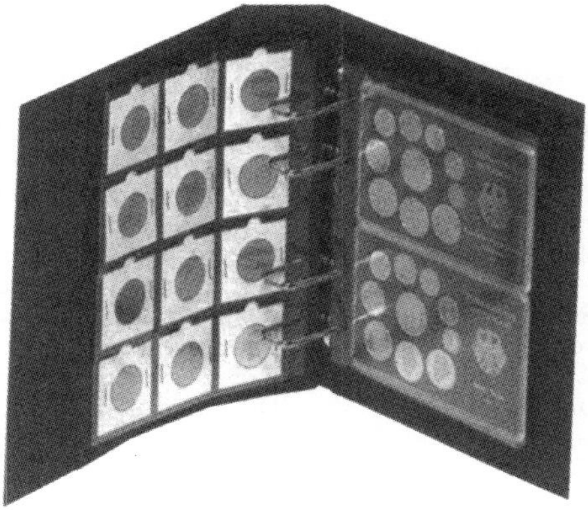

Albums can be carried around easily

treatment in a bid to restore them to as near the original condition as possible.

Fortunately the lesson has been learned and the coin albums now on the market are quite safe. Lindner offer a wide range of albums designed to house coins, medals or banknotes. The old problem about sagging pages is overcome by the use of a multi-ring binding welded to a very stout spine, while the sleeves contain neither Styrol nor PVC and will not affect any metals at all. In addition to pages with pockets of uniform size, the Karat range of albums operates on a slide principle which enables the user to insert vertical strips of different sizes on the same page, so that the coins of one country or series, or perhaps a thematic display of coins from different countries, can be displayed side by side.

Safe Albums offer a wide range of albums in the Coinholder System and Coin-Combi ranges. These, too, offer the choice of fixed pages with uniform-sized pockets, or interchangeable sliding inserts for different sizes side by side.

Cleaning Coins

This is like matrimony—it should not be embarked on lightly. Indeed, the advice given by the magazine *Punch* in regard to marriage is equally sound in this case—don't do it! It is far better to have a dirty coin than an irretrievably damaged one. Every dealer has horror stories of handling coins that previous owners have cleaned, to their detriment. The worst example I ever saw was a display of coins found by a metal detectorist who "improved" his finds by abrading them in the kind of rotary drum used by lapidarists to polish gemstones. If you really must remove the dirt and grease from coins, it is advisable to practise on coins of little value.

Warm water containing a mild household detergent or washing-up liquid will work wonders in removing surface dirt and grease from most coins, but silver is best washed in a weak solution of ammonia and warm water—one part ammonia to ten parts water. Gold coins can be cleaned with diluted citric acid, such as lemon juice. Copper or bronze coins present more of a problem, but patches of verdigris can usually be removed by careful washing in a 20 per cent solution of sodium sesquicarbonate. Wartime coins made of tin, zinc, iron or steel can be cleaned in a 5 per cent solution of caustic soda containing some aluminium or zinc foil or filings, but they must be rinsed afterwards in clean water and carefully dried. Cotton buds are ideal for gently prising dirt out of coin legends and crevices in the designs. Soft brushes (with animal bristles—*never* nylon or other artificial bristles) designed for cleaning silver are most suitable f gently cleaning coins.

Coins recovered from the soil or the sea b present special problems, due to chemical reacti between the metals and the salts in the earth or s water. In such cases, the best advice is to take the to the nearest museum and let the profession experts decide on what can or should be done.

Both Lindner and Safe Albums offer a range coin-cleaning kits and materials suitable for gol silver, copper and other base alloys respectivel Safe (living up to their name) also provide a ste warning that rubber gloves should be worn ar care taken to avoid breathing fumes or gettir splashes of liquid in your eyes or on your ski Obviously, the whole business of cleaning is matter that should not be entered into without t utmost care and forethought.

POLISHING: A WARNING

If cleaning should only be approached with the greatest trepidation, polishing is definitely *out!* Beginners sometimes fall into the appalling error of thinking that a smart rub with metal polish might improve the appearance of their coins. Short of actually punching a hole through it, there can hardly be a more destructive act. Polishing a coin may improve its superficial appearance for a few days, but such abrasive action will destroy the patina and reduce the fineness of the high points of the surface. Even if a coin is only polished once, it will never be quite the same again, and an expert can tell this a mile off.

Celtic
coinage of Britain

eltic coins were the first coins made in Britain. They were issued for a century and a alf before the Roman invasion, and possibly a little later in some areas. They were ›sued by 11 tribal groups or administrative authorities situated southeast of a line ·om the Humber to the Severn. In this short article Celtic specialist CHRIS RUDD ıtroduces this increasingly popular area.

The earliest coins were uninscribed and often ›stract in design. Later ones carried the names f local leaders and tribal centres, and in the ›utheast became increasingly Roman in style, ›metimes copying classical images quite closely.

Most Celtic coins were struck between two dies ı flans of gold, silver, billion and bronze. Some ere cast in strip moulds in tin-rich bronze alloy ılled "potin".

Because the Celts wrote no books and left no ·ritten records of their activities, little is known ›out the people and places behind their coins. /ho made them? When? Where? And why? These re questions that are still largely unanswered, xcept in the very vaguest terms. Celtic ıtaloguers talk about gold quarters, silver units ıd silver minims. But the truth is we don't even ıow what the Celts themselves called their coins.

British Celtic coins are among the most ıscinating ever fashioned and perhaps the least ımiliar to the average collector because of their ırity. Like the Celts themselves, Celtic coin esigns are wild, free flowing, flamboyant and full f fun. Yes, Celtic moneyers had a great sense of umour!

Celtic coins bear a vast variety of gods and oddesses, armed warriors, chariot wheels, idden faces, decapitated heads, suns, moons, tars, thunderbolts, floral motifs, magic signs and hallic symbols. Plus a menagerie of antelopes, ears, boars, bulls, cocks, crabs, cranes, dogs, olphins, ducks, eagles, hares, all kinds of horses ›ome with wings, some with human heads, many /ith three tails, a few breathing fire), goats, lions, zards, owls, rams, rats, ravens, snakes, stags, tarfish, worms and wolves. Not to mention ragons, griffins, hippocamps, sphinxes and ram-orned serpents.

Ask any metal detectorist how many Celtic coins he or she has found and you will immediately realise they are rarer than Roman coins in this country—at least a thousand times rarer on average. This is because far fewer Celtic coins were minted, in smaller runs, over a much shorter time span. Though some may have been made as early as 80 BC, the majority of British Celtic coins were struck from 54 BC to AD 43; barely 100 years of production, and most of that seems to have been sporadic.

However, the greater rarity of Celtic coins doesn't mean they are necessarily more costly than other ancient coins: in fact, they are often cheaper. You see, in the coin market, demand determines price. The more collectors that want a coin, the higher its price.

A recent survey revealed "worldwide there may be no more than 150 regular private collectors

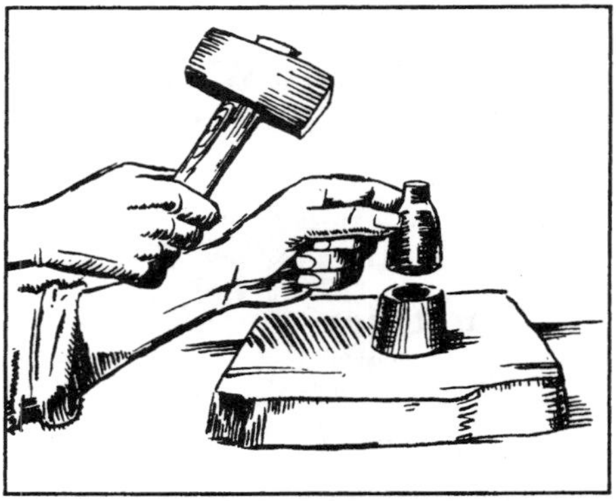

Method that may have been used for striking Celtic coins (drawing by Simon Pressey).

of Celtic coins, buying on average one or more coins per month". Whereas there are literally thousands of people collecting the other major series of ancient and medieval coins. That is why Celtic coins are still comparatively less costly than Greek, Anglo-Saxon and English hammered coins. The Celtic market is smaller, though expanding. For example a very fine Celtic gold stater typically costs half the price of a Greek gold stater or an English gold noble of comparable quality and rarity. The price differential can be even mo dramatic at major international auctions. But t disparity is diminishing as more and mo collectors are beginning to appreciate the hither unrecognised beauty, scarcity and good value British Celtic coins. So now could be a good tin to start collecting Celtic coins, before their pric begin climbing more steeply.

Thirty years ago collecting British Celtic coi was a rich man's hobby and understanding the

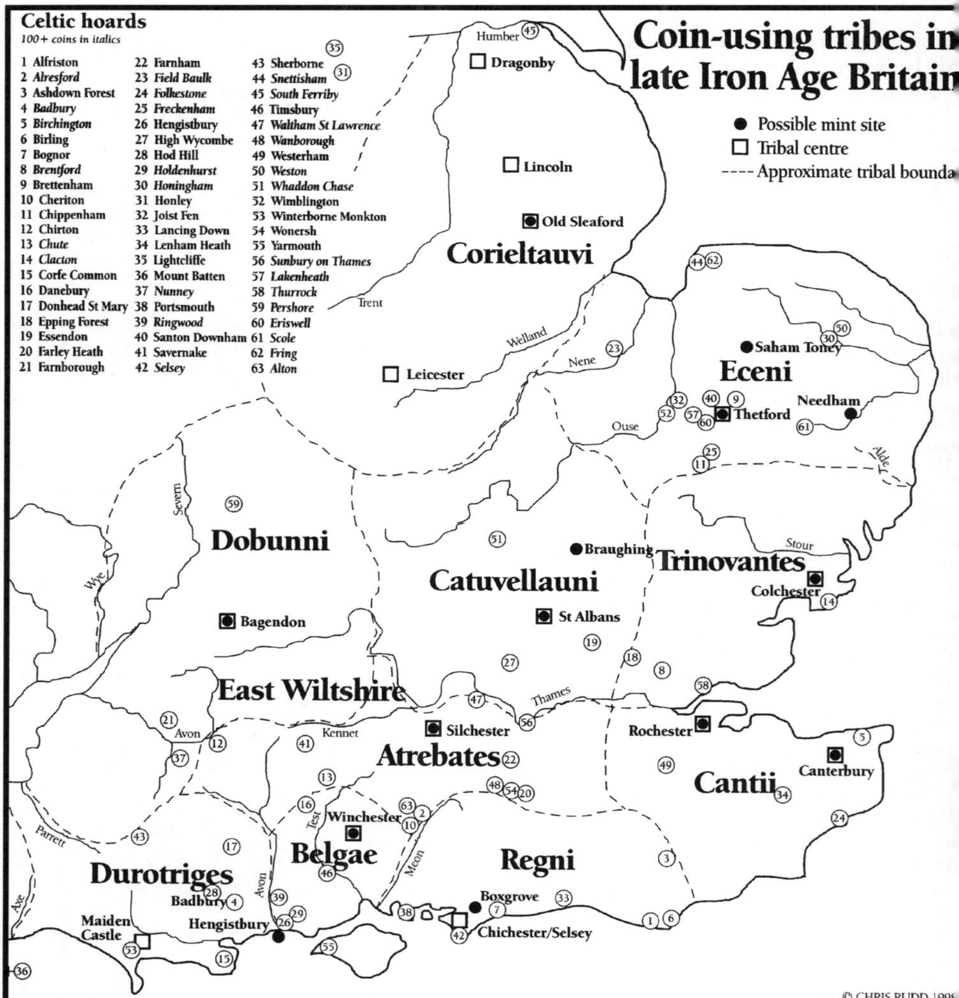

Eleven tribal groups minted coins in late Iron Age Britain, c. 80 BC–AD 45. The boundaries shown here a guesstimates, not actual, and often follow rivers, many of which are still known by their Celtic names.

Silver unit attributed to King Esuprastus of the Eceni, whose death resulted in the revolt of Queen Boudica, AD 60 (drawn four times actual size by Susan White).

as the lonely pursuit of a few scholarly ımismatists. Today, thanks to the popularity of etal detecting, Celtic coins are more plentiful and most everyone can afford to collect them. Most ıcient coin dealers sell Celtic coins, some for as tle as £20 each, and you will always find a few ıys of them at every coin fair.

British Celtic coins are also easier to study day, thanks to the publication of some excellent ›oks on the subject. The Celtic collector's bible *Celtic Coinage of Britain* by Robert D. Van Arsdell pink, 1989)—well researched, well written, well ustrated, always quoted in dealers' catalogues, ten controversial when dates are discussed and ›pefully to be republished soon in a revised lition. For the dedicated Celtic devotee *British ›n Age Coins in the British Museum* by Richard obbs (British Museum Press, 1996) is an valuable companion volume to Van Arsdell—ore cautious, less speculative.

By far the best introductory book is *Celtic ›inage in Britain* by Dr Philip de Jersey (Shire rchaeology, 1996) who manages the Celtic Coin ıdex, a photographic record of over 31,000 British ›ins at the Institute of Archaeology, Oxford. In ain language Dr Philip de Jersey explains how eltic coins and the images they carry can reveal formation on the political, economic and social :e of the Celts. *Celtic Coinage in Britain* contains ear twice-size photos of over a hundred Celtic coins, some of them rarely seen before. It gives the names, addresses and phone numbers of the museums in England, Scotland and Wales with the best and most accessible collections of Celtic coins.

In short, if you want to know more about British Celtic coins, *Celtic Coinage in Britain* is where you start reading and keep reading. This is the best little book ever written about British Celtic coins and outstanding value for money at £4.99.

How should you start collecting British Celtic coins? First, get a few of the commoner uninscribed types from each of the 11 tribal areas, aiming for the highest grade you can comfortably afford. Then you may wish to get an inscribed coin of each of the main rulers. You would also be well advised to acquire some Gaulish coins at the same time, because many British coins were influenced by Gallic prototypes.

How much do British Celtic coins cost? Very little, considering how scarce they are. Types with legends usually cost more than those without and top quality bronze is frequently more pricey than top quality silver (which may surprise you) because silver is commoner and generally survives better after two-thousand years underground.

Chris Rudd is a well-known dealer who specialises in Celtic coins.

Collecting Ancient coins

Ancient coins differ from most other series which are collected in Britain in that every piece has spent the major part of the last two thousand years in the ground. As JOHN CUMMINGS, dealer in ancient coins and antiquities explains here, the effect that burial has had on the surface of the coin determines more than anything else the value of a particular piece. With more modern coins, the only things which affect price are rarity and grade. There may be a premium for coins exhibiting particularly fine tone, or with outstanding pedigrees, but an 1887 crown in "extremely fine" condition has virtually the same value as every other piece with the same grade and of the same date. With ancient coins the story is very different.

A large number of different criteria affect the price of an ancient coin. Factors affecting prices can be broken down into several categories:

Condition

The most important factor by far in determining price. Ancient coins were struck by hand and can exhibit striking faults. Value suffers if the coin is struck with the designs off-centre, is weakly struck, or if the flan is irregular in shape. Many of the Celtic tribes issued coins of varying fineness and those made from low quality gold or silver are worth less than similar specimens where the metal quality is better. Conversely, coins on exceptional flans, particularly well struck, or with fine patinas command a premium.

Many ancient coins have suffered during their stay in the ground. It must be borne in mind that the prices given in the price guide are for uncorroded, undamaged examples. A Roman denarius should be graded using the same criteria as those used for grading modern coins. The surfaces must be good, and the coin intact. The fact that the coin is 2,000 years old is irrelevant as far as grading is concerned. Coins which are not perfectly preserved are not without value but the value for a given grade decreases with the degree of fault.

Rarity

As with all other series, rare coins usually command higher prices than common ones although this is not written in stone. A uniq variety of a small fourth century Roman bron coin, even in perfect condition, can be worth mu less than a more worn and common piece fro an earlier part of the empire. In the Celtic seri there is an almost infinite variety of minor typ and a unique variety of an uninscribed type w rarely outbid an inscribed issue of a known kin

Historical and local significance

Types which have historical or local interest ca command a price far above their scarcity valu Denarii of the emperor Tiberius are believed have been referred to in the New Testament ar command a far higher price than a less interestir piece of similar rarity. Similarly, pieces which ha British reverse types such as the "VICT BRIT reverse of the third century AD are mo expensive than their scarcity would indicate. Th 12 Caesars are ever popular especially in th American market and this affects pric throughout the world. In the Celtic series, coi of Cunobelin or Boudicca are far more popul than pieces which have no historical interest b which are far scarcer.

Reverse types

All Roman emperors who survived for reasonable time issued coins with many differe reverse types. The most common of these usuall show various Roman gods. When a coin has a unusual reverse it always enhances the valu rticularly popular are architectural scenes, imals, references to Judaism, and legionary pes.

tistic merit

Most Celtic tribes issued several distinct series hich generally speaking, improved in style up the time of the Roman invasion. Later issues hich exhibit fine "Celtic" style are usually more pular than the more stylised, earlier types. Typical of the former would be the beautiful gold staters of Tasciovanus and Cunobelin. The Roman coinage is blessed with a large number of bust varieties and these can have a startling effect on price. A common coin with the bust left instead of right can be worth several times the price of a normal example. The coinage of Hadrian has a large number of bust varieties some of which are extremely artistic and these can command a premium.

The coinage used in Britain from the time of the invasion in AD 43 was the same as that introduced throughout the Empire by the emperor Augustus around 20 BC. The simple divisions of 2 asses equal to one dupondius, 2 dupondii equal to 1 sestertius, 4 sestertii equal to one denarius and 25 denarii equal to one aureus continued in use until the reformation of the coinage by Caracalla in AD 214.

Aureus (gold)

Denarius (silver)

Sestertius (bronze)

Dupondius (copper)

As (copper)

Introducing *Hammered coinage*

The hammered currency of medieval Britain is among some of the most interesting coinage in the world. The turbulent history of these islands is reflected in the fascinating changes in size, design, fineness and workmanship, culminating in the many strange examples that emanated from the strife of the Civil War.

The Norman Conquest of England in 1066 and succeeding years had far-reaching effects on all aspects of life. Surprisingly, however, it had little impact on the coinage. William the Conqueror was anxious to emphasise the continuity of his reign, so far as the ordinary people were concerned, and therefore he retained the fabric, size and general design pattern of the silver penny. Almost 70 mints were in operation during this reign, but by the middle of the 12th century the number was reduced to 55 and under Henry II (1154–89) it fell to 30 and latterly to only eleven. By the early 14th century the production of coins had been centralised on London and Canterbury, together with the ecclesiastical mints at York and Canterbury. The silver penny was the principal denomination throughout the Norman period, pieces cut along the lines of the cross on the reverse continuing to serve as halfpence and farthings.

Eight types of penny were struck und William I and five under his son William Rufu both profiles (left and right) and facing portrai being used in both reigns allied to crosses various types. Fifteen types were minted und Henry I (1100–35), portraiture having no degenerated to crude caricature, the lin engraved on the coinage dies being built up b means of various punches. Halfpence modelle on the same pattern were also struck, but ver sparingly and are very rare.

On Henry's death the succession wa contested by his daughter Matilda and h nephew Stephen of Blois. Civil war broke out i 1138 and continued till 1153. Stephen controlle London and its mint, but Matilda and he supporters occupied the West Country an struck their own coins at Bristol. Several of th powerful barons struck their own coins, an there were distinct regional variants of the rega coinage. Of particular interest are the coins struc

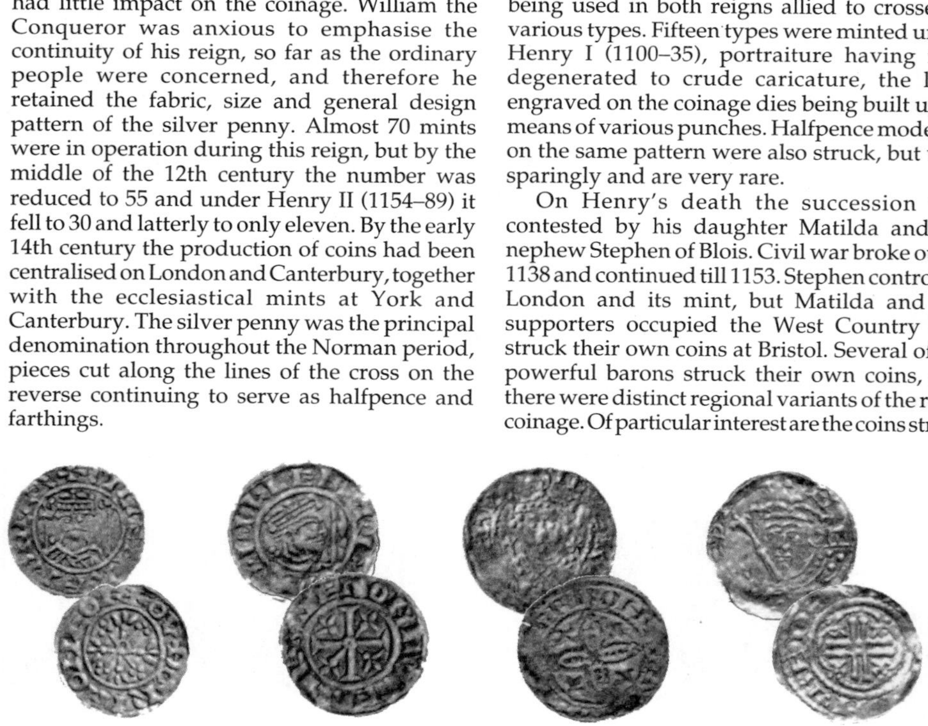

Silver pennies of, from left to right, William I, William Rufus, Henry I and Stephen.

›m obverse dies with Stephen's portrait erased defaced, believed to date from 1148 when the urper was under papal interdict.

Peace was restored in 1153 when it was agreed at Matilda's son Henry should succeed ephen. On the latter's death the following ar, Henry II ascended the throne. Coins of ephen's last type continued to be minted till 58, but Henry then took the opportunity to erhaul the coinage which had become egular and sub-standard during the civil war. ıe new "Cross Crosslet" coins, usually known the Tealby coinage (from the hoard of over)00 pennies found at Tealby, Lincolnshire in 07), were produced at 30 mints, but when the coinage was completed this number was duced to a dozen. The design of Henry's coins mained virtually the same throughout more an two decades, apart from minor variants. ıen, in 1180, a new type, known as the Short oss coinage, was introduced. This was a vast ıprovement over the poorly struck Cross osslet coins and continued without alteration, ›t only to the end of the reign of Henry II in 89, but throughout the reigns of his sons chard (1189–99) and John (1199–1216) and the st half of the reign of his grandson Henry III 216–46). Throughout that 66 year period, ›wever, there were minor variations in portraits ıd lettering which enable numismatists to tribute the HENRICUS coins to specific reigns ıd periods.

Tealby" type penny, left, and "Short Cross" penny Henry II.

The style and workmanship of the Short ross coinage deteriorated in the reign of Henry I. By the 1220s coin production was confined the regal mints at London and Canterbury, e sole exception being the ecclesiastical mint aintained by the Abbot of Bury St Edmunds. Halfpence and farthings were briefly struck in 1221–30, though halfpence are now extremely rare and so far only a solitary farthing has been discovered.

By the middle of this reign the coinage was in a deplorable state, being poorly struck, badly worn and often ruthlessly clipped. In 1247 Henry ordered a new coinage and in this the arms of the cross on the reverse were extended to the rim as a safeguard against clipping. This established a pattern of facing portrait and long cross on obverse and reverse respectively that was to continue till the beginning of the 16th century. Several provincial mints were re-activated to assist with the recoinage but they were all closed down again by 1250, only the regal mints at London and Canterbury and the ecclesiastical mints at Durham and Bury St Edmunds remaining active.

"Long Cross" pennies of Henry III, left, and Edward I.

In 1257 Henry tentatively introduced a gold penny (worth 20 silver pence and twice the weight of a silver penny). The coin was undervalued and soon disappeared from circulation.

The Long Cross coinage of Henry III continued under Edward I till 1279 when the king introduced a new coinage in his own name. The penny continued the style of its predecessors, though much better designed and executed; but new denominations were now added. Henceforward halfpence and farthings became a regular issue and, at the same time, a fourpenny coin known as the groat (from French *gros*) was briefly introduced (minting ceased in 1282 and was not revived till 1351). Due to the centralisation of coin production the name of the moneyer was now generally dropped, although it lingered on a few years at Bury St Edmunds. The provincial mints were again revived in 1299–1302 to recoin the lightweight foreign imitations of pennies which had flooded in from the Continent.

The coinage of Edward II (1307–27) differed only in minor respects from that of his father, and a similar pattern prevailed in the first years of Edward III. In 1335 halfpence and farthings below the sterling fineness were struck. More importantly, further attempts were made to introduce gold coins. In 1344 the florin or double

Pre-Treaty Noble of Edward III which contained reference to France in the legend.

leopard of six shillings was introduced, along with its half and quarter. This coinage was not successful and was soon replaced by a heavier series based on the noble of 80 pence (6*s*. 8*d*.), half a mark or one third of a pound. The noble originally weighed 138.5 grains but it was successively reduced to120 grains, at which weight it continued from 1351. During this reign the protracted conflict with France known as the Hundred Years' War erupted. Edward III, through his mother, claimed the French throne and inscribed this title on his coins. By the Treaty of Bretigny (1361) Edward temporarily gave up his claim and the reference to France

Noble of Edward IV, issued before he was forced to abandon the throne of England.

was dropped from the coins, but when war w renewed in 1369 the title was resumed, a remained on many English coins until the e of the 18th century. The silver coinage follow the pattern of the previous reign, but in 1351 t groat was re-introduced and with it came t twopence or half-groat. Another innovation w the use of mintmarks at the beginning of t inscriptions. Seven types of cross and one cro were employed from 1334 onwards and th sequence enables numismatists to date coi fairly accurately.

The full range of gold (noble, half-noble a quarter-noble) and silver (groat, half-gro penny, halfpenny and farthing) continued und Richard II (1377–99). Little attempt was made alter the facing portrait on the silver coins, now little more than a stylised caricatu anyway.

Noble of Henry IV which was reduced in weight due to the shortage of gold.

Under Henry IV (1399–1413) the pattern previous reigns prevailed, but in 1412 t weights of the coinage were reduced due to shortage of bullion. The noble was reduced 108 grains and its sub-divisions lighten proportionately. The penny was reduced by grains, and its multiples and sub-divisio correspondingly reduced. One interesti change was the reduction of the fleur de lis France from four to three in the heraldic shie on the reverse of the noble; this chan corresponded with the alteration in the arn used in France itself. The Calais mint, opened b Edward III in 1363, was closed in 1411. The was no change in the designs used for the coi of Henry V (1413–22) but greater use was no made of mintmarks to distinguish the vario

·riods of production. Coins were by now oduced mainly at London, although the iscopal mints at Durham and York were ·rmitted to strike pennies.

The supply of gold dwindled early in the ign of Henry VI and few nobles were struck :er 1426. The Calais mint was re-opened in 24 and struck a large amount of gold before ›sing finally in 1440. A regal mint briefly ·erated at York in 1423–24. Mintmarks were ›w much more widely used and tended to rrespond more closely to the annual trials of e Pyx. The series of civil upheavals known as e Wars of the Roses erupted in this period.

In 1461 Henry VI was deposed by the Yorkist ırl of March after he defeated the Lancastrians Mortimer's Cross. The Yorkists advanced on ›ndon where the victor was crowned Edward '. At first he continued the gold series of his edecessor, issuing nobles and quarter-nobles, ıt in 1464 the weight of the penny was reduced

roat of Richard III (1483–85).

12 grains and the value of the noble was ised to 100 pence (8*s*. 4*d*.).The ryal or rose-›ble of 120 grains, together with its half and ıarter, was introduced in 1465 and tariffed at n shillings or half a pound. The need for a coin orth a third of a pound, however, led to the sue of the angel of 80 grains, worth 6*s*. 8*d*., but ıis was initially unsucessful and very few ‹amples are now extant. The angel derived its ıme from the figure of the Archangel Michael ı the obverse; a cross surmounting a shield ›peared on the reverse.

In 1470 Edward was forced to flee to Holland ıd Henry VI was briefly restored. During this :ief period (to April 1471) the ryal was iscontinued but a substantial issue of angels ıd half-angels was made both at London and :istol. Silver coins were struck at York as well , London and Bristol, the issues of the provincial ıints being identified by the initials B or E :boracum, Latin for York). Edward defeated the Lancastrians at Tewkesbury and deposed the luckless Henry once more. In his second reign Edward struck only angels and half-angels as well as silver from the groat to halfpenny. In addition to the three existing mints, silver coins were struck at Canterbury, Durham and the archiepiscopal mint at York. Mintmarks were now much more frequent and varied. Coins with a mark of a halved sun and rose are usually assigned to the reign of Edward IV, but they were probably also struck in the nominal reign of Edward V, the twelve-year-old prince held in the Tower of London under the protection of his uncle Richard, Duke of Gloucester. Coins with this mark on the reverse had an obverse mark of a boar's head, Richard's personal emblem. The brief reign of Richard III (1483–5) came to an end with his defeat at Bosworth and the relatively scarce coins of this period followed the pattern of the previous reigns, distinguished by the sequence of mint marks and the inscription RICAD or RICARD.

In the early years of Henry VII's reign the coinage likewise followed the previous patterns, but in 1489 the first of several radical changes was effected, with the introduction of the gold sovereign of 20 shillings showing a full-length portrait of the monarch seated on an elaborate throne. For reverse, this coin depicted a Tudor rose surmounted by a heraldic shield. A similar reverse appeared on the ryal of 10 shillings, but the angel and angelet retained previous motifs. The silver coins at first adhered to the medieval pattern, with the stylised facing portrait and long cross, but at the beginning of the 16th century a large silver coin, the testoon or shilling of 12 pence, was introduced and adopted a realistic profile of the king, allied to a reverse showing a cross surmounted by the royal arms.

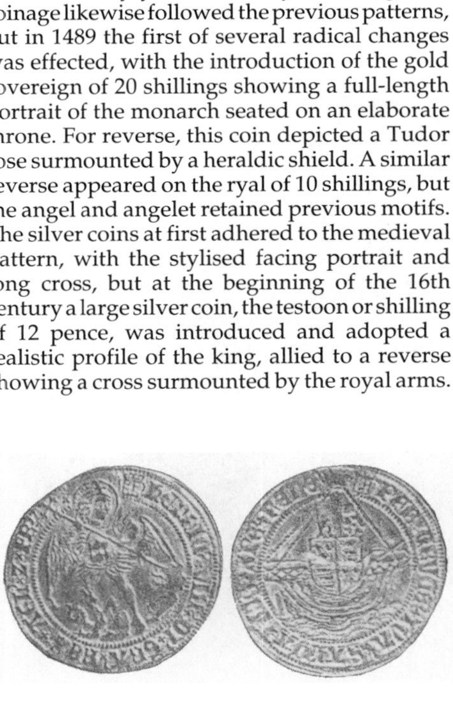

First coinage Angel of Henry VIII which retained the traditional 23.5 carat fineness.

The same design was also used for the later issue of groat and half groat.

This established a pattern which was to continue till the reign of Charles I. In the reign of Henry VIII, however, the coinage was subject to considerable debasement. This led to the eventual introduction of 22 carat (.916 fine) gold for the crown while the traditional 23 ½ carat gold was retained for the angel and ryal. This dual system continued until the angel was discontinued at the outset of the Civil War in 1642; latterly it had been associated with the ceremony of touching for "King's Evil" or scrofula, a ritual used by the early Stuart monarchs to bolster their belief in the divine right of kings.

Under the Tudors and Stuarts the range and complexity of the gold coinage increased, but it was not until the reign of Edward VI that the silver series was expanded. In 1551 he introduced the silver crown of five shillings, the first English coin to bear a clear date on the obverse. Under Mary dates were extended to the shilling and sixpence.

The mixture of dated and undated coins continued under Elizabeth I, a reign remarkable

The magnificent Rose-Ryal of James I.

for the range of denominations—nine gold a eight silver. The latter included the sixpen threepence, threehalfpence and threefarthin distinguished by the rose which appeared behi the Queen's head.

The coinage of James I was even mo complex, reflecting the king's attempts to un his dominions. The first issue bore the lege ANG: SCO (England and Scotland), but fro 1604 this was altered to MAG: BRIT (Gre Britain). This period witnessed ne denominations, such as the rose-ryal and spu ryal, the unite, the Britain crown and the this crown, and finally the laurel of 20 shillings a its sub-divisions.

In the reign of Elizabeth experiments beg with milled coinage under Eloi Mestrell. The continued sporadically in the 17th centu culminating in the beautiful coins struck Nicholas Briot (1631–39). A branch mint w established at Aberystwyth in 1637 to refine a coin silver from the Welsh mines. Relatio between King and Parliament deteriorated the reign of Charles I and led to the Civil W (1642). Parliament controlled London b continued to strike coins in the King's name. T Royalists struck coins, both in pre-war and ne types, at Shrewsbury, Oxford, Bristol, Worceste Exeter, Chester, Hereford and other Royali strongholds, while curious siege pieces we pressed into service at Newark, Pontefract a Scarborough.

After the execution of Charles I in 1649 t Commonwealth was proclaimed under Oliv Cromwell. Gold and silver coins were no inscribed in English instead of Latin. Patter portraying Cromwell and a crowned shie restored Latin in 1656. Plans for milled coina were already being considered before t Restoration of the monarchy in 1660. Hammere coinage appeared initially, resuming the style coins under Charles I, but in 1662 the han hammering of coins was abandoned in favour coins struck on the mill and screw press. T hammered coins of 1660–62 were undated a bore a crown mintmark, the last vestiges medievalism in British coinage.

Coins illustrated in the following listings are indicated with an asterisk (*)

A SIMPLIFIED PRICE GUIDE
TO

ANCIENT COINS USED IN BRITAIN

PART I
CELTIC

The prices given in this section are those that you would expect to pay from a reputable dealer and ›t the prices at which you could expect to sell coins.

The list below contains most of the commonly available types: a full comprehensive guide is beyond ɘ scope of this book. Prices are for coins with good surfaces which are not weakly struck or struck ›m worn dies. Examples which are struck from worn or damaged dies can be worth considerably ss. Particularly attractive examples of bronze Celtic coins command a very high premium. Where a ice is given for an issue of which there are many varieties, the price is for the most common type.

The illustrations are representative examples only and are indicated by an asterisk (*) in the listings.

UNINSCRIBED COINAGE

	F	VF	EF
)LD STATERS			
llo-Belgic A	£600	£1400	£5250
llo-Belgic E (Ambiani)	£135	£250	£400
ute type	£145	£265	£400
eriton type			
normally rather "brassy" metal	£200	£400	£850
rieltauvi (various types)	£150	£300	£500
rfolk "wolf" type			
ine gold	£200	£400	£750
brassy gold	£125	£250	£450
very debased	£75	£150	£350
'haddon Chase types	£200	£400	£850
nersh type	£200	£400	£750
eni (various types)	£250	£450	£825
mic type	£200	£350	£575
bunni	£250	£450	£800
)LD QUARTER STATERS			
rth Thames types	£155	£250	£425
rth Kent types	£155	£250	£425
eni	£145	£200	£375
ssex types	£100	£175	£320
bunni	£150	£250	£500
LVER COINAGE			
rth Thames types	£85	£155	£300
uth Thames types	£85	£155	£300
rotriges full stater			
ine silver	£50	£145	£265
base silver	£40	£85	£180
rotriges small silver	£35	£85	£150

Uninscribed Whaddon Chase type gold stater

Uninscribed Durotriges base silver stater

ins illustrated in the following listings are indicated with an asterisk (*)

	F	VF	EF
Dobunni	£40	£90	£200
(Note—Most examples are base in appearance. Prices for examples with fine surfaces are appreciably higher)			
Corieltauvi	£40	£100	£200
Eceni ("crescent" types)	£30	£65	£125
Eceni ("Norfolk god" types)	£50	£100	£250
Armorican Billon staters	£75	£150	£400

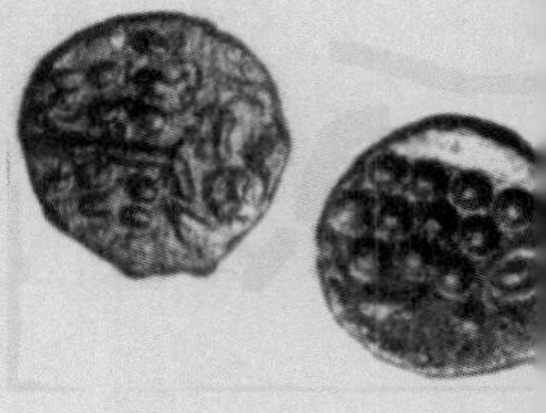

Durotriges cast bronze

POTIN COINAGE

	F	VF	EF
Kent	£20	£50	£100

BRONZE COINAGE

	F	VF	EF
Durotriges debased stater	£25	£45	£100
*Durotriges cast bronzes	£60	£120	£200
North Thames types. Various issues from:	£40	£90	£400

INSCRIBED CELTIC COINAGE

ATTREBATES & REGNI

	F	VF	EF
*Commios			
stater	£550	£1250	£2750
Tincomarus			
stater	£420	£850	£2000
quarter stater	£145	£250	£450
silver unit	£75	£140	£275
silver minim	£155	£285	£550
Eppillus			
quarter stater	£145	£235	£425
silver unit	£75	£145	£300
bronze			Rare
Verica			
stater	£255	£550	£1000
quarter stater	£155	£275	£425
silver unit	£55	£100	£225
Epaticcus			
stater	£1,000	£2000	£4000
*silver unit	£50	£100	£265
silver minim	£55	£110	£275
Caratacos			
silver unit	£165	£320	£465
silver minim	£110	£220	£325

Commios stater

CANTIACI

	F	VF	EF
Dubnovellaunos			
stater	£280	£565	£900
silver unit	£130	£210	£500
bronze unit	£55	£150	£350
Vosenos			
stater	£1000	£2500	£5000
quarter stater	£275	£585	£1200
silver unit	£135	£285	£650
bronze unit	£110	£215	£550
Sam			
silver unit	£175	£350	£750
bronze unit	£100	£250	£500
Eppillus			
stater	£1000	£2000	£4250
quarter stater	£145	£255	£500
silver unit	£65	£145	£350
bronze unit	£55	£125	£450
Amminus			
silver unit	£155	£320	£650
silver minim	£110	£215	£450
bronze unit	£80	£155	£500
Solidu			
silver unit	£500	£1000	£2250
silver minim	£500	£1000	£1500

Epaticcus silver unit

	F	VF	EF
ROTRIGES			
ab			
silver	£155	£320	£650
silver minim	£100	£250	£400
INOVANTES			
dedomaros			
stater	£265	£500	£800
quarter stater	£155	£320	£550
bnovellaunos			
stater	£255	£455	£775
quarter stater	£155	£310	£550
*bronze unit	£55	£130	£450
TUVELLAUNI			
sciovanos			
*stater	£225	£425	£1000
quarter stater	£130	£235	£450
silver unit	£80	£165	£375
bronze unit	£55	£135	£350
bronze half unit	£55	£135	£275
doco			
stater	£510	£1250	£2750
quarter stater	£210	£420	£755
silver unit	£155	£400	£750
bronze	£85	£215	£355
nobelin			
*stater	£200	£455	£1000
quarter stater	£145	£265	£420
silver unit	£85	£165	£360
bronze unit	£65	£145	£320
rippa			
quarter stater	£600	£1500	£3000
silver unit	£500	£1000	£2000
BUNNI			
ted			
stater	£310	£650	£1350
silver unit	£55	£120	£300
su			
stater	£450	£750	£1500
silver unit	£55	£125	£320
atti			
stater	£255	£525	£1250
mux			
stater	£800	£1650	£3150
rio			
stater	£265	£525	£1000
quarter stater	£200	£355	£625
duoc			
stater	£1000	£2250	£3550
silver unit	£200	£500	£850
CENI			
ro Cam			
silver unit	£110	£265	£550
nted			
stater	£425	£1000	£2500
silver unit	£35	£65	£185
silver half unit	£45	£95	£200
en			
silver unit	£40	£75	£185
silver half unit	£45	£95	£200
aemu			
silver unit	£65	£125	£285
esu			
silver unit	£65	£125	£285

Dubnovellaunos bronze unit

Tasciovanos stater

Cunobelin stater

	F	VF	EF
Esuprastus			
silver unit	£420	£1,000	£1850
Ale Sca			
silver unit	£355	£765	£1550
CORIELTAUVI			
Aunt Cost			
stater	£255	£565	£1000
silver unit	£85	£185	£315
silver half unit	£85	£160	£300
Esuprasu			
stater	£330	£675	£1250
silver unit	£155	£310	£550
Vep Corf			
stater	£410	£1000	£2150
*silver unit	£80	£185	£300
silver half unit	£100	£215	£450
Dumno Tigir Seno			
stater	£755	£1850	£3150
silver unit	£100	£185	£500
Volisios Dumnocoveros			
*stater	£310	£725	£1550
silver unit	£100	£185	£475
silver half unit	£100	£185	£450
Volisios Dumnovellaunos			
stater	£300	£675	£1250
silver half unit	£150	£335	£655
Volisios Cartivellaunos			
stater	£1000	£2000	£4000
silver half unit	£300	£620	£1150
Iat Iso			
silver unit	£155	£420	£1150

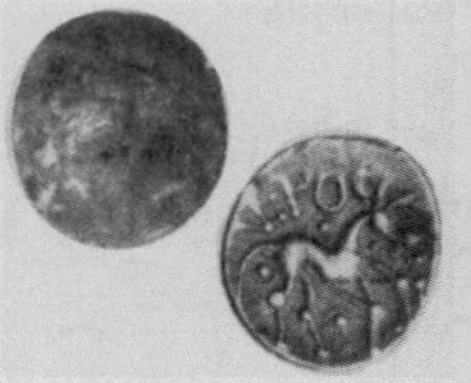

Vep Corf silver unit

Volisios Dumnocoveros state

Illustrations by courtesy of Chris Rudd.

A SIMPLIFIED PRICE GUIDE TO

ANCIENT COINS USED IN BRITAIN

PART II ROMAN BRITAIN

In certain cases, especially with large bronze coins, the price for coins in extremely fine condition are *uch* higher than the price for the same coin in very fine condition as early bronze coins are seldom und in hoards and perfect undamaged examples are rarely available.

The illustrations provided are a representative guide to assist with identification only and are indicated an asterisk (*) in the listings.

	F	VF	EF
epublican			
denarius (Roma/Biga)	£18	£45	£140
denarius (other types)	£20	£50	£160
lius Caesar			
aureus	£350	£850	£1750
denarius ("elephant" type)	£65	£150	£375
denarius (with portrait)	£210	£550	£1400
ark Antony			
denarius ("Galley" type)	£45	£110	£300
denarius (with portrait)	£100	£275	£650
ctavian/Augustus			
aureus (Caius & Lucius Caesar)	£490	£1250	£2800
denarius (Caius & Lucius Caesar)	£45	£130	£340
*other types	£60	£175	£400
dupondius or as (large SC)	£45	£100	£300
quadrans	£15	£35	£95
via			
Ae as	£120	£350	£1400
berius			
aureus (Tribute type)	£400	£1300	£2500
denarius (Tribute penny)	£70	£175	£425
ae as	£55	£150	£450
rusus			
as	£60	£175	£450
ermanicus			
*as	£60	£170	£425
grippa			
as	£50	£150	£450
aligula			
denarius	£350	£1000	£2500
*as	£50	£250	£750

Augustus

Germanicus

Caligula

	F	VF	EF
Claudius			
aureus ("DE BRITANN" type)	£850	£2100	£5250
denarius similar	£300	£800	£2100
denarius other types	£250	£650	£1700
sestertius	£140	£425	£1550
as	£45	£125	£375
quadrans	£15	£40	£110
Irregular British as	£20	£65	£195
Nero			
aureus	£450	£1200	£2750
sestertius	£145	£375	£1750
as	£45	£130	£350
denarius	£80	£250	£600
Civil War			
denarius	£165	£450	£1100
Galba			
denarius	£90	£325	£875
*sestertius	£185	£550	£2500
as	£75	£200	£725
Otho			
denarius	£190	£525	£1600
Vitellius			
denarius	£90	£290	£870
sestertius	£650	£2000	£7000
as	£130	£350	£1000
Vespasian			
aureus	£475	£1100	£2750
denarius	£20	£65	£190
sestertius	£100	£275	£850
as	£40	£110	£325
Titus			
aureus	£450	£1250	£3000
denarius	£40	£120	£325
sestertius	£140	£375	£1100
dupondius or as	£50	£140	£425
Domitian			
aureus	£450	£1200	£3000
denarius	£22	£55	£175
*sestertius	£90	£275	£900
dupondius or as	£35	£100	£295
ae semis	£30	£80	£250
Nerva			
aureus	£800	£2500	£7000
denarius	£40	£110	£350
as	£55	£180	£565
Trajan			
aureus	£375	£950	£2800
denarius	£20	£56	£150
sestertius	£60	£190	£575
dupondius or as	£25	£75	£290
Hadrian			
aureus	£500	£1100	£3000
denarius	£20	£55	£165
sestertius	£65	£210	£650
dupondius or as	£35	£85	£300
as "Britannia"	£150	£450	£1750
Sabina			
denarius	£25	£70	£225
*sestertius	£110	£300	£1000
as or dupondius	£50	£165	£475
Aelius			
denarius	£65	£200	£500
sestertius	£135	£400	£1200
as or dupondius	£50	£155	£500

Gal

Domiti

Sabi

	F	VF	EF
ntoninus Pius			
aureus	£300	£750	£2500
denarius	£15	£45	£140
sestertius	£38	£120	£450
as or dupondius	£22	£65	£250
as "Britannia'	£50	£150	£600
ustina Senior			
denarius	£15	£45	£140
sestertius	£30	£125	£450
as or dupondius	£20	£60	£225
arcus Aurelius			
aureus	£375	£850	£2500
*denarius	£15	£40	£120
sestertius	£40	£140	£475
as or dupondius	£22	£65	£230
ustina Junior			
*denarius	£15	£45	£135
sestertius	£36	£130	£400
as or dupondius	£18	£55	£200
ucius Verus			
denarius	£20	£60	£200
sestertius	£55	£175	£650
as or dupondius	£25	£75	£300
ucilla			
denarius	£20	£55	£175
sestertius	£45	£160	£550
ommodus			
denarius	£15	£40	£120
*sestertius	£35	£110	£425
sestertius (Vict. Brit)	£95	£275	£800
as or dupondius	£20	£55	£200
rispina			
denarius	£20	£60	£190
as or dupondius	£30	£85	£265
ertinax			
*denarius	£190	£525	£1350
idius Julianus			
denarius	£375	£825	£1800
escennius Niger			
denarius	£260	£650	£1500
lodius Albinus			
denarius	£40	£100	£275
sestertius	£125	£450	£1650
eptimius Severus			
aureus	£500	£1250	£3750
denarius	£13	£30	£90
denarius (VICT BRIT)	£25	£70	£185
sestertius	£60	£200	£625
as	£45	£125	£350
ulia Domna			
denarius	£13	£32	£90
sestertius	£70	£220	£650
as or dupondius	£45	£130	£400
aracalla			
*denarius	£12	£30	£90
denarius (VICT BRIT)	£28	£75	£200
sestertius	£80	£220	£750
as	£40	£115	£350
antoninianus	£25	£65	£175
lautilla			
denarius	£22	£55	£150
eta			
denarius	£13	£32	£100

Marcus Aurelius

Faustina Junior

Commodus

Pertinax

Caracalla

	F	VF	EF
denarius (VICT BRIT)	£32	£80	£220
sestertius	£100	£275	£825
as or dupondius	£70	£185	£550
Macrinus			
denarius	£25	£80	£225
*sestertius	£195	£500	£2000
Diadumenian			
*denarius	£70	£175	£475
Elagabalus			
antoninianus	£20	£50	£150
denarius	£12	£30	£90
Julia Paula			
denarius	£30	£85	£250
Aquilla Severa			
denarius	£50	£135	£375
Julia Soaemias			
denarius	£22	£55	£140
Julia Maesa			
denarius	£15	£40	£115
Severus Alexander			
aureus	£350	£900	£2700
*denarius	£12	£30	£90
sestertius	£28	£80	£260
as or dupondius	£24	£60	£200
Orblana			
denarius	£55	£145	£375
Julia Mamaea			
denarius	£13	£32	£100
Maximinus I			
denarius	£15	£40	£100
*sestertius	£30	£90	£300
as	£27	£75	£250
Maximus			
denarius	£50	£140	£400
sestertius	£55	£150	£430
Balbinus & Pupienus			
antoninanus	£60	£175	£450
denarius	£50	£150	£400
Gordian III			
antoninianus	£8	£20	£55
denarius	£10	£28	£75
sestertius	£20	£65	£175
Philip I			
antoninianus "Animal Den" lion stag antelope wolf & twins	£20	£45	£120
antoninianus	£8	£20	£55
*sestertius	£22	£70	£195
Otacilla Severa			
antoniniaus	£10	£25	£65
sestertius	£25	£75	£250
Philip II			
antoninianus	£10	£25	£65
Trajan Decius			
antoninianus	£8	£20	£60
Herennius Etruscus			
antoninianus	£15	£40	£120
Hostilian			
antoninianus	£30	£85	£250
Trebonianus Gallus			
antoninianus	£10	£25	£65
Volusian			
antoninianus	£12	£27	£70

Macrin

Diadumenia

Severus Alexande

Maximin

Philip

	F	VF	EF
emillan			
*antoninianus	£45	£130	£300
alerian I			
antoninianus	£8	£20	£55
iva Mariniana			
antoninianus	£40	£110	£300
allienus			
*silver antoninianus	£8	£20	£55
ae antoninianus	£5	£15	£40
ae denarius	£45	£125	£375
alonina			
ae antoninianus	£7	£18	£45
alerian II			
billon antoninianus	£12	£35	£95
aloninus			
antoninianus	£12	£35	£95
acrianus			
billon antoninianus	£35	£95	£250
uietus			
billon antoninianus	£35	£95	£250
ostumus			
silver antoninianus	£8	£22	£60
*ae antoninianus	£5	£15	£40
sestertius	£45	£145	£450
aelianus			
antoninianus	£115	£285	£700
arius			
antoninianus	£35	£90	£235
ictorinus			
ae antoninianus	£5	£15	£40
laudius II Gothicus			
ae antoninianus	£4	£14	£38
etricus I			
ae antoninianus	£5	£15	£40
etricus II			
ae antoninianus	£7	£17	£45
uintillus			
*ae antoninianus	£13	£35	£85
urelian			
ae antoninianus	£6	£17	£50
abalathus & Aurelian			
ae antoninianus	£25	£60	£175
everina			
*ae antoninianus	£12	£32	£90
acitus			
ae antoninianus	£10	£25	£70
lorian			
ae antoninianus	£25	£70	£195
robus			
ae antoninianus	£5	£16	£45
antoninianus (military or imp. busts)	£10	£25	£65
arus			
ae antoninlanus	£12	£32	£90
lumerian			
ae antoninianus	£11	£30	£85
arinus			
ae antoninianus	£11	£28	£75
lagna Urbica			
ae antoninianus	£60	£160	£400
iocletian			
ae argenteus	£80	£225	£550
ae antoninianus	£7	£18	£50
ae follis (London Mint)	£12	£30	£90
Ae follis (other mints)	£10	£25	£70

Aemillian

Gallienus

Postumus

Quintillus

Severina

	F	VF	EF
Maximianus			
ae follis (London mint)	£12	£30	£90
*ae follis (other mints)	£10	£25	£70
Carauslus			
denarius	£275	£800	£2000
antoninianus	£25	£55	£250
legionary antoninianus	£70	£185	£750
Allectus			
antoninianus	£25	£65	£300
quinarius	£25	£60	£250
Constantius I			
ae follis (London mint)	£14	£35	£110
ae follis (other mints)	£10	£25	£70
Galerius			
ae follis (London mint)	£12	£30	£90
ae follis (other mints)	£8	£22	£60
Galeria Valeria			
follis	£30	£75	£200
Severus II			
ae follis (London mint)	£38	£95	£255
*ae follis (other mints)	£30	£75	£200
Maximinus II			
ae follis (London mint)	£14	£35	£110
*ae follis (other mints)	£7	£18	£50
Maxentius			
follis	£8	£22	£60
Romulus			
ae follis	£35	£90	£275
Licinius I			
follis	£7	£18	£50
ae 3	£6	£16	£45
Licinius II			
ae 3	£9	£22	£60
Constantine I			
follis (London mint)	£8	£20	£60
follis (other mints)	£6	£15	£45
ae 3	£5	£13	£40
ae 3 (London mint)	£8	£20	£60
Urbs Roma ae 3/4	£4	£12	£35
Fausta			
ae 3 (London mint)	£60	£150	£375
ae 3 (other mints)	£16	£40	£120
Helena			
*ae 3 (London mint)	£60	£150	£375
ae 3 (other mints)	£16	£40	£120
Theodora			
ae 4	£8	£22	£60
Crispus			
ae 3 (London mint)	£10	£25	£75
*ae 3	£7	£18	£55
Deimatius			
ae 3/4	£14	£35	£90
Hanniballianus			
ae 4	£90	£250	£650
Constantine II			
ae 3 (London Mint)	£10	£25	£75
ae 3	£7	£18	£50
ae 4	£3	£8	£30
Constans			
*centenionalis	£10	£25	£70
ae 4	£3	£8	£30
Constantius II			
*siliqua	£22	£60	£150
centenionalis	£8	£20	£55
half-centenionalis	£9	£18	£50
ae 4	£3	£8	£30

Maximian

Severus

Maximinus

Helena

Crispus

agnentius			
double centenionalis	£40	£125	£400
centenionalis	£12	£30	£90
ecentius			
double centenionalis	£55	£175	£550
centenionalis	£15	£40	£125
etranio			
ae 2 or centenionalis	£50	£150	£450
onstantius Gallus			
centenionalis	£12	£30	£85
ulian II			
*siliqua	£24	£60	£165
ae 1	£45	£135	£375
ae 3 (helmeted bust)	£10	£25	£85
ovian			
ae 1	£80	£225	£550
ae 3	£13	£35	£90
alentinian I			
gold solidus	£110	£275	£600
siliqua	£26	£65	£145
ae 3	£5	£15	£50
alens			
gold solidus	£110	£275	£600
*siliqua	£22	£60	£145
ae 3	£5	£15	£50
rocopius			
ae 3	£55	£160	£475
ratian			
silver milliarense	£150	£450	£1150
*siliqua	£24	£60	£150
ae 3	£5	£15	£50
alentinian II			
siliqua	£25	£65	£150
ae 2	£12	£28	£80
ae 4	£5	£12	£35
heodosius I			
siliqua	£28	£75	£175
elia Flaccilla			
ae 2	£25	£70	£220
lagnus Maximus			
solidus	£700	£1800	£4500
siliqua	£50	£80	£195
*ae 2	£28	£70	£175
lavius Victor			
silver sliqua	£100	£275	£680
ugenius			
silver siliqua	£120	£300	£750
rcadius			
gold solidus	£100	£250	£550
silver siliqua	£25	£65	£160
ae 2	£11	£28	£75
udoxia			
ae 3	£22	£60	£180
lonorius			
gold solidus	£100	£250	£550
silver siliqua	£30	£75	£190
ae 4	£6	£15	£45
onstantine III			
silver siliqua	£120	£300	£750

Julian II

Valens

Gratian

Magnus Maximus

ae = bronze; ae 1, 2, 3, 4 = bronze coins in descending order of size.

llustrations by courtesy of Classical Numismatic Group/Seaby Coins.

A SIMPLIFIED PRICE GUIDE
TO

ENGLISH HAMMERED COINS

PART I
959–1485

INTRODUCTION

We have taken our starting point for hammered coin prices back to the Anglo-Saxon reign of Edgar; who could reasonably claim to be the first king of All England. Also it is from this time onwards that we start to get regular "portraits" as well as moneyers and mints on most issues. This gives a total of eight rulers to the list of kings prior to the Norman Conquest and most of these have coin issues that can be purchased quite reasonably. It is also worth pointing out here that of course coins had previously been struck in England for approximately 1000 years prior to our listings by Celtic, Roman and earlier Saxon rulers, details of which can be found in more specific publications.

PRICING

The prices given in the following pages are intended to be used as a "Pocket book guide" to the values of the *most common* coins within any denomination of any one reign. The price quoted is what a collector may expect to pay for such a piece in the condition indicated. For more detailed information we recommend the reader to one of the many specialist publications.

GRADING

The prices quoted are for three different grades of condition: Fine (F), Very Fine (VF) and Extremely Fine (EF). A "Fine" coin is assumed to be a fairly worn, circulated, piece but with all or most of the main features and lettering still clear. "Very Fine" is a middle grade with a small amount of wear and most details fairly clear. For this edition we have included the prices for coins in Extremely Fine condition where appropriate, although very few hammered coins actually turn up in this grade (i.e. nearly mint state with hardly any wear). In some instances the prices quoted are theoretically based and are only included to provide a guide. It is important to note that on all hammered coins the very nature of striking, i.e. individually, by hand, means hammered coinage is rarely a straight grade and when listed by a dealer the overall condition will often be qualified by terms such as: *weak in parts, struck off-centre, cracked or chipped flan, double struck*, etc. When applicable the price should be adjusted accordingly.

HISTORY

Below the heading for each monarch we have given a few historical notes as and when they apply to significant changes in the coinage.

EDGAR
(959–957

	F	VF	EF
Edgar Penny, non portrait (2 line inscription)	£140	£300	—

EDWARD THE MARTYR
(975–978)

	F	VF	EF
Edward, Penny, Portrait	£650	£1450	—

AETHELRED II
(978–1016)

	F	VF	EF
Aethelred II, Penny, First hand type	£85	£200	—

CNUT
(1016–1035)

	F	VF	EF
Cnut, Penny	£50	£110	—

HAROLD I
(1035–40)

	F	VF	EF
arold I, Penny	£180	£435	—

HARTHACANUTE
(1035–42)

	F	VF	EF
arthacanute, Penny, English Mint	£350	£675	—
arthacanute, Penny, Danish type	£150	£425	—

Danish type

EDWARD THE CONFESSOR
(1042–66)

	F	VF	EF
:dward the Confessor, Penny	£70	£150	—

HAROLD II
(1066)

	F	VF	EF
Iarold II, Penny	£420	£925	—

WILLIAM I
(1066–87)

The Norman Conquest had very little immediate effect on the coinage of England. The Anglo-Saxo standard of minting silver pennies was very high and the practice of the moneyer putting his name and mi town on the reverse continued as before, except with William's portrait of course. It is worth noting he that non-realistic, stylised portraits were used until the reign of Henry VII.

There are eight major types of William I penny of which the last, the PAXS type, is by far the commones

	F	VF	EF
William I, Penny	£140	£300	£550

WILLIAM II
(1087–1100)

Very little change from his father's reign except that five new types were issued, most of which were much more crudely designed than previous, all are scarce.

	F	VF	EF
William II, Penny	£400	£825	—

HENRY I
(1100–35)

There are fifteen different types of penny for this reign of which the last two are the most common. Mo issues are of a very poor standard both in workmanship and metal, the prices reflect a poor quality of issu

	F	VF	EF
Henry I, Penny	£130	£300	—

STEPHEN
(1135–54)

his is historically a very complicated time for the coinage, mainly due to civil war and a consequential lack central control in the country which resulted in very poor quality and deliberately damaged pieces. Coins ere struck not only in the name of Stephen and his main rival claimant Matilda but also by their supporters. he commonest issue is the "Watford" type; so named, as are many issues, after the area in which a hoard as found.

	F	VF	EF
tephen, Penny	£170	£400	—

HENRY II
(1154–89)

here were two distinct issues struck during this reign. The first, Cross and Crosslets or "Tealby" coinage named after Tealby in Lincolnshire), continued to be very poorly made and lasted 20 years. However, in 180 the new and superior "Short Cross" issue commenced, being issued from only twelve major towns.

	F	VF	EF
enry II, Penny, Tealby	£70	£180	—
enry II, Penny, Short Cross	£40	£100	—

RICHARD I
(1189–1199)

here were no major changes during this reign, in fact pennies continued to be struck with his father Henry's ame throughout the reign. The coins struck under Richard tend to be rather crude in style.

	F	VF	EF
Richard I, Penny	£50	£130	—

JOHN (1199–1216)

As with his brother before him, there were no major changes during the reign of King John, and pennie with his father's name were struck throughout the reign, although they tended to be somewhat neater style than those struck during the reign of Richard I.

	F	VF	EF
John, Penny	£35	£80	£170

HENRY III (1216–72)

The coinage during Henry III's reign continued as before with the short cross issue. However, in 1247 new long cross design was introduced to prevent clipping. This design was to last in one form or anothe for many centuries.

	F	VF	EF
Henry III, Penny, Short Cross	£20	£45	£120
Henry III, Penny, Long Cross	£20	£40	£90

EDWARD I (1272–1307)

After a few years of issuing similar pieces to his father, in 1279 Edward I ordered a major re-coinage. Thi consisted of well-made pennies, halfpennies and farthings in relatively large quantities, and for a brie period a groat (four pence) was produced. The pennies are amongst the most common of all hammere coins.

	F	VF	EF
Edward I (and Edward II)			
Groat (often damaged)	£1150	£4200	—
Penny	£18	£40	£85
Halfpenny	£20	£45	£140
Farthing	£15	£40	£125

Edward I halfpenny

EDWARD II
(1307–1327)

ne coinage of Edward II differs in only a very few minor details from that of Edward I and are of similar alue.

EDWARD III
(1327–77)

his was a long reign which saw major changes in the coinage, the most significant being the introduction f a gold coinage (based on the Noble, valued at 6s 8d, and its fractions) and a regular issue of a large lver groat (and half groat). The mints were limited to a few episcopal cities but coins of English type were so struck in the newly-acquired Calais.

	F	VF	EF
old			
Noble	£475	£1000	£2000
Half Noble	£300	£675	£1350
Quarter Noble	£170	£380	£725
ilver			
Groat	£45	£125	£350
Half Groat	£25	£75	£250
Penny	£20	£40	£125
Half Penny	£15	£40	£115
Farthing	£30	£60	£140

Gold Noble

RICHARD II
(1377–1399)

'he denominations continued during this reign much as before. However, coins are quite rare mainly due the lack of bullion gold and silver going into the mints, mainly because of an inbalance with European veights and fineness.

	F	VF	EF
iold			
Noble	£650	£1300	£3000
Half Noble	£600	£1500	—
Quarter Noble	£300	£700	£1200
ilver			
Groat	£280	£775	—
Half Groat	£200	£480	—
Penny	£50	£165	—
Half Penny	£30	£90	—
Farthing	£100	£230	—

Groat

HENRY IV
(1399–1413)

Because of the continuing problems with the scarcity of gold and silver the coinage was reduced in weig
in 1412, towards the end of the reign. All coins of this reign are quite scarce.

	F	VF
Gold		
Noble	£1100	£2750
Half Noble	£2150	£5000
Quarter Noble	£425	£900
Silver		
Groat	£1400	£4000
Half Groat	£425	£925
Penny	£175	£550
Half Penny	£150	£400
Farthing	£600	£1350

Noble

HENRY V
(1413–22)

Monetary reform introduced towards the end of his father's reign in 1412 improved the supply of bullio
and hence coins of Henry V are far more common. All of the main denominations continued as before

	F	VF	EF
Gold			
Noble	£550	£1100	£2200
Half Noble	£500	£950	—
Quarter Noble	£250	£570	£950
Silver			
Groat	£100	£300	—
Half Groat	£90	£250	—
Penny	£30	£85	—
Half Penny	£20	£70	—
Farthing	£120	£370	—

Half Groat

HENRY VI
(1422–61 and again 1470–71)

Although there were no new denominations during these reigns (see Edward IV below), Henry's first reig
saw eleven different issues, each for a few years and distinguished by privy marks, i.e. crosses, pellets
annulets, etc.

ENRY VI *continued*

	F	VF	EF
ld			
First reign—			
Noble	£450	£1000	£1900
Half Noble	£300	£800	£1400
Quarter Noble	£170	£400	£700
2nd reign—			
Angel	£1000	£2500	—
Half Angel	£1500	£4000	—
ver			
Groat	£30	£80	£170
Half Groat	£25	£65	£150
Penny	£20	£65	£135
Half Penny	£15	£45	£100
Farthing	£85	£220	—

Groat

EDWARD IV
(1461–70 and again 1471–83)

ie significant changes during these reigns were the replacement of the noble by the rose ryal (and valued at 10s) and the introduction of the angel at the old noble value. We also start to see mint-marks initial marks appearing, usually at the top of the coin, they were used to denote the period of issue for ting purposes and often lasted for 2–3 years.

	F	VF	EF
ld			
Ryal	£500	£1100	£1750
Half Ryal	£375	£800	£1450
Quarter Ryal	£275	£600	£1000
Angel	£400	£900	£1800
Half Angel	£320	£680	£1400
ver			
Groat	£40	£110	£265
Half Groat	£35	£90	£225
Penny	£35	£75	£175
Half Penny	£20	£70	—
Farthing	£230	£500	—

Gold Ryal

RICHARD III
(1483–85)

ie close of the Yorkist Plantagenet and the beginning of the Medieval period come together at this ne. There are no new significant numismatic changes but most coins of Richard whilst not really rare, ntinue to be very popular and priced quite high.

	F	VF	EF
ld			
Angel	£1350	£3250	—
Half Angel	£2600	£7500	—
ver			
Groat	£380	£850	—
Half Groat	£450	£1100	—
Penny	£170	£425	—
Half Penny	£140	£350	—
Farthing	£725	£1850	—

Groat

PART II: 1485–1663

Among the more significant features of the post-Renaissance period as it affected coinage is t introduction of realistic portraiture during the reign of Henry VII. We also have a much wider and vari number of new and revised denominations, for example eleven different gold denominations of Henry V and the same number of silver for Elizabeth I. Here we only mention the introduction or changes in the ma denominations, giving a value for all of them, once again listing the commonest type.

HENRY VII (1485–1509)

The gold sovereign of 20 shillings makes its first appearance in 1489 as does the testoon (later shilling in about 1500. The silver penny was re-designed to a rather crude likeness of the sovereign.

	F	VF	EF
Gold			
Sovereign	£7250	£18,500	—
Ryal	£7500	£22,500	—
Angel	£350	£800	£1500
Half Angel	£300	£700	£1300
Silver			
Testoon 1/-	£5300	£11,000	—
Groat	£50	£130	£375
Half Groat	£30	£80	£200
Penny	£25	£75	£160
Half Penny	£20	£55	—
Farthing	£140	£440	—

Profile Groat

Sovereign-style penny

HENRY VIII (1509–47)

After a long initial period of very little change in the coinage, in 1526 there were many, with an attempt bring the gold/silver ratio in line with the continental currencies. Some gold coins only lasted a short tin and are very rare. The crown (in gold) makes its first appearance. Towards the end of the reign we se large issues of debased silver coins (with a high copper content) bearing the well-known facing portrait the ageing King. These tend to turn up in poor condition.

	F	VF	EF
Gold			
Sovereign	£2300	£6525	—
Half Sovereign	£425	£1000	—
Angel	£350	£800	£1600
Half Angel	£275	£700	£1300
Quarter Angel	£325	£775	—
George Noble	£3500	£9500	—
Half George Noble	Rare	Rare	—
Crown of the rose	Rare	Rare	—
Crown of the double rose	£330	£775	£1350
Half Crown of the double rose	£300	£750	—
Silver			
Testoon 1/-	£525	£1750	—
Groat	£70	£200	£425
Half Groat	£40	£110	£250
Penny	£30	£90	£180
Half Penny	£25	£70	—
Farthing	£220	£600	—

Facing Groat

Crown of the double rose

EDWARD VI
(1547–53)

me of the coins struck in the first few years of this short reign could really be called Henry VIII posthumous sues as there is continuity in both name and style from his father's last issue. However, overlapping this riod are portrait issues of the boy King, particularly shillings (usually poor quality coins). This period also es the first dated English coin (shown in Roman numerals). In 1551 however, a new coinage was roduced with a restored silver quality from the Crown (dated 1551) down to the new sixpence and eepence.

	F	VF	EF
ld			
Sovereign (30s)	£2750	£7000	—
Half Sovereign	£725	£2000	—
Crown	£875	£2250	—
Half Crown	£850	£2100	—
Angel	£3750	£11,000	—
Half Angel	—	—	—
Sovereign (20s)	£1750	£4500	—
ver			
Crown	£500	£1350	—
Half Crown	£400	£1000	—
Shilling	£85	£300	£750
Sixpence	£90	£350	—
Groat	£600	£1600	—
Threepence	£170	£550	—
Half Groat	£240	£600	—
Penny	£50	£170	—
Half Penny	£150	£475	—
Farthing	£750	£2,250	—

Base Shilling, obverse

Fine Shilling

MARY
(1553–54)

e early coins of Mary's sole reign are limited and continue to use the same denominations as Edward, cept that the gold ryal was reintroduced.

	F	VF
ld		
Sovereign (30s)	£2500	£6750
Ryal	£7500	—
Angel	£850	£2200
Half Angel	£1800	£4750
ver		
Groat	£100	£350
Half Groat	£625	£1600
Penny	£425	£1350

Groat

PHILIP & MARY
(1554–58)

After a very short reign alone, Mary married Philip of Spain and they technically ruled jointly (although n for very long in practise) until her death. After her marriage we see both her and Philip on the shillings a sixpences.

	F	VF
Gold		
Angel	£2000	£5000
Half Angel	£4500	—
Silver		
Shilling	£230	£850
Sixpence	£250	£875
Groat	£100	£350
Half Groat	£300	£825
Penny	£70	£220

Shilling

ELIZABETH I
(1558–1603)

As might be expected with a long reign there are a number of significant changes in the coinage wh include several new denominations—so many in silver that every value from the shilling downwards v marked and dated to distinguish them. Early on we have old base Edward VI shillings countermarked t new reduced value (not priced here). Also due to a lack of small change and the expense of makin miniscule farthing we have a new threehalfpence and threefarthings. Finally we see the beginnings c milled (machine produced) coinage for a brief period from 1561–71.

	F	VF	EF
Gold			
Sovereign (30s)	£2250	£5500	—
Ryal (15s)	£4000	£11,000	—
Angel	£500	£1100	—
Half Angel	£475	£1000	—
Quarter Angel	£400	£875	—
Pound (20s)	£1250	£3000	—
Half Pound	£675	£1600	—
Crown	£625	£1,450	—
Half Crown	£600	£1,400	—
Silver			
Crown	£825	£2200	—
Half Crown	£550	£1400	—
Shilling	£70	£230	£550
Sixpence	£45	£135	£300
Groat	£45	£150	£275
Threepence	£35	£110	£200
Half Groat	£25	£60	—
Threehalfpence	£30	£90	—
Penny	£20	£65	£135
Threefarthings	£55	£150	—
Half Penny	£25	£60	£100

Shilling

Milled Sixpence

JAMES I
(1603–25)

:hough the size of the gold coinage remains much the same as Elizabeth's reign, the name and weight value of the denominations have several changes, i.e. Pound = Sovereign = Unite = Laurel. A new four illing gold coin (thistle crown) was introduced. A number of the silver coins now have their value in Roman merals on the coin. Relatively few angels were made from this period onwards and they are usually found rced.

	F	VF	EF
ld			
Sovereign (20s)	£875	£2200	—
Unite	£350	£750	£1500
Double crown/half unite	£300	£600	£1200
Crown	£165	£380	£800
Thistle Crown	£185	£450	£775
Half Crown	£150	£300	—
Rose Ryal (30s)	£1250	£2800	—
Spur Ryal (15s)	£2150	£6250	—
Angel (pierced)	£400	£800	—
Half Angel (Unpierced)	£1400	£4000	—
Laurel	£325	£700	—
Half Laurel	£300	£650	—
Quarter Laurel	£180	£400	£750
ver			
Crown	£450	£1100	—
Half Crown	£180	£550	—

	F	VF	EF
Shilling	£55	£190	—
Sixpence	£45	£150	—
Half Groat	£18	£45	£80
Penny	£18	£35	£70
Half Penny	£15	£30	£50

CHARLES I
(1625–49)

This reign is probably the most difficult to simplify as there are so many different issues and whole boo have been produced on this period alone. From the beginning of the King's reign and throughout the Ci War, a number of mints operated for varying lengths of time, producing both regular and irregular issue The Tower mint was taken over by Parliament in 1642 but before this a small quantity of milled coina was produced alongside the regular hammered issues. The Court then moved to Oxford from where, the next three years, large quantities of gold and silver were struck (including rare triple unites and lar silver pounds). The most prolific of the provincial mints were those situated at Aberystwyth, York, Oxfo Shrewsbury, Bristol, Exeter, Truro, Chester and Worcester as well as some smaller mints mainly situat in the West Country. Among the more interesting coins of the period are the pieces struck on unusual shaped flans at Newark and Pontefract whilst those towns were under siege. As many of the coins stru during the Civil War were crudely struck on hastily gathered bullion and plate, they provide a fascinati area of study. The prices indicated below are the minimum for the commonest examples of ea denomination irrespective of town of origin.

	F	VF	EF
Gold			
Triple Unite (£3)	£3000	£7750	—
Unite	£350	£850	—
Double crown/Half unite	£325	£675	—
Crown	£160	£375	—
Angel (pierced)	£480	£1100	—
Silver			
Pound (20 shillings)	£1300	£3000	—
Half Pound	£650	£1300	—
Crown	£270	£675	—
Half Crown	£50	£150	—
Shilling	£35	£130	£350
Sixpence	£35	£135	£300
Groat	£40	£120	£200
Threepence	£40	£110	£175
Half Groat	£20	£45	£100
Penny	£15	£30	£90
Half Penny	£15	£35	£55

Many of the coins of Charles' reign, particularly those produced during the Civil War, are poorly struck. However, the sixpence shown above is a superb example with a good portrait.

"Declaration" type shilling

Above: a Newark sieg shilling.

Left: Milled shilling by Nicholas Briot.

THE COMMONWEALTH (1649–60)

ter the execution of Charles I, Parliament changed the design of the coinage. They are simple non-rtrait pieces with an English legend.

	F	VF	EF
ld			
Unite	£675	£1200	—
Double crown/Half unite	£500	£1100	—
Crown	£425	£950	—
ver			
Crown	£500	£1100	£2250
Half Crown	£150	£425	£1150
Shilling	£115	£250	£550
Sixpence	£100	£240	£500
Half Groat	£30	£80	£170
Penny	£30	£75	£150
Half Penny	£25	£65	£110

Unite

CHARLES II (1660–85)

though milled coins had been produced for Oliver Cromwell in 1656–58, after the Restoration of the onarchy hammered coins continued to be produced until 1663, when the machinery was ready to anufacture large quantities of good milled pieces.

	F	VF	EF
old			
Unite	£750	£1900	—
Double crown/Half unite	£625	£1800	—
Crown	£600	£1700	—
lver			
Half Crown	£130	£450	—
Shilling	£100	£300	—
Sixpence	£95	£275	—
Fourpence	£30	£70	£120
Threepence	£30	£70	£115
Twopence	£20	£40	£75
Penny	£25	£50	£100

Halfcrown

A COMPREHENSIVE PRICE GUIDE
TO THE COINS OF

THE
UNITED KINGDOM
1656–2003

including

ENGLAND
SCOTLAND
ISLE OF MAN
GUERNSEY, JERSEY, ALDERNEY

also

IRELAND

When referring to this price guide one must bear a number of important points in mind. The points listed here have been taken into consideration during the preparation of this guide and we hope that the prices given will provide a true reflection of the market at the time of going to press. Nevertheless, the publishers can accept no liability for the accuracy of the prices quoted.

1. "As struck" examples with flaws will be worth less than the indicated price.
2. Any coin which is particularly attractive or in superb state will command a *higher* price than that shown.
3. These prices refer strictly to the British market, and do not reflect outside opinions.
4. Some prices given for coins not seen in recent years are estimates based on a knowledge of the market.
5. In the case of coins of high rarity, prices are not generally given.
6. In the listing, "—" indicates, where applicable, one of the following:
    a. Metal or bullion value only
    b. Not usually found in this grade
    c. Not collected in this condition
7. Proof coins are listed in FDC under the UNC column.
8. All prices are quoted in £ sterling, exclusive of VAT (where applicable).

FIVE GUINEAS

CHARLES II (1660–85)

	F	VF	EF
1668 First bust	£1100	£2500	£7000
1668 — Elephant	£1100	£2200	£7500
1669 —	£1200	£2750	—
1669 — Elephant	£1500	£2800	—
*1670 —	£1100	£2000	£7000
1671 —	£1200	£2500	—
1672 —	£1100	£2500	£7000
1673 —	£1100	£2500	£7000
1674 —	£1200	£2750	£7500
1675 —	£1200	£2500	£7000
1675 — Elephant	£1500	£2800	—
1675 — Elephant & Castle		Extremely rare	
1676 —	£1200	£1800	—
1676 — Elephant & Castle	£1200	£2600	—
1677 —	£1200	£2500	—
1677/5 —		Extremely rare	
1677 — Elephant & Castle	£1300	£2800	—
1678 —	£1200	£2600	£7000
1678 — Elephant & Castle	£1500	£3000	—
1679 — 2nd Bust	£1500	£2800	£6500
1680 —	£1200	£2500	£7000
1680 — Elephant & Castle		Extremely rare	
1681 —	£1200	£2500	£6500
1681 — Elephant & Castle	£1500	£3000	—
1682 —	£1200	£2500	£6500
1682 — Elephant & Castle	£1200	£2500	—
1683 —	£1500	£2700	£6500
1683 — Elephant & Castle	£1500	£2800	—
1684 —	£1200	£2200	£6500

JAMES II (1685–88)

	F	VF	EF
1686	£1300	£2750	£7000
1687	£1150	£2500	£7000
1687 Elephant & Castle	£1250	£2200	£6500
1688	£1150	£2500	£7000
1688 Elephant & Castle	£1250	£2800	£7000

WILLIAM AND MARY (1688–94)

	F	VF	EF
*1691	£1000	£2100	£6000
1691 Elephant & Castle	£1100	£2200	£6000
1692	£1000	£2400	£6000
1692 Elephant & Castle	£1250	£2400	£6000
1693	£1000	£2200	£5500
1693 Elephant & Castle	£1250	£2400	£6000
1694	£1200	£2700	£6000
1694 Elephant & Castle	£1250	£2750	£6500

WILLIAM III (1694–1702)

	F	VF	EF
1699 First bust	£1100	£2500	£5000
1699 — Elephant & Castle	£1300	£3000	£5500
1700 —	£1100	£3000	£5500
1701 Second bust "fine work"	£1200	£3250	£6500

ANNE (1702–14)

Pre-Union with Scotland

	F	VF	EF
1703 VIGO below bust		Extremely rare	

	F	VF	EF
'05	£1500	£2750	£6750
)6	£1250	£2500	£6500
st-Union shields			
)6	£1400	£2600	£6000
)9 Broader shields	£1250	£2600	£6000
11 Broader bust	£1250	£2600	£5000
13 —	£1250	£2600	£6000
14 —	£1250	£2600	£6000
14/3	£1250	£2600	£6000

GEORGE I (1714–27)

	F	VF	EF
16	£1500	£3000	£7500
17	£1500	£3500	£7750
20	£1500	£3500	£7750
26	£1500	£3250	£7250

GEORGE II (1727–60)

	F	VF	EF
29 Young head	£1000	£2500	£6000
29 Plain edge Proof			V. Rare
29 — E.I.C. below head	£1000	£2600	£6000
31 —	£1100	£2500	£6000
35 —	£1100	£2500	£6000
38 —	£1100	£2500	£6000
41 —	£1000	£2500	£6000
46 Old head, LIMA	£1050	£2500	£5500
48 —	£1000	£2200	£5500
53 —	£1000	£2200	£5500

GEORGE III (1760–1820)

	F	VF	EF
70 Patterns	—	—	£40000
73	—	—	£40000
77	—	—	£40000

TWO GUINEAS

CHARLES II (1660–85)

	F	VF	EF
1664 First bust	£650	£1800	£4000
*1664 — Elephant	£600	£140	£4500
1665 —			Extremely rare
1669 —			Extremely rare
1671 —	£700	£2000	£4250
1675 Second bust	£700	£2200	£4250
1676 —	£600	£1800	—
1676 — Elephant & Castle	£600	£1800	—
1677 —	£600	£1800	£4500
1677 — Elephant & Castle			Extremely rare
1678 —	£600	£1800	—
1678 — Elephant			Extremely rare
1678 — Elephant & Castle	£550	£1800	—
1679 —	£600	£1800	—
1680 —	£700	£1200	£5000
1681 —	£600	£1800	£4000
1682 — Elephant & Castle	£600	£1800	—
1683 —	£600	£1800	£4000
1683 — Elephant & Castle	£750	—	—
1684 —	£750	£2000	£4000
1684 — Elephant & Castle	£7500	£2200	—

JAMES II (1685–88)

	F	VF	EF
1687	£700	£2000	£4500
*1688/7	£750	£2000	£5000

WILLIAM AND MARY (1688–94)

	F	VF	EF
1691 Elephant & Castle			Extremely rare
1693	£700	£2000	£4000
1693 Elephant & Castle	£700	£2000	£4000
1694	£700	£2000	£4250
1694 Elephant & Castle	£700	£2000	£4250

WILLIAM III (1694–1702)

	F	VF	EF
1701 "fine work"	£950	£2400	£4500

ANNE (1702–14)

	F	VF	EF
1709	£500	£1100	£3500
1711	£500	£1100	£3000
1713	£500	£1150	£3500
1714	£600	£1400	£4000

GEORGE I (1714–27)

	F	VF	EF
1717	£600	£1200	£4000
1720	£500	£1250	£4000
*1726	£500	£1200	£3750

GEORGE II (1727–60)

	F	VF	EF
4 Young head 4 over 3	£800	£2200	—
5 —	£400	£850	£2500
38 —	£375	£650	£1700
9 —	£350	£700	£1750
9 Intermediate head	£350	£650	£1500
0 —	£350	£700	£1500
8 Old head	£375	£800	£2100
3 —	£500	£1400	£3000

GEORGE III (1760–1820)

	F	VF	EF
8 Patterns only	—	—	£17500
3 Patterns only	—	—	£17500
7 Patterns only	—	—	£17500

GUINEAS

CHARLES II (1660–85)

	F	VF	EF
3 First bust	£575	£1600	—
3 — Elephant below	£575	£1600	—
4 Second bust	£400	£1500	—
4 — Elephant		Extremely rare	
4 Third bust	£400	£1000	£3250
4 — Elephant	£500	£1250	£3950
5 —	£400	£1000	£3250
5 — Elephant	£400	£1100	£4000
6 —	£400	£1100	£3250
7 —	£400	£1100	£3250
8 —	£400	£1100	£3250
8 — Elephant		Extremely rare	
9 —	£400	£1250	—
70 —	£400	£1100	£3250
1 —	£400	£1100	£3250
2 —	£425	£1400	—
2 Fourth bust	£300	£900	£3000
3 Third bust	£500	£1500	—
3 Fourth bust	£350	£900	£3000
4 —	£350	£1250	—
4 — Elephant & Castle		Extremely rare	
5 —	£300	£1000	£3250
75 — Elephant & Castle	£400	£1300	—
6 —	£300	£700	£2750
6 — Elephant & Castle	£350	£1000	£3000
7 —	£275	£800	£2800
7 — Elephant		Extremely rare	
7 — Elephant & Castle	£350	£1100	£3250
8 —	£350	£1000	£3000
8 — Elephant		Extremely rare	
8 — Elephant & Castle	£425	£1300	—
9 —	£250	£800	£2800

Charles II, third bust

Charles II, fourth bust, elephant & castle below

	F	VF	EF
1679 — Elephant & Castle	£375	£1250	—
1680 —	£250	£800	£2800
1680 — Elephant & Castle	£500	£1500	—
1681 —	£325	£1000	£3000
1681 — Elephant & Castle	£375	£1250	—
1682 —	£300	£900	£3000
1682 — Elephant & Castle	£350	£1250	£2800
1683 —	£275	£800	£2800
1683 — Elephant & Castle	£500	£1400	£4000
1684 —	£300	£900	£3300
1684 — Elephant & Castle	£325	£1100	£3250

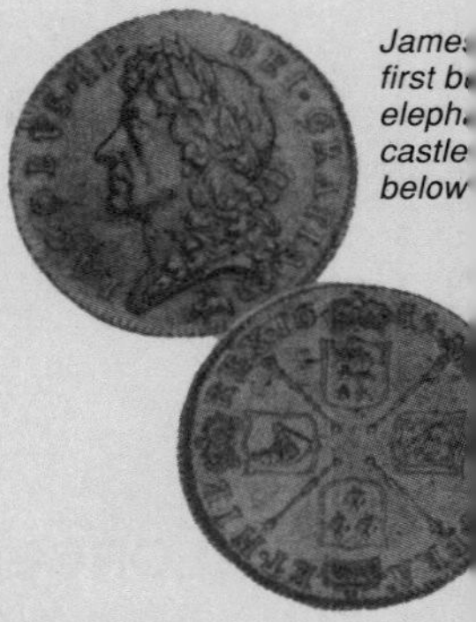

Jame first b eleph castle below

JAMES II (1685–1688)

1685 First bust	£300	£1000	£2750
*1685 — Elephant & Castle	£375	£1100	£3000
1686 —	£325	£1000	£3000
1686 — Elephant & Castle		Extremely rare	
1686 Second bust	£270	£900	£2500
1686 — Elephant & Castle	£450	£1500	£4000
1687 —	£275	£900	£2500
1687 —Elephant & Castle	£325	£900	£3000
*1688 —	£275	£900	£3000
1688 — Elephant & Castle	£325	£1000	£3000

Jam seco

WILLIAM AND MARY (1688–94)

1689	£300	£900	£3000
1689 Elephant & Castle	£300	£1000	£3000
1690	£300	£9000	£3000
1690 Elephant & Castle	£500	£1250	£4000
1691	£350	£900	£3000
1691 Elephant & Castle	£350	£1250	£3000
1692	£350	£1000	£3000
1692 Elephant	£500	£1250	£3500
1692 Elephant & Castle	£400	£1250	£3250
1693	£325	£1100	£3000
1693 Elephant		Extremely rare	
1693 Elephant & Castle		Extremely rare	
1694	£300	£1100	£2750
1694 Elephant & Castle	£400	£1100	£3250
1694/3 Elephant & Castle	£400	£1100	£3250

WILLIAM III (1694–1702)

1695 First bust	£250	£1000	£2500
1695 — Elephant & Castle	£350	£1250	£3000
1696 —	£225	£1000	£2500
1696 — Elephant & Castle		Extremely rare	
1697 —	£225	£1000	£3000
1697 Second bust	£220	£1000	£3000
1697 — Elephant & Castle	£700	£2400	—
1698 —	£225	£900	£2200
1698 — Elephant & Castle	£350	£1000	£3000
1699 —	£300	£1000	£2500
1699 — Elephant & Castle		Extremely rare	
1700 —	£225	£900	£2400
1700 — Elephant & Castle	£700	£2250	—
1701 —	£225	£900	£2200
1701 — Elephant & Castle		Extremely rare	
1701 Third bust "fine work"	£450	£1200	£3250

ANNE (1702–1714)

	F	VF	EF
2 (Pre-Union) First bust	£300	£900	£2850
3 — VIGO below	£4000	£8000	—
5 —	£350	£1000	£3000
6 —	£375	£1100	£3000
7 —	£425	£1100	£3000
7 — (Post-Union)	£240	£700	£2000
7 — Elephant & Castle	£750	£1750	—
7 Second bust		Extremely rare	
8 First bust		Extremely rare	
8 Second bust	£225	£600	£1800
8 — Elephant & Castle	£700	£1250	£3250
9 —	£225	£750	£2000
9 — Elephant & Castle	£700	£1250	£3250
0 Third bust	£225	£500	£1600
1 —	£225	£500	£1600
2 —	£225	£500	£1600
13 —	£225	£500	£1600
4 —	£225	£500	£1600

GEORGE I (1714–27)

	F	VF	EF
4 First bust (Prince Elector)	£700	£1500	£3500
5 Second bust	£240	£700	£2000
5 Third bust	£225	£700	£2000
6 —	£225	£700	£2000
6 Fourth bust	£210	£700	£2000
7 —	£210	£375	£1750
8 —		Extremely rare	
9 —	£225	£700	£1800
0 —	£225	£700	£1800
1 —	£225	£700	£1800
1 — Elephant & Castle		Extremely rare	
2 —	£225	£650	£2000
2 — Elephant & Castle		Extremely rare	
3 —	£225	£700	£2200
3 Fifth bust	£225	£750	£2200
4 —	£225	£750	£2200
5 —	£225	£750	£2200
6 —	£225	£700	£2000
6 — Elephant & Castle	£700	£2200	—
7 —	£275	£800	£2500

GEORGE II (1727–60)

	F	VF	EF
7 First young head, early large shield	£500	£1250	£3000
7 — Larger lettering, early small shield	£375	£800	£2250
8 — —	£375	£800	£2250
9 2nd young head E.I.C. below	£400	£1000	£3000
9 — Proof			Rare
0 —	£300	£800	£2200
1 —	£225	£700	£2000
1 — E.I.C. below	£400	£800	£2600
2 —	£275	£750	£2200
2 — E.I.C. below	£325	£800	£2600
2 — Larger lettering obverse	£250	£700	£2000
2 — — E.I.C. below	£325	£1000	£2600
3 — —	£200	£500	£1750
4 — —	£200	£500	£1750
5 — —	£225	£600	£1750
6 — —	£225	£700	£2000
7 — —	£250	£700	£2000

	F	VF	EF
1738 — —	£250	£700	£1800
1739 Intermediate head	£250	£450	£1750
1739 — E.I.C. below	£275	£750	£3000
1740 —	£225	£500	£1850
1741/39 —		Extremely rare	
1743 —		Extremely rare	
1745 — Larger lettering obv. Older bust	£250	£600	£2000
1745 — LIMA below	£600	£1500	£4000
1746 — (GEORGIVS) Larger lettering obv.	£225	£500	£1800
1747 Old head, large lettering	£200	£350	£1250
1748 —	£200	£350	£1250
1749 —	£200	£350	£1250
1750 —	£200	£350	£1250
1751 — small lettering	£200	£350	£1250
1753 —	£200	£350	£1250
1755 —	£200	£400	£1500
1756 —	£200	£350	£1250
1758 —	£200	£350	£1250
1759 —	£200	£350	£1250
1760 —	£200	£350	£1250

GEORGE III (1760–1820)

	F	VF	EF
1761 First head	£500	£1800	£3250
1763 Second head	£400	£900	£2500
1764 —	£325	£900	£2000
1765 Third head	£170	£375	£900
1766 —	£150	£325	£750
1767 —	£175	£400	£950
1768 —	£150	£325	£750
1769 —	£150	£325	£750
1770 —	£175	£400	£900
*1771 —	£150	£350	£750
1772 —	£150	£325	£750
1773 —	£150	£300	£675
1774 Fourth head	£100	£200	£450
1775 —	£100	£200	£450
1776 —	£110	£220	£500
1777 —	£100	£200	£450
1778 —	£100	£250	£500
1779 —	£110	£250	£475
1781 —	£110	£250	£450
1782 —	£110	£250	£450
1783 —	£110	£250	£450
1784 —	£110	£250	£450
1785 —	£110	£250	£450
1786 —	£110	£250	£450
1787 Fifth head, "Spade" reverse	£95	£200	£350
1788 —	£90	£200	£350
1789 —	£90	£200	£350
1790 —	£90	£200	£350
1791 —	£90	£200	£350
1792 —	£90	£200	£350
1793 —	£90	£200	£350
1794 —	£90	£200	£350
1795 —	£110	£220	£500
1796 —	£120	£250	£500
1797 —	£100	£200	£350
*1798 —	£85	£175	£325
1799 —	£125	£275	£500
*1813 Sixth head, "Military" reverse	£225	£700	£1200

(Beware of counterfeits of this series—many dangerous copies exist)

HALF GUINEAS

CHARLES II (1660–85)

	F	VF	EF
9 First bust	£300	£650	£2500
70 —	£240	£650	£2000
1 —	£350	£1000	—
2 —	£350	£1000	—
2 Second bust	£250	£700	£2200
3 —	£400	£1200	—
4 —	£400	£1200	—
5 —	Extremely rare		
6 —	£260	£600	—
6 — Elephant & Castle	£500	£1500	—
7 —	£260	£650	£2000
7 — Elephant & Castle	£400	£1200	—
8 —	£275	£700	£2200
8 — Elephant & Castle	£350	£1000	—
9 —	£250	£600	£2000
0 —	£400	£1200	—
0 — Elephant & Castle	Extremely rare		
1 —	£400	£1200	—
2 —	£375	£850	£2200
2 — Elephant & Castle	£450	£1350	—
3 —	£270	£675	£2200
3 — Elephant & Castle	Extremely rare		
4 —	£250	£500	£2000
4 — Elephant & Castle	£350	£800	£2750

JAMES II (1685–88)

	F	VF	EF
6	£275	£625	£2500
6 Elephant & Castle	£600	£2000	£4500
7	£350	£1000	£3000
8	£320	£1000	£3000

WILLIAM AND MARY (1688–94)

	F	VF	EF
9 First busts	£325	£800	£2500
0 Second busts	£375	£900	£2400
1 —	£425	£900	£2400
1 — Elephant & Castle	£325	£900	£2200
2 —	£350	£900	£2500
92 — Elephant	Extremely rare		
2 — Elephant & Castle	£325	£1000	£2750
3 —	Extremely rare		
4 —	£300	£1000	£2000

WILLIAM III (1694–1702)

	F	VF	EF
5	£175	£425	£1750
5 Elephant & Castle	£425	£850	£2250
6 —	£250	£600	£2000
7 Larger Harp rev.	£275	£600	£2200
8	£175	£450	£1500
8 Elephant & Castle	£350	£800	£2250
99	Extremely rare		
0	£175	£450	£1850
1	£175	£450	£1850

ANNE (1702–14)

	F	VF	EF
1702 (Pre-Union)	£250	£750	£2500
1703 VIGO below bust	£3000	£7000	£12500
1705	£250	£700	£2500
1707 (Post-Union)	£210	£600	£1500
1708	£240	£700	£1700
1709	£200	£500	£1400
1710	£200	£500	£1400
*1711	£210	£500	£1350
1712	£220	£500	£1400
1713	£200	£450	£1400
1714	£200	£350	£1400

GEORGE I (1714–27)

	F	VF	EF
1715 First bust	£200	£425	£1150
1717 —	£200	£375	£850
*1718 —	£200	£375	£1050
1719 —	£175	£350	£1050
1720 —	£275	£650	£1100
1721 —		Extremely rare	
1721 — Elephant & Castle		Extremely rare	
1722 —	£200	£700	£1850
1723 —		Extremely rare	
1724 —	£275	£550	£1850
1725 Second bust	£175	£350	£1050
1726 —	£175	£350	£1050
1727 —	£180	£400	£1100

GEORGE II (1727–60)

Georg
young

Georg
head

	F	VF	EF
1728 Young head	£200	£475	£1500
1729 —	£220	£525	£1700
1729 — E.I.C.	£300	£750	£2200
1730 —	£500	£1200	—
1730 — E.I.C.	£500	£1200	—
1731 —	£300	£750	£2200
1731 — E.I.C.		Extremely rare	
1732 —	£200	£500	£1700
1732 — E.I.C.		Extremely rare	
1733 —		Extremely rare	
1734 —	£175	£425	£1500
1735 —		Extremely rare	
1736 —	£200	£450	£1500
*1737 —		Extremely rare	
1738 —	£175	£425	£1500
1739 —	£175	£425	£1500
1739 — E.I.C.		Extremely rare	
1740 Intermediate head	£250	£650	£2200
1743 —		Extremely rare	
1745 —	£250	£700	£2200
1745 — LIMA	£650	£1650	£3500
1746 —	£175	£400	£1250
1747 Old head	£275	£600	£1500
1748 —	£150	£350	£1000
1749 —		Extremely rare	
*1750 —	£170	£400	£1000
1751 —	£170	£400	£1000
1752 —	£170	£400	£1000
1753 —	£150	£350	£850

	F	VF	EF
5 —	£150	£300	£850
6 —	£155	£300	£850
8 —	£150	£300	£850
9 —	£145	£275	£850
0 —	£145	£275	£850

GEORGE III (1760–1820)

	F	VF	EF
2 First head	£250	£700	£1850
3 —	£300	£750	£2000
4 Second head	£150	£300	£650
5 —	£300	£650	£1250
6 —	£175	£300	£750
8 —	£175	£300	£750
69 —	£160	£350	£700
2 —		Extremely rare	
3 —	£175	£300	£750
4 —	£250	£500	£1500
4 Third head		Extremely rare	
5 —	£350	£800	£2000
5 Fourth head	£75	£150	£325
5 — Proof		Extremely rare	
6 —	£75	£150	£325
7 —	£75	£150	£325
8 —	£90	£180	£400
9 —	£100	£200	£500
1 —	£90	£175	£425
3 —	£350	£900	—
4 —	£75	£170	£325
5 —	£70	£175	£325
6 —	£70	£155	£320
7 Fifth head, "Spade" rev.	£65	£140	£275
8 —	£65	£140	£300
9 —	£75	£175	£400
0 —	£65	£140	£275
1 —	£65	£140	£300
2 —	£400	—	—
3 —	£65	£140	£280
4 —	£65	£160	£300
5 —	£100	£200	£475
96 —	£70	£160	£300
7 —	£70	£140	£275
8 —	£70	£140	£275
0 —	£140	£400	£850
01 Sixth head, Shield in Garter rev.	£55	£95	£180
2 —	£55	£95	£200
3 —	£55	£95	£200
4 Seventh head	£55	£95	£200
5		Extremely Rare	
6 —	£55	£95	£200
8 —	£55	£95	£200
9 —	£55	£95	£200
0 —	£55	£95	£200
1 —	£100	£225	£425
3 —	£100	£225	£450

George III, second head

George III, fifth head, "spade" reverse

George III, sixth head

THIRD GUINEAS

GEORGE III (1760–1820)

DATE	F	VF	EF
*1797 First head,date in legend	£45	£75	£175
1798 — —	£45	£75	£175
1799 — —	£65	£100	£225
1800 — —	£40	£75	£175
1801 Date under crown	£40	£75	£175
1802 —	£40	£75	£175
1803 —	£40	£75	£175
1804 Second head	£40	£75	£175
1806 —	£40	£75	£175
1808 —	£40	£75	£175
1809 —	£40	£75	£175
*1810 —	£40	£75	£175
1811 —	£160	£375	£800
1813 —	£90	£175	£350

George III, date in legend

George III, date under crown

QUARTER GUINEAS

GEORGE I (1714–27)

1718	£70	£145	£280

GEORGE III (1760–1820)

*1762	£50	£125	£275

FIVE POUNDS

DATE	Mintage	F	VF	EF	UNC
GEORGE III (1760–1820)					
1820 (pattern only)	—			Extremely rare	
GEORGE IV (1820–30)					
*1826 proof only	—	—	—	£6,000	£10,000
VICTORIA (1837–1901)					
1839 Proof Only	—	—	—	£16,000	£25,000
1887	53,844	£325	£470	£675	£850
1887 Proof	797	—	—	—	£2,000
1887 S on ground on rev. (Sydney Mint)				Excessively rare	
1893	20,405	£400	£650	£900	£13250
1893 Proof	773	—	—	—	£2,500
EDWARD VII (1902–10)					
1902	34,910	—	£400	£550	£750
1902 Matt proof	8,066	—	—	—	£750

TE	MINTAGE	F	VF	EF	UNC

GEORGE V (1911–36)

1 Proof only	2,812	—	—	—	£1,500

GEORGE VI (1937–52)

37 Proof only	5,501	—	—	—	£675

er issues are listed in the Decimal section.

TWO POUNDS

GEORGE III (1760–1820)

20 (pattern only)	—	—	—	Extremely rare	

GEORGE IV (1820–30)

23 St George reverse	—	£225	£425	£825	£1600
26 Proof only, shield reverse	—	—	—	£2750	£4000

WILLIAM IV (1830–37)

31 Proof only	225	—	—	£3000	£5000

VICTORIA (1837–1901)

87	91,345	£170	£240	£375	£475
87 Proof	797	—	—	—	£850
87 S on ground of rev. (Sydney Mint)				Excessively rare	
93	52,212	£240	£350	£500	£675
93 Proof	773	—	—	—	£1000

EDWARD VII (1902–10)

02	45,807	£140	£180	£275	£350
02 Matt proof	8,066	—	—	—	£350

GEORGE V (1911–36)

11 Proof only	2,812	—	—	—	£600

GEORGE VI (1937–52)

937 Proof only	5,501	—	—	—	£360

ter issues are listed in the Decimal section.

SOVEREIGNS

GEORGE III (1760–1820)

DATE	MINTAGE	F	VF	EF	UNC
1817	3,235,239	£100	£180	£475	£750
1818	2,347,230	£100	£180	£500	£750
1819	3,574		Exceedingly rare		
1820	931,994	£100	£180	£500	£750

GEORGE IV (1820–30)

DATE	MINTAGE	F	VF	EF	UNC
1821 First bust, St George reverse	9,405,114	£95	£175	£450	£850
1821 — Proof	*incl. above*	—	—	£1500	£2500
1822 —	5,356,787	£95	£175	£450	£850
1823 —	616,770	£150	£415	£2000	—
1824 —	3,767,904	£90	£175	£500	£850
1825 —	4,200,343	£175	£450	£1500	—
1825 Second bust, shield reverse	*incl. above*	£90	£160	£425	£750
1826 —	5,724,046	£90	£160	£425	£750
*1826 — Proof	—	—	—	£1500	£2500
1827 —	2,266,629	£100	£175	£425	£750
1828 —	386,182	£700	£1800	£4750	—
1829 —	2,444,652	£110	£200	£475	£750
1830 —	2,387,881	£110	£200	£475	£750

WILLIAM IV (1830–37)

DATE	MINTAGE	F	VF	EF	UNC
1831	598,547	£150	£225	£500	£900
*1831 Proof	—	—	—	£1750	£2750
1832	3,737,065	£150	£225	£500	£850
1833	1,225,269	£150	£225	£500	£800
1835	723,441	£150	£225	£500	£850
1836	1,714,349	£150	£225	£500	£850
1837	1,172,984	£150	£225	£500	£800

VICTORIA (1837–1901)

Many of the gold coins struck at the colonial mints found their way into circulation in Britain, for the sake of completeness these coins are listed here. These can easily be identified by a tiny initial letter for the appropriate mint which can be found below the base of the reverse shield or, in the case of the St George reverse, below the bust on the obverse of the Young Head issues, or on the "ground" below the horse's hoof on the later issues.

YOUNG HEAD ISSUES

Shield reverse

(Note—Shield back sovereigns in Fine/VF condition, common dates, are normally traded as bullion + a percentage)

DATE	MINTAGE	F	VF	EF	UNC
1838	2,718,694	£75	£150	£350	£850
1839	503,695	£125	£350	£850	£2000
*1839 Proof	—	—	—	—	£2000
1841	124,054	£600	£1100	£2500	—
1842	4,865,375	—	£75	£150	£250
1843	5,981,968	—	£75	£150	£250
1843 "Narrow shield" variety	*incl. above*	£275	£600	£1500	—
1844	3,000,445	£60	£75	£150	£250
1845	3,800,845	£60	£75	£150	£250
1846	3,802,947	£60	£75	£150	£270

TE	MINTAGE	F	VF	EF	UNC
7	4,667,126	£60	£75	£140	£250
8	2,246,701	£60	£75	£160	£340
9	1,755,399	£60	£75	£150	£325
0	1,402,039	£60	£75	£140	£275
1	4,013,624	£60	£75	£140	£250
2	8,053,435	£60	£75	£140	£250
3	10,597,993	£60	£75	£140	£250
3 Proof	—	—	—	—	£3500
4	3,589,611	£75	£150	£350	£600
5	8,448,482	£70	£125	£200	£350
6	4,806,160	£60	£75	£140	£250
7	4,495,748	£60	£75	£140	£250
8	803,234	£60	£80	£175	£375
9	1,547,603	£60	£75	£140	£300
9 "Ansell" (additional line on ower part of hair ribbon)	—	£160	£320	£1500	—
0	2,555,958	£60	£75	£200	£300
1	7,624,736	£60	£75	£140	£250
2	7,836,413	—	£75	£140	£250
3	5,921,669	—	£75	£140	£250
3 Die No 827 on Truncation ..				Extremely Rare	
3 with Die number below shield	*incl. above*	£60	£75	£125	£240
4 —	8,656,352	£60	£75	£125	£240
5 —	1,450,238	£60	£75	£125	£240
6 —	4,047,288	£60	£75	£125	£240
8 —	1,653,384	£60	£75	£125	£240
9 —	6,441,322	£60	£75	£125	£240
70 —	2,189,960	£60	£75	£125	£240
71 —	8,767,250	£60	£75	£125	£240
72 —	8,767,250	£60	£75	£140	£240
72 no Die number	*incl. above*	£60	£75	£140	£240
73 with Die number	2,368,215	£55	£70	£130	£240
74 —	520,713	£800	—	—	—

below (Melbourne Mint)

72	748,180	£60	£75	£175	£350
73	—			Extremely rare	
74	1,373,298	£60	£75	£150	£350
79				Extremely rare	
80	3,053,454	£200	£500	£1750	—
81	2,325,303	£70	£100	£200	£300
82	2,465,781	£60	£75	£175	£325
83	2,050,450	£100	£200	£600	—
84	2,942,630	£60	£75	£150	£400
85	2,967,143	£60	£75	£150	£400
86	2,902,131	£300	£1000	£2500	—
87	1,916,424	£200	£700	£2000	£3500

below (Sydney Mint)

71	2,814,000	£60	£65	£140	£350
72	1,815,000	£60	£65	£140	£350
73	1,478,000	£60	£65	£140	£350
75	2,122,000	£60	£65	£140	£350
77	1,590,000	£60	£65	£140	£350
78	1,259,000	£60	£65	£150	£350
79	1,366,000	£60	£65	£140	£350
80	1,459,000	£60	£65	£140	£350
81	1,360,000	£60	£75	£170	£350
82	1,298,000	£60	£65	£140	£350
83	1,108,000	£60	£75	£170	£350
84	1,595,000	£60	£65	£140	£350
85	1,486,000	£60	£65	£140	£350
86	1,667,000	£60	£65	£140	£350
87	1,000,000	£60	£75	£170	£300

"S" below the shield indicates that the coin was struck at the Sydney Mint

DATE	MINTAGE	F	VF	EF	UNC
St George & Dragon reverse					
1871	*incl. above*	—	£60	£85	£160
1872	*incl. above*	—	£60	£85	£160
1873	*incl. above*	—	£60	£85	£160
1874	*incl. above*	—	£60	£85	£160
1876	3,318,866	—	£60	£85	£160
1878	1,091,275	—	£60	£85	£175
1879	20,013	£100	£300	£600	—
1880	3,650,080	—	£60	£85	£160
1884	1,769,635	—	£60	£85	£160
1885	717,723	—	£60	£85	£160
M below (Melbourne Mint)					
1872	*incl. above*	—	£60	£100	£160
1873	752,199	—	£60	£100	£150
1874	*incl. above*	—	£60	£100	£150
1875	*incl. above*	—	£60	£100	£150
1876	2,124,445	—	£60	£100	£160
1877	1,487,316	—	£60	£100	£150
1878	2,171,457	—	£60	£100	£150
1879	2,740,594	—	£60	£100	£150
1880	*incl. above*	—	£60	£100	£150
1881	*incl. above*	—	£60	£100	£150
1882	*incl. above*	—	£60	£100	£150
1883	*incl. above*	—	£60	£100	£150
1884	*incl. above*	—	£60	£100	£150
1885	*incl. above*	—	£60	£100	£150
1886	*incl. above*	—	£60	£100	£150
1887	*incl. above*	—	£60	£100	£150
S below (Sydney Mint)					
1871	2,814,000	—	£60	£110	£200
1872	*incl. above*	—	£60	£110	£200
1873	*incl. above*	—	£60	£110	£200
1874	1,899,000	—	£60	£100	£300
1875	inc above	—	£60	£100	£175
1876	1,613,000	—	£60	£100	£200
1877	—			Extremely rare	
1879	*incl. above*	—	£60	£100	£200
1880	*incl. above*	—	£60	£100	£200
1881	*incl. above*	—	£60	£100	£200
1882	*incl. above*	—	£60	£100	£200
1883	*incl. above*	—	£60	£100	£200
1884	*incl. above*	—	£60	£100	£200
1885	*incl. above*	—	£60	£100	£200
1886	*incl. above*	—	£60	£100	£200
1887	*incl. above*	—	£60	£100	£200
JUBILEE HEAD ISSUES					
*1887	1,111,280	—	—	£70	£90
1887 Proof	797	—	—	—	£700
1888	2,717,424	—	—	£60	£90
1889	7,257,455	—	—	£60	£90
1890	6,529.887	—	—	£60	£90
1891	6,329,476	—	—	£60	£90
1892	7,104,720	—	—	£60	£90
M below (Melbourne Mint)					
1887	940,000	£60	£85	£125	—
1888	2,830,612	£55	£70	£110	£120
1889	2,732,590	£55	£70	£110	£120
1890	2,473,537	£55	£70	£110	£120
1891	2,749,592	£55	£70	£110	£120
1892	3,488,750	£55	£70	£110	£120
1893	1,649,352	£55	£70	£110	£120

"M" below the horse's hoof above the date indicates th the coin was struck at the Melbourne Mint

ATE	MINTAGE	F	VF	EF	UNC
below (Sydney Mint)					
87	1,002,000	£55	£100	£125	£200
88	2,187,000	—	£75	£100	£120
89	3,262,000	—	£75	£100	£120
90	2,808,000	—	£75	£100	£120
91	2,596,000	—	£75	£100	£120
92	2,837,000	—	£75	£100	£120
93	1,498,000	—	£75	£100	£120
D HEAD ISSUES					
893	6,898,260	—	—	£65	£85
93 Proof	773	—	—	—	£650
94	3,782,611	—	—	£65	£85
95	2,285,317	—	—	£65	£85
96	3,334,065	—	—	£65	£85
98	4,361,347	—	—	£65	£85
99	7,515,978	—	—	£65	£85
00	10,846,741	—	—	£65	£85
01	1,578,948	—	—	£65	£85
below (Melbourne Mint)					
93	1,914,000	—	—	£90	£100
94	4,166,874	—	—	£90	£100
95	4,165,869	—	—	£90	£100
96	4,456,932	—	—	£90	£100
97	5,130,565	—	—	£90	£100
98	5,509,138	—	—	£90	£100
99	5,579,157	—	—	£90	£100
00	4,305,904	—	—	£90	£100
01	3,987,701	—	—	£90	£100
below (Perth Mint)					
99	690,992	£60	£85	£225	£800
00	1,886,089	—	—	£90	£150
01	2,889,333	—	—	£90	£150
below (Sydney Mint)					
93	1,346,000	—	—	£75	£100
94	3,067,000	—	—	£75	£100
95	2,758,000	—	—	£75	£100
96	2,544,000	—	—	£100	£140
97	2,532,000	—	—	£75	£100
98	2,548,000	—	—	£75	£100
99	3,259,000	—	—	£75	£100
00	3,586,000	—	—	£75	£100
01	3,012,000	—	—	£75	£100

EDWARD VII (1902–10)

902	4,737,796	—	—	£60	£75
902 Matt proof	15,123	—	—	—	£125
903	8,888,627	—	—	£60	£75
904	10,041,369	—	—	£60	£75
905	5,910,403	—	—	£60	£75
906	10,466,981	—	—	£60	£75
907	18,458,663	—	—	£60	£75
908	11,729,006	—	—	£60	£75
909	12,157,099	—	—	£60	£75
910	22,379,624	—	—	£60	£75
below (Ottawa Mint)					
908 Satin finish Proof only	636		Extremely rare		
909	16,273	—	£80	£220	—
910	28,012	—	£80	£220	—

DATE	MINTAGE	F	VF	EF	UNC
M below (Melbourne Mint)					
1902	4,267,157	—	—	£75	£110
1903	3,521,780	—	—	£75	£110
1904	3,743,897	—	—	£75	£110
1905	3,633,838	—	—	£75	£110
1906	3,657,853	—	—	£75	£110
1907	3,332,691	—	—	£75	£110
1908	3,080,148	—	—	£75	£110
1909	3,029,538	—	—	£75	£110
1910	3,054,547	—	—	£75	£110
P below (Perth Mint)					
1902	3,289,122	—	—	£75	£110
1903	4,674,783	—	—	£75	£110
1904	4,506,756	—	—	£75	£110
1905	4,876,193	—	—	£75	£110
1906	4,829,817	—	—	£75	£110
1907	4,972,289	—	—	£75	£110
1908	4,875,617	—	—	£75	£110
1909	4,524,241	—	—	£75	£110
1910	4,690,625	—	—	£75	£110
S below (Sydney Mint)					
1902	2,813,000	—	—	£75	£110
1902 Proof	*incl. above*			Extremely rare	
1903	2,806,000	—	—	£75	£110
1904	2,986,000	—	—	£75	£110
1905	2,778,000	—	—	£75	£110
1906	2,792,000	—	—	£75	£110
1907	2,539,000	—	—	£75	£110
1908	2,017,000	—	—	£75	£110
1909	2,057,000	—	—	£75	£110
1910	2,135,000	—	—	£75	£110

GEORGE V (1911–36)

(Extra care should be exercised when purchasing as good quality forgeries exist of virtually all dates and mintmarks)

1911	30,044,105	—	—	£60	£80
1911 Proof	3,764	—	—	—	£300
1912	30,317,921	—	—	£60	£80
1913	24,539,672	—	—	£60	£80
1914	11,501,117	—	—	£60	£80
1915	20,295,280	—	—	£60	£80
1916	1,554,120	—	—	£60	£85
1917	1,014,714	£1250	£2000	£3250	—
1925	4,406,431	—	—	£60	£80
C below (Ottawa Mint)					
1911	256,946	—	£70	£90	£125
1913	3,715	£100	£120	£400	—
1914	14,891	£100	£180	£300	—
1916	6,111			Extremely rare	
1917	58,845	—	£70	£110	£125
1918	106,516	—	£70	£110	£125
1919	135,889	—	£70	£110	£125
I below (Bombay Mint)					
1918	1,295,372	—	—	£75	—
M below (Melbourne Mint)					
1911	2,851,451	—	—	£75	£100
1912	2,469,257	—	—	£75	£100
1913	2,323,180	—	—	£75	£100
1914	2,012,029	—	—	£75	£100
1915	1,637,839	—	—	£75	£100

ATE	MINTAGE	F	VF	EF	UNC
16	1,273,643	—	—	£75	£100
17	934,469	—	—	£75	£100
18	4,969,493	—	—	£75	£100
19	514,257	—	—	£90	£125
20	530,266	—	£700	£1500	—
21	240,121	—	—	£4000	—
22	608,306	—	£1000	£3000	—
23	510,870	—	—	£75	£110
24	278,140	—	—	£80	£125
25	3,311,622	—	—	£75	£100
26	211,107	—	—	£75	£100
28	413,208	—	£550	£1250	£2000
29	436,719	—	£500	£1500	£2000
30	77,547	—	£75	£150	£2000
31	57,779	—	£140	£300	£2000
below (Perth Mint)					
11	4,373,165	—	—	£75	£100
12	4,278,144	—	—	£75	£100
13	4,635,287	—	—	£75	£100
14	4,815,996	—	—	£75	£100
15	4,373,596	—	—	£75	£100
16	4,096,771	—	—	£75	£100
17	4,110,286	—	—	£75	£100
18	3,812,884	—	—	£75	£100
19	2,995,216	—	—	£75	£100
20	2,421,196	—	—	£75	£100
21	2,134,360	—	—	£75	£100
22	2,298,884	—	—	£75	£100
23	2,124,154	—	—	£75	£100
24	1,464,416	—	—	£80	£120
25	1,837,901	—	—	£90	£175
26	1,313,578	—	£100	£200	£1000
27	1,383,544	—	—	£110	£350
28	1,333,417	—	—	£100	£140
29	1,606,625	—	—	£75	£100
30	1,915,352	—	—	£75	£100
31	1,173,568	—	—	£75	£100
below (Sydney Mint)					
911	2,519,000	—	—	£70	£90
912	2,227,000	—	—	£70	£90
913	2,249,000	—	—	£70	£90
914	1,774,000	—	—	£70	£90
915	1,346,000	—	—	£70	£90
916	1,242,000	—	—	£70	£90
917	1,666,000	—	—	£70	£90
918	3,716,000	—	—	£70	£90
919	1,835,000	—	—	£70	£90
920	—		Excessively rare		
921	839,000	—	£600	£1250	—
922	578,000		Extremely rare		
923	416,000		Extremely rare		
924	394,000	—	£400	£800	£1250
925	5,632,000	—	—	£75	£100
926	1,031,050		Extremely rare		
A below (Pretoria Mint)					
923	719		Extremely rare		
923 Proof	655		Extremely rare		
924	3,184		Extremely rare		
925	6,086,264	—	£60	£80	£95
926	11,107,611	—	£60	£80	£95
927	16,379,704	—	£60	£80	£95
928	18,235,057	—	£60	£80	£95

DATE	MINTAGE	F	VF	EF	UNC
1929	12,024,107	—	—	£80	£95
1930	10,027,756	—	—	£80	£95
1931	8,511,792	—	—	£80	£95
1932	1,066,680	—	—	£90	£110

GEORGE VI (1937–52)

*1937 Proof only	5,501	—	—	£275	£350

ELIZABETH II (1952–)

Pre Decimal Issues

1957	2,072,000	—	—	—	£65
1958	8,700,140	—	—	—	£60
1959	1,358,228	—	—	—	£70
1962	3,000,000	—	—	—	£60
1963	7,400,000	—	—	—	£60
1964	3,000,000	—	—	—	£60
1965	3,800,000	—	—	—	£60
1966	7,050,000	—	—	—	£60
1967	5,000,000	—	—	—	£60
1968	4,203,000	—	—	—	£60

Later issues are included in the Decimal section.

HALF SOVEREIGNS

GEORGE III (1760–1820)

1817	2,080,197	£55	£90	£200	£325
1818	1,030,286	£55	£90	£200	£350
1820	35,043	£55	£90	£200	£350

GEORGE IV (1820–30)

1821 First bust, ornate shield reverse	231,288	£200	£600	£1500	£2650
1821 — Proof	*unrecorded*	—	—	£2000	£3000
1823 First bust, Plain shield rev.	224,280	£70	£150	£400	£675
1824 —	591,538	£70	£150	£425	£675
1825 —	761,150	£70	£150	£425	£675
1826 bare head, shield with full legend reverse	344,830	£70	£130	£400	£600
1826 — Proof	*unrecorded*	—	—	£750	£1000
1827 —	492,014	£75	£150	£400	£650
1828 —	1,224,754	£70	£135	£400	£675

WILLIAM IV (1830–37)

1831 Proof only	*uncrecorded*	—	—	£750	£1400
1834	133,899	£100	£200	£500	£800
1835	772,554	£100	£300	£425	£775
1836	146,865	£90	£200	£500	£850
1836 obverse from 6d die	*incl. above*	£600	£1200	£2270	—
1837	160,207	£100	£200	£475	£750

VICTORIA (1837–1901)

YOUNG HEAD ISSUES

Shield reverse

DATE	MINTAGE	F	VF	EF	UNC
1838	273,341	£60	£90	£225	£450
1839 Proof only	1,230	—	—	—	£1200
1841	508,835	£65	£90	£260	£500
1842	2,223,352	—	£65	£200	£300
1843	1,251,762	£65	£90	£260	£500
1844	1,127,007	£60	£70	£240	£350
1845	887,526	£100	£300	£700	£1000
1846	1,063,928	£60	£80	£220	£375
1847	982,636	£60	£80	£220	£375
1848	410,595	£60	£80	£220	£375
1849	845,112	—	£75	£180	£325
1850	179,595	£100	£200	£500	£800
1851	773,573	—	£75	£200	£350
1852	1,377,671	—	£80	£200	£350
1853	2,708,796	—	£70	£180	£300
1853 Proof	*unrecorded*	—	—	—	£2800
1854	1,125,144		Extremely rare		
1855	1,120,362	—	£75	£180	£325
1856	2,391,909	—	£75	£180	£325
1857	728,223	—	£80	£190	£350
1858	855,578	—	£80	£190	£350
1859	2,203,813	—	£70	£180	£325
1860	1,131,500	—	£70	£180	£325
1861	1,130,867	—	£70	£180	£325
1862	*unrecorded*	£275	£800	£2500	—
1863	1,571,574	—	£70	£180	£325
1863 with Die number	*incl. above*	—	£65	£180	£325
1864 —	1,758,490	—	£70	£180	£325
1865 —	1,834,750	—	£70	£180	£325
1866 —	2,058,776	—	£70	£180	£325
1867 —	992,795	—	£70	£180	£325
1869 —	1,861,764	—	£65	£180	£325
1870 —	1,159,544	—	£65	£175	£275
1871 —	2,062,970	—	£60	£150	£275
1872 —	3,248,627	—	£65	£150	£275
1873 —	1,927,050	—	£60	£150	£275
1874 —	1,884,432	—	£60	£150	£275
1875 —	516,240	—	£60	£150	£275
1876 —	2,785,187	—	£60	£150	£250
1877 —	2,197,482	—	£60	£130	£275
1878 —	2,081,941	—	£60	£130	£275
1879 —	35,201	—	£60	£140	£275
1880 —	1,009,049	—	£60	£140	£275
1880 no Die number	*incl. above*	—	£60	£140	£275
1883 —	2,870,457	—	£60	£135	£225
1884 —	1,113,756	—	£60	£125	£225
1885 —	4,468,871	—	£60	£125	£225

M below (Melbourne Mint)

DATE	MINTAGE	F	VF	EF	UNC
1873	165,034	£50	£110	£350	—
1877	80,016	£50	£110	£350	—
1881	42,009	£60	£175	£450	—
1882	107,522	£60	£100	£400	—
1884	48,009	£60	£100	£350	—
1885	11,003	£70	£200	£800	—
1886	38,008	£60	£110	£450	—
1887	64,013	£75	£225	£800	£1750

S below (Sydney Mint)

DATE	MINTAGE	F	VF	EF	UNC
1871	*unrecorded*	£60	£95	£400	—
1872	356,000	£65	£110	£400	—

Date	Mintage	F	VF	EF	UNC
1875	*unrecorded*	£55	£90	£450	—
1879	94,000	£55	£90	£450	—
1880	80,000	£55	£900	£400	—
1881	62,000	£55	£100	£400	—
1882	52,000	£100	£400	£1500	—
1883	220,000	£55	£80	£450	—
1886	82,000	£55	£80	£375	—
1887	134,000	£55	£80	£1500	—
JUBILEE HEAD ISSUES					
1887	871,770	—	£45	£65	£80
1887 Proof	797	—	—	—	£350
1890	2.266,023	—	£50	£70	£125
1891	1,079,286	—	£50	£70	£125
1892	13,680,486	—	—	£60	£120
1893	4,426,625	—	—	£65	£120
M below (Melbourne Mint)					
1887	*incl. above*	£50	£100	£275	£450
1893	110,024	£60	£125	£375	—
S below (Sydney Mint)					
1887	*incl. above*	£50	£90	£250	£400
1889	64,000	£60	£100	£250	—
1891	154,000	£60	£120	£275	—
OLD HEAD ISSUES					
1893	*incl. above*	—	£40	£55	£90
1893 Proof	773	—	—	—	£500
1894	3,794,591	—	£40	£60	£90
1895	2,869,183	—	£40	£60	£90
1896	2,946,605	—	£40	£60	£90
1897	3,568,156	—	£40	£60	£90
1898	2,868,527	—	£40	£60	£90
1899	3,361,881	—	£40	£60	£90
1900	4,307,372	—	£40	£60	£90
1901	2,037,664	—	£40	£60	£90
M below (Melbourne Mint)					
1893	*unrecorded*			Extremely rare	
1896	218,946	£50	£100	£300	—
1899	97,221	£50	£100	£300	—
1900	112,920	£50	£100	£300	—
P below (Perth Mint)					
1899				Proof Unique	
1900	119,376	£125	£300	£500	—
S below (Sydney Mint)					
1893	250,000	£60	£100	£275	—
1897	*unrecorded*	£50	£90	£275	—
1900	260,00	£50	£80	£275	—

EDWARD VII (1902–10)

1902	4,244,457	—	—	£45	£55
1902 Matt proof	15,123	—	—	—	£100
1903	2,522,057	—	—	£45	£55
1904	1,717,440	—	—	£45	£55
1905	3,023,993	—	—	£45	£55
1906	4,245,437	—	—	£45	£55
1907	4,233,421	—	—	£45	£55
1908	3,996,992	—	—	£45	£55
1909	4,010,715	—	—	£45	£55
1910	5,023,881	—	—	£45	£55

DATE		F	VF	EF	UNC
M below (Melbourne Mint)					
1906	82,042	—	£40	£80	£150
1907	405,034	—	£40	£80	£150
1908	*incl. above*	—	£40	£80	£200
1909	186,094	—	£40	£80	£150
P below (Perth Mint)					
1904	60,030	£100	£150	£550	—
1908	24,668	£100	£150	£550	—
1909	44,022	£70	£130	£350	—
S below (Sydney Mint)					
1902	84,000	—	£45	£100	£200
1902 Proof				Extremely rare	
1903	231,000	—	£45	£100	£150
1906	308,00	—	£45	£100	£175
1908	538,000	—	£45	£100	£175
1910	474,000	—	£45	£100	£175

GEORGE V (1911–36)

DATE		F	VF	EF	UNC
1911	6,104,106	—	£35	£50	£75
1911 Proof	3,764	—	—	—	£175
1912	6,224,316	—	£35	£50	£75
1913	6,094,290	—	£35	£50	£75
1914	7,251,124	—	£35	£50	£75
1915	2,042,747	—	£35	£50	£75
M below (Melbourne Mint)					
1915	125,664	—	—	£70	£125
P below (Perth Mint)					
1911	130,373	—	—	£70	£100
1915	136,219	—	—	£70	£100
1918	*unrecorded*	£120	£275	£600	—
S below (Sydney Mint)					
1911	252,000	—	—	£70	£110
1912	278,000	—	—	£70	£110
1914	322,000	—	—	£70	£110
1915	892,000	—	—	£70	£110
1916	448,000	—	—	£70	£110
SA below (Pretoria Mint)					
1923 Proof only	655	—	—	—	£350
1925	946,615	—	—	£40	£75
1926	806,540	—	—	£40	£75

GEORGE VI (1937–52)

DATE		F	VF	EF	UNC
1937 Proof only	5,501	—	—	—	£165

Later issues are included in the Decimal section.

CROWNS

DATE	F	VF	EF	UNC
OLIVER CROMWELL				
1658 8 over 7 (always)	£1250	£2200	£3250	—
1658 Dutch Copy			Extremely rare	
1658 Patterns. In Various Metals			Extremely rare	
CHARLES II (1660–85)				
1662 First bust, rose (2 varieties)	£75	£300	£2250	—
1662 — no rose (2 varieties)	£75	£300	£2250	—
1663 —	£75	£300	£2250	—
1664 Second bust	£75	£300	£2500	—
1665 —	£175	£550	—	—
*1666 —	£100	£375	£2600	—
1666 — error RE.X for REX			Extremely rare	
1666 — Elephant below bust	£200	£600	£3500	—
1667 —	£75	£300	£2200	—
1668/7 — 8 over 7	£80	£275	—	—
1668 —	£75	£300	£2200	—
1669/8 — 9 over 8	£175	—	—	—
1669 —	£125	£300	£2500	—
1670/69 — 70 over 69	£100	£400	—	—
1670 —	£75	£300	£2000	—
1671	£75	£300	£2000	—
1671 Third bust	£75	£300	£2000	—
1672 —	£75	£300	£2000	—
1673 —	£75	£300	£2000	—
1674 —			Extremely rare	
1675 —	£225	—	—	—
1675/3 —	£225	£750	—	—
1676 —	£70	£250	£2000	—
1677 —	£75	£250	£2000	—
1677/6 — 7 over 6	£100	£400	—	—
1678/7 —	£80	£325	—	—
1678/7 — 8 over 7	£100	—	—	—
1679 —	£75	£275	£2000	—
1679 Fourth bust	£75	£275	£2000	—
1680 Third bust	£70	£275	£2000	—
1680/79 — 80 over 79	£100	—	—	—
1680 Fourth bust	£70	£280	£2000	—
1680/79 — 80 over 79	£100	—	—	—
1681 —	£70	£280	£2000	—
1681 — Elephant & Castle below bust	£1000	£2750	—	—
1682/1 —	£75	£300	£2000	—
1682 — edge error QVRRTO for QVARTO	£175	—	—	—
1683 —	£100	£350	£2000	—
1684 —	£125	£650	—	—
JAMES II (1685–88)				
1686 First bust	£110	£350	£1800	—
1686 — No stops on obv	£150	£500	—	—
1687 Second bust	£100	£400	£1800	—
1688/7 — 8 over 7	£100	£350	—	—
*1688 —	£100	£400	£1800	—
WILLIAM AND MARY (1688–94)				
1691	£200	£550	£2250	—
1692	£200	£550	£2250	—
1692 2 over upside down 2	£200	£550	£2250	—

WILLIAM III (1694–1702)

DATE	F	VF	EF	UNC
1695 First bust	£60	£175	£750	—
1696 — no stops on obv.	£150	—	—	—
1996 — no stops obv./rev.	£250	—	—	—
1696 — GEI for DEI	£125	£500	—	—
1696 —	£60	£175	£750	—
1696 Second bust				Unique
1696 Third bust	£60	£175	£750	—
1697 —	£250	£750	£1500	—
1700 Third bust variety edge year DUODECIMO	£80	£250	£800	—
1700 — edge year DUODECIMO TERTIO	£80	£250	£800	—

ANNE (1702–14)

DATE	F	VF	EF	UNC
1703 First bust, VIGO	£175	£550	£2000	—
1705 — Plumes in angles on rev.	£300	£750	£2750	—
1706 — Roses & Plumes in angles on rev.	£140	£350	£1000	—
1707 — —	£140	£350	£1100	—
1707 Second bust, E below	£85	£300	£750	—
1707 — Plain	£85	£275	£800	—
1708 — E below	£85	£275	£800	—
1708/7 — 8 over 7	£110	£400	—	—
1708 — Plain	£85	£275	£800	—
1708 — — error BR for BRI		Extremely rare		
1708 — Plumes in angles on rev.	£125	£400	£1100	—
*1713 Third bust, Roses & Plumes in angles on rev.	£150	£440	£1150	—

GEORGE I (1714–27)

DATE	F	VF	EF	UNC
1716	£240	£475	£1750	—
1718 8 over 6	£240	£475	£2000	—
1720 20 over 18	£240	£475	£2000	—
1723 SSC in angles on rev. (South Sea Co.)	£280	£475	£1500	—
1726	£250	£550	£2500	—

GEORGE II (1727–60)

DATE	F	VF	EF	UNC
1732 Young head, Plain, Proof	—	—	£3000	
1732 — Roses & Plumes in angles on rev .	£150	£375	£950	—
1734 — —	£150	£375	£950	—
1735 — —	£150	£375	£925	—
1736 — —	£165	£400	£1000	—
1739 — Roses in angles on rev	£150	£350	£950	—
1741 — —	£150	£350	£950	—
1743 Old head, Roses in angles on rev	£130	£325	£750	—
*1746 — — LIMA below bust	£135	£325	£750	—
1746 — Plain, Proof	—	—	£1750	—
1750 — —	£200	£400	£1000	—
1751 — —	£225	£475	£1200	—

GEORGE III (1760–1820)

DATE	F	VF	EF	UNC
Dollar with oval counterstamp	£90	£200	£425	—
Dollar with octagonal counterstamp	£100	£200	£475	—
1804 Bank of England Dollar, Britannia rev.	£90	£140	£300	—
1818 LVIII	£25	£70	£240	£475
1818 LIX	£25	£70	£240	£475
1819 LIX	£25	£70	£240	£475
1819 LIX 9 over 8	£25	£90	£250	—
1819 no stops on edge	£50	£120	£250	£550
1819 LX	£25	£70	£250	£475
1820 LX	£25	£70	£240	£475
1820 LX 20 over 19	£30	£75	£250	—

DATE	MINTAGE	F	VF	EF	UNC
GEORGE IV (1820–30)					
1821 First bust, St George rev. SECUNDO on edge	437,976	£22	£80	£300	£675
1821 —— Proof	*Incl. above*	—	—	—	£2000
1821 —— Proof TERTIO (error edge)	*Incl above*	—	—	—	£3000
1822 —— SECUNDO	124,929	£22	£80	£350	£900
1822 —— TERTIO	*Incl above*	£22	£80	£340	£800
1823 —— Proof only					Extremely rare
1826 Second bust, shield rev, SEPTIMO Proof only		—	—	£1750	£2500
WILLIAM IV (1830–37)					
					FDC
1831 Proof only W.W. on truncation		—	—		£4500
1831 Proof only W. WYON on truncation		—	—		£4500
1834 Proof only		—	—	—	—
VICTORIA (1837–1901)					
YOUNG HEAD ISSUES					
1839 Proof only	—	—	—	—	£2800
1844 Star stops on edge	94,248	£32	£150	£650	£1850
1844 Cinquefoil stops on edge	*incl. above*	£30	£150	£650	£1850
1845 Star stops on edge	159,192	£32	£150	£650	£1950
1845 Cinquefoil stops on edge	*incl. above*	£30	£150	£650	£1950
1847	140,976	£40	£160	£650	£2200
1847 "Gothic" Proof only UNDECIMO edge	8,000	£325	£650	£900	£1750
1847 Plain edge, Proof only	—	—	—	£1000	£1800
1853 D. SEPTIMO edge, Proof only	460	—	—	—	£5000
1853 Plain edge, Proof only	—	—	—	—	£7000
JUBILEE HEAD ISSUES					
*1887	173,581	£10	£22	£45	£70
1887 Proof	1,084	—	—	—	£300
1888 Narrow date	131,899	£12	£25	£60	£125
1888 Wide date		£15	£30	£80	£140
1889	1,807,224	£10	£20	£40	£75
1890	997,862	£12	£25	£60	£120
1891	556,394	£12	£25	£60	£120
1892	451,334	£12	£25	£70	£140
OLD HEAD ISSUES (Regnal date on edge in Roman numerals)					
1893 LVI	497,845	£12	£25	£100	£225
1893 LVII	*incl. above*	£14	£35	£175	£375
1893 Proof	1,312	—	—	—	£350
1894 LVII	144,906	£14	£45	£140	£375
1894 LVIII	*incl. above*	£14	£45	£140	£375
1895 LVIII	252,862	£12	£35	£120	£300
1895 LIX	*incl. above*	£12	£35	£120	£300
1896 LIX	317,599	£14	£35	£130	£375
1896 LX	*incl. above*	£12	£35	£120	£300
1897 LX	262,118	£12	£35	£120	£300
1897 LXI	*incl. above*	£12	£35	£120	£300
1898 LXI	166,150	£14	£40	£120	£350
1898 LXII	*incl. above*	£12	£35	£120	£300
1899 LXII	166,300	£12	£35	£120	£300
1899 LXIII	*incl. above*	£12	£35	£120	£300
1900 LXIII	353,356	£12	£35	£120	£300
1900 LXIV	*incl. above*	£12	£35	£120	£300
EDWARD VII (1901–10)					
1902	256,020	£22	£45	£85	£135
1902 "Matt Proof"	15,123	—	—	—	£125

Victoria, young head

Victoria, Jubilee head

GEORGE V (1910–36)

DATE	MINTAGE	F	VF	EF	UNC
1927 Proof only	15,030	—	£55	£90	£145
1928	9,034	£50	£75	£125	£225
1929	4,994	£50	£75	£125	£200
1930	4,847	£50	£75	£125	£220
1931	4,056	£50	£75	£125	£190
1932	2,395	£80	£175	£270	£450
1933	7,132	£50	£75	£125	£190
*1934	932	£325	£600	£1100	£1750
1935 Jubilee issue	714,769	£8	£12	£16	£25
1935 Specimen in box	—	—	—	—	£35
1935 Proof. Raised Edge inscription	2,500	—	—	£150	£200
1936	2,473	£80	£180	£240	£450

GEORGE VI (1936–52)

DATE	MINTAGE	F	VF	EF	UNC
1937 Coronation	418,699	£9	£14	£20	£30
1937 Proof	26,402	—	—	—	£30
1951 Festival of Britain, Proof-like	1,983,540	—	—	£3	£5

ELIZABETH II (1952–)

Pre-Decimal issues (Five Shillings)

DATE	MINTAGE	F	VF	EF	UNC
*1953	5,962,621	—	—	£3	£6
1953 Proof	40,000	—	—	—	£15
1960	1,024,038	—	—	£3	£6
1960 Polished dies	70,000	—	—	—	£8
1965 Churchill	19,640,000	—	—	—	£1

Later issues are listed in the Decimal section.

DOUBLE FLORINS

VICTORIA (1837–1901)

DATE	MINTAGE	F	VF	EF	UNC
1887 Roman I	483,347	£10	£18	£40	£65
1887 Roman I Proof	*incl. above*	—	—	—	£250
1887 Arabic 1	*incl. above*	£10	£18	£40	£65
1887 Arabic 1 Proof	*incl. above*	—	—	—	£200
1888	243,340	£12	£30	£75	£85
1888 Second I in VICTORIA an inverted 1	*incl. above*	£20	£35	£75	£250
1889	1,185,111	£15	£23	£40	£75
1889 inverted 1	*incl. above*	£20	£35	£75	£275
1890	782,146	£12	£33	£55	£105

Patterns were also produced in 1911, 1914 and 1950 and are all extremely rare.

HALFCROWNS

OLIVER CROMWELL

DATE	MINTAGE	F	VF	EF	UNC
1656				Extremely rare	
1658		£600	£1000	£1800	—
1658 Proof in Gold				Extremely rare	

CHARLES II (1660–1685)

DATE	MINTAGE	F	VF	EF	UNC
1663 First bust		£70	£325	£1500	—
1663 — no stops on obv.		£100	£400	—	—
1664 Second bust		£75	£400	£1850	—
1666 Third bust		£500	—	—	—
1666 — Elephant		£400	£1000	£4000	—
1667/4 — 7 over 4				Extremely rare	
1668/4 — 8 over 4		£75	—	—	—
1669 —		£175	£650	—	—
1669/4 — 9 over 4		£150	£500	—	—
1670 —		£60	£275	£1500	—
1670 — MRG for MAG		£300	£900	—	—
1671 —		£60	£250	£1800	—
1671/0 — 1 over 0		£75	£350	£1800	—
1672 —		£60	£300	£1800	—
1672 Fourth bust		£70	£300	£2000	—
1673 —		£60	£200	£1500	—
1673 — Plumes both sides				Extremely rare	
1673 — Plume below bust		£1000	—	—	—
1674 —		£80	£275	—	—
1675 —		£70	£225	£1200	—
1676 —		£70	£200	£1000	—
1676 — inverted 1 in date		£75	£225	£1200	—
1677 —		£60	£200	£1000	—
1678 —		£140	£500	—	—
1679 — GRATTA error				Extremely rare	
1679 —		£60	£200	£1000	—
1680 —		£110	£450	—	—
1681/0 — 1 over 0		£120	—	—	—
1681 —		£85	£200	£1000	—
1681 — Elephant & Castle		£1200	—	—	—
1682 —		£80	£250	£2000	—
1683 —		£80	£200	£2000	—
1683 — Plume below bust				Extremely rare	
1684/3 — 4 over 3		£125	£450	£1800	—

JAMES II (1685–1688)

DATE	MINTAGE	F	VF	EF	UNC
1685 First bust		£85	£300	£1150	—
1686 —		£85	£300	£1100	—
1686/5 — 6 over 5		£100	£400	—	—
1686 — V over S		£175	£450	—	—
1687 —		£100	£350	£1000	—
1687/6 — 7 over 6		£125	£400	—	—
1687 Second bust		£100	£275	£1000	—
1688 —		£100	£275	£1000	—

WILLIAM AND MARY (1688–1694)

DATE	MINTAGE	F	VF	EF	UNC
1689 First busts; first shield		£60	£175	£750	—
1689 — — no pearls in crown		£60	£175	£750	—
1689 — — FRA for FR		£100	£200	£650	—
1689 — — No stop on obv		£60	£175	£700	—
1689 — Second shield		£60	£175	£750	—

DATE	MINTAGE	F	VF	EF	UNC
1689 — — no pearls in crown		£60	£275	£800	—
1690 — —		£90	£400	£1200	—
1690 — — error GRETIA for GRATIA		£150	£500	£1800	—
1691 Second busts		—	£275	—	—
1692 —		£75	£275	£1000	—
1693 —		£75	£175	£1000	—
1693 — 3 over inverted 3		£100	£400	—	—

WILLIAM III (1694–1702)

DATE	MINTAGE	F	VF	EF	UNC
1696 First bust, large shields, early harp		£35	£100	£450	—
1696 — — — B (Bristol) below bust		£50	£170	£550	—
1696 — — — C (Chester)		£40	£175	£550	—
1696 — — — E (Exeter)		£40	£175	£600	—
1696 — — — N (Norwich)		£65	£250	—	—
1696 — — — y (York)		£45	£200	£550	—
1696 — — — — Scottish arms at date				Extremely rare	
1696 — — ordinary harp		£65	£200	—	—
1696 — — — C		£70	£250	—	—
1696 — — — E		£70	£250	—	—
1696 — — — N		£100	£500	—	—
1696 — Small shields, ordinary harp		£35	£150	£400	—
1696 — — — B		£50	£200	£650	—
1696 — — — C		£50	£225	£700	—
1696 — — — E		£70	£250	—	—
1696 — — — N		£60	£250	£700	—
1696 — — — y		£60	£250	£700	—
1696 Second bust				Only one known	
1697 First bust, large shields, ordinary harp		£45	£170	£400	—
1697 — — — GRR for GRA				Extremely rare	
1697 — — — B		£45	£200	£500	—
1697 — — — C		£50	£250	£550	
1697 — — — E		£55	£225	£550	—
1697 — — — N		£50	£225	£550	—
1697 — — — y		£50	£225	£550	—
1698 — —		£50	£150	£300	—
1698/7 — — 8 over 7				Extremely rare	
1699 — —		£75	£200	£600	—
1699 — — Scottish arms at date				Extremely rare	
1700 — —		£55	£170	£450	—
1701 — —		£60	£200	£550	—
1701 — — No stops on rev		£80	£220	—	—
1701 — — Elephant & Castle below				Fair £1000	
1701 — — Plumes in angles on rev.		£100	£400	£950	—

ANNE (1702–1714)

DATE	MINTAGE	F	VF	EF	UNC
1703 Plain (pre-Union)		£200	£850	—	—
1703 VIGO below bust		£70	£200	£700	—
1704 Plumes in angles on rev.		£100	£350	£850	—
1705 —		£80	£250	£750	—
1706 Roses & Plumes in angles on rev.		£55	£200	£500	—
*1707 —		£60	£175	£450	—
1707 Plain (post-Union)		£45	£125	£400	—
1707 E below bust		£45	£125	£425	—
1707 — SEPTIMO edge				Extremely rare	
1708 Plain		£45	£150	£400	—
1708 E below bust		£40	£150	£425	—
1708 Plumes in angles on rev.		£50	£200	£525	—
1709 Plain		£40	£150	£400	—
1709 E below bust		£100	£500	—	—
1710 Roses & Plumes in angles on rev.		£50	£160	£500	—
1712 —		£50	£160	£500	—
1713 Plain		£50	£160	£500	—
1713 Roses & Plumes in angles on rev.		£50	£160	£500	—
1714 —		£50	£160	£500	—
1714/3 4 over 3		£100	£300	—	—

DATE	MINTAGE	F	VF	EF	UNC

GEORGE I (1714–1727)

1715 Roses & Plumes in angles on rev.		£150	£400	£1000	—
1715 Plain edge				Extremely rare	
1717 —		£150	£400	£1000	—
*1720 —		£150	£400	£1000	—
1720/17 20 over 17		£150	£425	—	—
1723 SSC in angles on rev.		£150	£4000	£900	—
1726 Small Roses & Plumes in angles on rev..		£1250	£3250	—	—

GEORGE II (1727–1760)

1731 Young head, Plain, proof only		—	—	£1850	—
1731 — Roses & Plumes in angles on rev.		£65	£200	£600	—
1732 — —		£65	£200	£600	—
1734 — —		£65	£200	£600	—
1735 — —		£65	£200	£600	—
1736 — —		£65	£200	£600	—
1739 — Roses in angles on rev.		£55	£175	£550	—
1741/39 — — 41 over 39		£100	£200	—	—
1741 — —		£55	£175	£550	—
1743 Old head, Roses in angles on rev.		£50	£100	£400	—
1745 — —		£50	£100	£400	—
1745 — LIMA below bust		£55	£100	£250	—
1746 — —		£55	£100	£250	—
1746/5 — — 6 over 5		£55	£110	£300	—
1746 — Plain, Proof		—	—	£800	—
1750 — —		£80	£350	£650	—
1751 — —		£90	£300	£850	—

GEORGE III (1760–1820)

1816 "Bull head"	—	£12	£45	£140	£275
1817 —	8,092,656	£12	£45	£140	£275
1817 "Small head"	*incl. above*	£12	£45	£140	£275
1818 —	2,905,056	£12	£45	£140	£275
1819/8 — 9 over 8	*incl. above*			Extremely rare	
1819 —	4,790,016	£12	£45	£140	£275
1820 —	2,396,592	£20	£65	£200	£450

GEORGE IV (1820–30)

1820 First bust, first reverse	*incl. above*	£15	£40	£150	£280
1821 — —	1,435,104	£15	£40	£150	£280
1821 — — Proof	*incl. above*	—	—	—	£650
1823 — —	2,003,760	£500	£800	£2500	—
1823 — Second reverse	*incl. above*	£15	£45	£150	£300
1824 — —	465,696	£20	£60	£160	£400
1824 Second bust, third reverse .	*incl. above*			Extremely rare	
*1825 — —	2,258,784	£15	£38	£125	£275
1826 — —	2,189,088	£15	£38	£125	£275
1826 — — Proof	*incl. above*	—	—	£325	£550
1828 — —	49,890	£40	£80	£225	£550
1829 — —	508,464	£45	£85	£200	£425

WILLIAM IV (1830–37)

1831	—			Extremely rare	
1831 Proof (W.W. in script & block)	—	—	—	—	£700
1834 W.W. in block	993,168	£16	£55	£175	£350
1834 W.W. in script	*incl. above*	£16	£50	£160	£300
1835	281,952	£16	£55	£175	£325
*1836	1,588,752	£16	£45	£160	£325
1836/5 6 over 5	*incl. above*	£25	£70	£300	—
1837	150,526	£16	£60	£200	£450

DATE	MINTAGE	F	VF	EF	UNC
VICTORIA (1837–1901)					
YOUNG HEAD ISSUES					
1839 (two varieties)	—	£400	£800	£2000	—
1839 Proof	—	—	—	—	£1000
1840	386,496	£30	£170	£250	£400
1841	42,768	£300	£600	£1500	£2200
1842	486,288	£30	£80	£240	£400
1843	454,608	£70	£160	£700	£1100
*1844	1,999,008	£20	£50	£160	£400
1845	2,231,856	£20	£50	£160	£400
1846	1,539,668	£25	£60	£200	£450
1848 Plain 8	367,488	£50	£120	£450	£850
1848/6	*incl. above*	£35	£100	£300	£700
1849	261,360	£40	£80	£300	£550
1849 Small date	*incl. above*	£50	£100	£400	£650
1850	484,613	£30	£70	£250	£425
1853 Proof only	—	—	—	—	£1800
1874	2,188,599	£15	£35	£100	£200
1875	1,113,483	£15	£35	£100	£200
1876	633,221	£15	£35	£100	£200
1876/5 6 over 5	*incl. above*	£20	£50	£175	£375
1877	447,059	£15	£35	£100	£200
1878	1,466,323	£15	£35	£100	£200
1879	901,356	£20	£40	£140	£275
1880	1,346,350	£15	£35	£90	£175
1881	2,301,495	£15	£35	£90	£175
1882	808,227	£15	£35	£90	£175
1883	2,982,779	£15	£35	£90	£175
1884	1,569,175	£15	£35	£90	£175
1885	1,628,438	£15	£35	£90	£175
1886	891,767	£15	£35	£90	£175
1887	1,438,046	£15	£35	£90	£175
JUBILEE HEAD ISSUES					
1887	*incl. above*	£5	£8	£16	£35
1887 Proof	1,084	—	—	—	£125
1888	1,428,787	£8	£15	£35	£65
1889	4,811,954	£8	£14	£35	£65
1890	3,228,111	£8	£14	£45	£70
1891	2,284,632	£8	£15	£45	£80
1892	1,710,946	£8	£14	£45	£80
OLD HEAD ISSUES					
1893	1,792,600	£6	£14	£40	£75
1893 Proof	1,312	—	—	—	£135
1894	1,524,960	£10	£24	£55	£100
1895	1,772,662	£8	£18	£50	£90
1896	2,148,505	£7	£15	£45	£80
1897	1,678,643	£7	£15	£40	£80
1898	1,870,055	£7	£15	£40	£80
1899	2,865,872	£7	£15	£40	£80
1900	4,479,128	£7	£15	£40	£80
1901	1,516,570	£7	£15	£40	£80
EDWARD VII (1901–10)					
1902	1,316,008	£6	£18	£50	£70
1902 "Matt Proof"	15,123	—	—	—	£60
*1903	274,840	£50	£140	£450	£1000
1904	709,652	£45	£125	£350	£650
1905	166,008	£160	£400	£850	£1500
1906	2,886,206	£8	£30	£100	£2500
1907	3,693,930	£8	£30	£100	£250
1908	1,758,889	£12	£40	£175	£450
1909	3,051,592	£8	£30	£110	£350
1910	2,557,685	£8	£25	£70	£175
GEORGE V (1910–36)					
First issue					
1911	2,914,573	£6	£18	£35	£75
1911 Proof	6,007	—	—	—	£75
1912	4,700,789	£6	£12	£35	£80

George V first type reverse

DATE	MINTAGE	F	VF	EF	UNC
1913	4,090,169	£6	£12	£40	£90
1914	18,333,003	£3	£8	£25	£45
1915	32,433,066	£3	£8	£20	£40
1916	29,530,020	£3	£8	£20	£40
1917	11,172,052	£3	£8	£22	£45
1918	29,079,592	£3	£8	£20	£40
1919	10,266,737	£4	£10	£25	£60
***Second issue**—debased silver*					
1920	17,982,077	£2	£7	£15	£40
1921	23,677,889	£2	£7	£16	£45
1922	16,396,724	£2	£7	£16	£45
1923	26,308,526	£6	£7	£15	£30
1924	5,866,294	£6	£12	£40	£90
1925	1,413,461	£8	£25	£110	£275
1926	4,473,516	£4	£14	£35	£80
***Third issue** —Modified effigy*					
1926	*incl. above*	£4	£10	£30	£75
1927	6,837,872	£3	£8	£24	£45
***Fourth issue**—New shield reverse*					
1927 Proof	15,000	—	—	—	£35
1928	18,762,727	£2	£5	£12	£25
1929	17,632,636	£2	£5	£12	£25
1930	809,051	£5	£35	£100	£250
1931	11,264,468	£2	£5	£15	£25
1932	4,793,643	£2	£5	£18	£60
1933	10,311,494	£2	£5	£15	£35
1934	2,422,399	£3	£8	£35	£80
1935	7,022,216	£2	£5	£12	£16
*1936	7,039,423	£2	£5	£10	£16

George V, fourth issue, new sh reverse

GEORGE VI (1936–52)

DATE	MINTAGE	F	VF	EF	UNC
1937	9,106,440	—	£2	£4	£10
1937 Proof	26,402	—	—	—	£12
1938	6,426,478	£1	£3	£10	£17
1939	15,478,635	—	£1	£3	£8
1940	17,948,439	—	£1	£3	£6
1941	15,773,984	—	£1	£3	£6
1942	31,220,090	—	£1	£3	£6
1943	15,462,875	—	£1	£3	£6
*1944	15,255,165	—	£1	£3	£6
1945	19,849,242	—	£1	£3	£6
1946	22,724,873	—	£1	£3	£6
Cupro-nickel					
1947	21,911,484	—	£1	£2	£4
1948	71,164,703	—	£1	£2	£4
1949	28,272,512	—	£1	£2	£6
1950	28,335,500	—	£1	£2	£6
1950 Proof	17,513	—	£1	£2	£9
1951	9,003,520	—	£1	£2	£6
1951 Proof	20,000	—	—	—	£9
1952			Only one known		

ELIZABETH II (1952–)

DATE	MINTAGE	F	VF	EF	UNC
1953	4,333,214	—	—	£1	£3
1953 Proof	40,000	—	—	—	£5
1954	11,614,953	—	£1	£3	£15
1955	23,628,726	—	—	£1	£4
1956	33,934,909	—	—	£1	£4
1957	34,200,563	—	—	£1	£4
1958	15,745,668	—	£1	£3	£16
1959	9,028,844	—	£1	£5	£18
1960	19,929,191	—	—	£1	£2
1961	25,887,897	—	—	—	£1
1961 Polished dies	*incl. above*	—	—	£1	£2
1962	24,013,312	—	—	—	£1
1963	17,625,200	—	—	—	£1
1964	5,973,600	—	—	—	£1
1965	9,778,440	—	—	—	£1
1966	13,375,200	—	—	—	£1
1967	33,058,400	—	—	—	—

FLORINS

)ATE	MINTAGE	F	VF	EF	UNC

VICTORIA (1837–1901)

'OUNG (CROWNED) HEAD ISSUES

Godless" type (without D.G.—"Dei Gratia")					
848 "Godless" Pattern only plain edge	—			Very rare	
848 "Godless" Pattern only milled edge	—			Extremely rare	
1849	413,820	£10	£30	£80	£175
Gothic" type i.e. date in Roman numerals in obverse legend					
brit." in legend. No die no.					
851 mdcccli Proof	1,540			Extremely rare	
852 mdccclii	1,014,552	£15	£40	£120	£250
853 mdcccliii	3,919,950	£15	£40	£120	£250
853 — Proof	*incl. above*	—	—	—	£1200
854 mdcccliv	550,413	£500	—	—	—
855 mdccclv	831,017	£15	£40	£120	£250
856 mdccclvi	2,201,760	£15	£40	£120	£250
857 mdccclvii	1,671,120	£15	£40	£120	£250
858 mdccclviii	2,239,380	£15	£40	£120	£250
859 mdccclix	2,568,060	£15	£40	£120	£250
860 mdccclx	1,475,100	£18	£45	£150	£350
862 mdccclxii	594,000	£70	£180	£600	£1200
863 mdccclxiii	938,520	£200	£400	£1200	£1800
brit" in legend. Die no. below bust					
864 mdccclxiv	1,861,200	£15	£40	£120	£250
864 Gothic Piedfort flan	*incl. above*			Extremely rare	
865 mdccclxv	1,580,044	£15	£40	£120	£250
866 mdccclxvi	914,760	£15	£40	£120	£250
1867 mdccclxvii	423,720	£25	£70	£250	£500
867—only 42 arcs in border	*incl. above*			Extremely rare	
'britt" in legend. Die no. below bust					
1868 mdccclxviii	896,940	£15	£40	£120	£250
1869 mdccclxix	297,000	£20	£45	£160	£325
1870 mdccclxx	1,080,648	£15	£38	£100	£210
1871 mdccclxxi	3,425,605	£15	£38	£100	£210
1872 mdccclxxii	7,199,690	£12	£38	£100	£210
1873 mdccclxxiii	5,921,839	£12	£38	£100	£210
1874 mdccclxxiv	1,642,630	£12	£38	£100	£175
1874 — iv over iii in date	incl. above	£25	£60	£140	£220
1875 mdccclxxv	1,117,030	£12	£38	£100	£210
1876 mdccclxxvi	580,034	£12	£38	£100	£225
1877 mdccclxxvii	682,292	£12	£38	£100	£210
1877 — 48 arcs in border no W.W.	*incl. above*	£15	£45	£125	£300
1877 — 42 arcs	*incl. above*	£15	£45	£125	£275
1877 — — no die number	*incl. above*			Extremely rare	
1878 mdccclxxviii with die number	1,786,680	£14	£40	£140	£250
1879 mdcccixxix no die no	1,512,247			Extremely rare	
1879 — 48 arcs in border	*incl. above*	£12	£35	£140	£250
1879 — no die number	*incl. above*			Extremely rare	
1879 — 38 arcs, no W.W..	*incl. above*	£12	£45	£140	£250
1880 mdccclxxx Younger portrait	—			Extremely rare	
1880 — 34 arcs, Older portrait	2,167,170	£12	£40	£100	£210
1881 mdccclxxxi — —	2,570,337	£12	£40	£100	£210
1881 — xxΓi broken puncheon	*incl. above*	£20	£60	£140	£220
1883 mdccclxxxiii — —	3,555,667	£12	£40	£100	£210
1884 mdccclxxxiv — —	1,447,379	£12	£40	£100	£210
1885 mdccclxxxv — —	1,758,210	£12	£40	£100	£210
1886 mdccclxxxvi — —	591,773	£12	£40	£90	£210
1887 mdccclxxxvii — —	1,776,903	£18	£65	£200	£400
1887 — 46 arcs	*incl. above*	£20	£70	£225	£425

"Godless" florin

"Gothic" florin

DATE	MINTAGE	F	VF	EF	UNC
JUBILEE HEAD ISSUES					
1887	*incl. above*	£4	£8	£18	£32
1887 Proof	1,084	—	—	—	£100
1888	1,547,540	£4	£8	£30	£60
1889	2,973,561	£4	£10	£30	£60
1890	1,684,737	£7	£20	£60	£150
1891	836,438	£12	£40	£100	£240
1892	283,401	£20	£55	£170	£400
VICTORIA—OLD HEAD ISSUES					
1893	1,666,103	£5	£14	£32	£75
1893 Proof	1,312	—	—	—	£100
1894	1,952,842	£8	£22	£55	£120
1895	2,182,968	£7	£20	£55	£100
1896	2,944,416	£6	£16	£40	£80
1897	1,699,921	£6	£16	£40	£80
1898	3,061,343	£6	£16	£40	£80
1899	3,966,953	£6	£16	£40	£80
*1900	5,528,630	£6	£16	£40	£80
1901	2,648,870	£6	£16	£40	£80

EDWARD VII (1901–10)

*1902	2,189,575	£6	£14	£35	£65
1902 "Matt Proof"	15,123	—	—	—	£50
1903	1,995,298	£10	£30	£75	£240
1904	2,769,932	£10	£30	£75	£250
1905	1,187,596	£30	£75	£325	£750
1906	6,910,128	£9	£30	£80	£200
1907	5,947,895	£11	£30	£80	£220
1908	3,280,010	£10	£40	£140	£400
1909	3,482,829	£9	£35	£140	£350
1910	5,650,713	£7	£24	£65	£130

GEORGE V (1910–36)

First issue					
1911	5,951,284	£3	£8	£25	£60
1911 Proof	6,007	—	—	—	£60
1912	8,571,731	£3	£11	£30	£70
1913	4,545,278	£5	£16	£35	£80
1914	21,252,701	£3	£14	£22	£40
1915	12,367,939	£3	£14	£22	£40
1916	21,064,337	£3	£14	£22	£40
1917	11,181,617	£3	£14	£25	£50
1918	29,211,792	£3	£14	£22	£40
1919	9,469,292	£3	£15	£30	£65
***Second issue** —debased silver*					
1920	15,387,833	£2	£12	£32	£55
1921	34,863,895	£2	£12	£30	£45
1922	23,861,044	£2	£12	£30	£45
1923	21,546,533	£2	£10	£25	£45
1924	4,582,372	£4	£14	£50	£100
1925	1,404,136	£10	£32	£125	£275
1926	5,125,410	£5	£15	£40	£80
***Fourth issue**—new reverse*					
1927 Proof only	101,497	—	—	—	£35
1928	11,087,186	£2	£4	£12	£25
1929	16,397,279	£2	£4	£12	£25
1930	5,753,568	£2	£5	£15	£40
1931	6,556,331	£2	£5	£12	£30
1932	717,041	£7	£16	£100	£225
1933	8,685,303	£2	£5	£14	£32
1935	7,540,546	£2	£5	£10	£20
*1936	9,897,448	£2	£4	£9	£16

GEORGE VI (1936–52)

ATE	MINTAGE	F	VF	EF	UNC
937	13,006,781	—	£1	£3	£6
937 Proof	26,402	—	—	—	£8
938	7,909,388	£1	£2	£8	£16
939	20,850,607	£1	£2	£3	£5
940	18,700,338	£1	£2	£3	£5
941	24,451,079	£1	£2	£3	£5
942	39,895,243	£1	£2	£3	£5
943	26,711,987	£1	£2	£3	£5
1944	27,560,005	£1	£2	£3	£5
945	25,858,049	£1	£2	£3	£5
946	22,300,254	£1	£2	£3	£5
947	22,910,085	—	—	£1	£3
948	67,553,636	—	—	£1	£3
949	28,614,939	—	—	£1	£5
950	24,357,490	—	—	£2	£7
950 Proof	17,513	—	—	£1	£8
951	27,411,747	—	—	£2	£8
951 Proof	20,000	—	—	—	£8

ELIZABETH II (1952–)

ATE	MINTAGE	F	VF	EF	UNC
953	11,958,710	—	—	—	£2
953 Proof	40,000	—	—	—	£5
954	13,085,422	—	—	£5	£15
955	25,887,253	—	—	£1	£3
956	47,824,500	—	—	£1	£3
957	33,071,282	—	—	£4	£15
958	9,564,580	—	—	£3	£14
959	14,080,319	—	—	£4	£15
960	13,831,782	—	—	£1	£3
961	37,735,315	—	—	£1	£2
962	35,147,903	—	—	£1	£2
963	26,471,000	—	—	£1	£2
964	16,539,000	—	—	£1	£2
965	48,163,000	—	—	—	£1.50
966	83,999,000	—	—	—	£1.50
967	39,718,000	—	—	—	£1.50

SHILLINGS

OLIVER CROMWELL

658	£358	£550	£1000	—
658 Dutch Copy			Extremely rare	

CHARLES II (1660–85)

1663 First bust	£50	£130	£450	—
663 — GARTIA error			Extremely rare	
663 — Irish & Scottish shields transposed	£125	£450	—	—
666 — Elephant below bust	£200	£550	£1500	—
666 "Guinea" head, elephant	£500	£1000	—	—
666 Second bust			Extremely rare	
668 —	£50	£130	£425	—
668/7 — 8 over 7	£55	£125	—	—
668 Second bust	£50	£130	£425	—
669/6 First bust variety			Extremely rare	
669			Extremely rare	
669 Second bust			Extremely rare	
670 —	£65	£220	£600	—
671 —	£80	£250	£750	—
671 — Plume below, plume in centre rev.	£200	£400	£1250	—
672 —	£60	£150	£500	—
673 —	£75	£250	£675	—

DATE	F	VF	EF	UNC
1673 — Plume below, plume in centre rev.	£200	£400	£1250	—
1673/2 — 3 over 2	£100	£350	—	—
1674/3 — 4 over 3	£100	£350	—	—
1674 —	£75	£250	£675	—
1674 — Plume below bust, plume in centre rev.	£200	£400	£1250	—
1674 — Plume rev. only	£200	£400	£1250	—
1674 Third bust	£225	£575	—	—
1675 Second bust	£90	£275	—	—
1675/4 — 5 over 4	£140	£450	—	—
1675 — Plume below bust, plume in centre rev.	£200	£400	£1250	—
1675 Third bust	£175	£450	—	—
1675/3 — 5 over 3	£200	£500	—	—
1676 Second bust	£60	£160	£425	—
1676/5 — 6 over 5	£80	£270	—	—
1676 — Plume below bust, plume in centre rev.	£200	£400	£1450	—
1677 —	£65	£160	£500	—
1677 — Plume below bust	£200	£450	£1400	—
1678 —	£70	£220	£650	—
1678/7 — 8 over 7	£80	£300	—	—
1679 —	£60	£170	£500	—
1679 — Plume below bust, plume in centre rev.	£200	£450	£1400	—
1679 — Plume below bust	£200	£450	£1400	—
1679 — 9 over 7	£80	£300	—	—
1680 —	£225	—	—	—
1680 — Plume below bust, plume in centre rev.	£200	£475	£1500	—
1680/79 — — 80 over 79	£300	£800	—	—
1681 —	£80	£275	£800	—
1681 — — Elephant & Castle	£800	—	—	—
1681 — 1 over 0	£80	£275	£800	—
1681/0 Elephant & Castle below bust	£800	£275	£800	—
1682/1 — 2 over 1	£200	£600	—	
1682 —	£200	£600	—	
1683 —	£700	—	—	—
1683 Fourth bust	£150	£375	£900	—
1684 —	£120	£335	£850	—

William III First bust

William III Second bust

JAMES II (1685–88)

1685	£80	£210	£600	—
1685 Plume in centre rev. rev		Extremely rare		
1685 No stops on rev.	£125	£400	—	—
1686	£80	£225	£600	—
1686/5 6 over 5	£80	£225	£600	—
1687	£85	£240	£600	—
1687/6 7 over 6	£85	£240	£600	—
1688	£85	£240	£550	—
1688/7 last 8 over 7	£90	£250	—	—

William III Third bust

WILLIAM & MARY (1688–94)

1692	£85	£250	£650	—
1692 inverted 1	£90	£260	£675	—
1693	£85	£230	£650	—

William III Fourth bust

WILLIAM III (1694–1702)

Provincially produced shillings carry privy marks or initials below the bust: B: Bristol. C: Chester. E: Exeter. N: Norwich. Y or y: York.

1695 First bust	£25	£60	£200	—
1696 —	£20	£55	£200	—
1696 — no stops on rev.	£30	£85	£270	—
1696 — MAB for MAG		Extremely rare		
1696 — 1669 error		Extremely rare		
1696 — 1669 various GVLELMVS errors		Extremely rare		
1696 — B below bust	£30	£75	£300	—
1696 — C	£30	£75	£300	—

William III Fifth bust

ATE	F	VF	EF	UNC
696 — E	£30	£75	£300	—
696 — N	£30	£75	£325	—
696 — y	£30	£80	£300	—
696 — Y	£25	£90	£350	—
696 Second bust		Only one known		
696 Third bust C below	£75	£175	£500	—
696 — Y	£300	—	—	—
697 First bust	£24	£60	£200	—
697 — GRI for GRA error			Extremely rare	
697 — Scottish & Irish shields transposed			Extremely rare	
697 — Irish arms at date			Extremely rare	
697 — no stops on rev	£30	£80	£200	—
697 — GVLELMVS error			Extremely rare	
697 — B	£30	£80	£300	—
697 — C	£30	£80	£300	—
697 — E	£30	£80	£300	—
697 — N	£30	£80	£300	—
697 — — no stops on obv.			Extremely rare	
697 — y	£30	£80	£300	—
697 — — arms of France & Ireland transposed			Extremely rare	
697 — Y	£30	£80	£300	—
697 Third bust	£25	£80	£225	—
697 — B	£30	£80	£325	—
697 — C	£30	£75	£350	—
697 — — Fr.a error	£40	£100	—	—
697 — — no stops on obv.	£60	£125	—	—
697 — — arms of Scotland at date			Extremely rare	
697 — E	£30	£80	£325	—
697 — N	£30	£85	£350	—
697 — y	£30	£80	£325	—
697 Third bust variety	£25	£60	£200	—
697 — B	£30	£85	£350	—
697 — C	£50	£200	—	—
698 —	£40	£100	£325	—
698 — Plumes in angles of rev.	£60	£275	£700	—
698 Fourth bust "Flaming hair"	£110	£300	£900	—
699 —	£90	£260	£800	—
699 Fifth bust	£60	£120	£450	—
699 — Plumes in angles on rev.	£70	£200	£600	—
699 — Roses in angles on rev.	£70	£200	£650	—
700 —	£35	£80	£250	—
700 — Small round oo in date	£35	£80	£250	—
700 — no stop after DEI			Extremely rare	
700 — Plume below bust	£800	—	—	—
701 —	£55	£140	£325	—
701 — Plumes in angles on rev.	£75	£200	£500	—

ANNE (1702–14)

702 First bust (pre-Union with Scotland)	£35	£85	£300	—
702 — Plumes in angles on rev.	£35	£90	£300	—
702 — VIGO below bust	£35	£80	£275	—
702 — — colon before ANNA			Extremely rare	
703 Second bust, VIGO below	£35	£80	£275	—
704 — Plain	£200	—	—	—
704 — Plumes in angles on rev.	£40	£120	£400	—
705 — Plain	£40	£120	£350	—
705 — Plumes in angles on rev.	£35	£110	£350	—
705 — Roses & Plumes in angles on rev.	£35	£110	£350	—
707 — —	£30	£110	£350	—
707 Second bust (post-Union) E below bust	£25	£55	£250	—
707 — E* below bust	£60	£150	£450	—
707 Third bust, Plain	£25	£60	£175	—
707 — Plumes in angles on rev.	£35	£100	£400	—
707 — E below bust	£25	£65	£250	—
707 "Edinburgh" bust, E* below			Extremely rare	
708 Second bust, E below	£25	£60	£275	—
708 — E* below bust	£30	£100	£350	—
708/7 — — 8 over 7			Extremely rare	

Anne, VIGO below bust

Anne, E below bust

DATE	MINTAGE	F	VF	EF	UNC
1708 — Roses & Plumes in angles on rev.		£70	£200	£425	—
1708 Third bust, Plain		£25	£60	£200	—
1708 — Plumes in angles on rev.		£35	£90	£275	—
1708 Third bust, E below bust		£35	£120	£280	—
1708/7 — — 8 over 7		£60	£150	—	—
1708 — Roses & Plumes in angles on rev.		£30	£100	£300	—
1708 "Edinburgh" bust, E* below		£35	£100	£325	—
1709 Third bust, Plain		£25	£70	£275	—
1709 "Edinburgh" bust, E* below		£35	£100	£350	—
1709 — E no star (filled in die?)		£60	£150	£350	—
1710 Third bust, Roses & Plumes in angles		£35	£80	£300	—
1710 Fourth bust, Roses & Plumes in angles ...		£35	£100	£300	—
1711 Third bust, Plain		£60	£120	£350	—
1711 Fourth bust, Plain		£20	£40	£130	—
1712 — Roses & Plumes in angles on rev.		£30	£70	£225	—
1713 — —		£30	£65	£225	—
1713/2 — 3 over 2		£40	£125	—	—
1714 — —		£30	£65	£225	—
1714/3 —				Extremely rare	

GEORGE I (1714–27)

DATE	MINTAGE	F	VF	EF	UNC
*1715 First bust, Roses & Plumes in angles on rev.		£35	£90	£325	—
1716 — —		£60	£175	£500	—
1717 — —		£40	£100	£325	—
1718 — —		£30	£80	£375	—
1719 — —		£70	£200	£650	—
1720 — —		£30	£80	£240	—
1720/18 — —		£40	£90	£300	—
1720 — Plain		£22	£65	£240	—
1721 — Roses & Plumes in angles on rev.		£40	£100	£500	—
1721/0 — — 1 over 0		£40	£100	£500	—
1721 — Plain		£100	£225	£850	—
172170 — — 1 over 0		£100	£225	£800	—
1721/19 — — 21 over 19		£125	£250	—	—
1722 — Roses & Plumes in angles on rev.		£50	£150	£555	—
1723 — —		£50	£150	£500	—
1723 — SSC in angles of rev.		£15	£40	£125	—
1723 — SSC rev., Arms of France at date		£60	£130	£500	—
1723 Second bust, SSC in angles on rev.		£30	£80	£300	—
1723 — Roses & Plumes in angles		£40	£125	£500	—
1723 — WCC (Welsh Copper Co) below bust ..		£275	£600	£2500	—
1724 — Roses & Plumes in angles on rev.		£40	£100	£350	—
1724 — WCC below bust		£275	£600	£2500	—
1725 — Roses & Plumes in angles on rev.		£40	£120	£375	—
1725 — — no stops on obv.		£50	£150	£350	—
1725 — WCC below bust		£275	£600	£2500	—
1726 — —.		£275	£600	£2500	—
1726 — Roses & Plumes in angles on rev.		£200	£700	—	—
1727 — —				Extremely rare	
1727 — — no stops on obv.				Extremely rare	

GEORGE II (1727–60)

DATE	MINTAGE	F	VF	EF	UNC
1727 Young head, Plumes in angles on rev.		£35	£110	£320	—
1727 — Roses & Plumes in angles on rev.		£35	£100	£300	—
1728 — —		£35	£100	£350	—
1728 — Plain		£40	£110	£350	—
1729 — Roses & Plumes in angles on rev.		£35	£100	£300	—
1731 — —		£35	£80	£250	—
1731 — Plumes in angles on rev.		£40	£125	£400	—
1732 — Roses & Plumes in angles on rev.		£35	£80	£250	—
1734 — —		£35	£80	£250	—
1735 — —		£35	£80	£250	—
1736 — —		£35	£80	£250	—
1736/5 — — 6 over 5		£40	£85	£260	—
1737 — —		£35	£80	£250	—
*1739 — Roses in angles on rev.		£30	£65	£225	—
1739/7 — — 9 over 7				Extremely rare	
1741 — —		£30	£65	£225	—
1741/39 — — 41 over 39				Extremely rare	
1743 Old head, Roses in angles on rev.		£18	£45	£175	—
1745 — —		£18	£45	£175	—

George II Young head

ATE	MINTAGE	F	VF	EF	UNC
745 — — LIMA beow bust		£15	£40	£150	—
745/3 — — — 5 over 3		£25	£60	£250	—
746 — — —		£30	£100	£400	—
746/5 — — — 6 over 5		£50	£125	—	—
746 — Plain, Proof		—	—	£425	—
747 — Roses in angles on rev.		£18	£50	£200	—
750 — Plain		£18	£50	£220	—
750/6 — — 0 over 6		£30	£80	£240	—
751 — —		£28	£80	£250	—
758 — —		£8	£20	£75	—

George II Old head

GEORGE III (1760–1820)

ATE	MINTAGE	F	VF	EF	UNC
763 "Northumberland" bust		£200	£375	£600	—
787 rev. no semée of hearts in 4th shield		£7	£16	£50	—
787 — No stop over head		£7	£16	£50	
787 — No stop at date		£7	£16	£50	
787 — No stops on obv		£15	£30	£70	—
787 rev. with semée of hearts in shield		£7	£16	£50	—
798 "Dorrien Magens" bust		—	—	£3500	—
EW COINAGE—shield in garter reverse					
316	—	£5	£15	£40	£85
317	3,031,360	£5	£15	£40	£85
317 GEOE for GEOR	*incl. above*	£70	£160	£300	—
318	1,342,440	£6	£16	£60	£120
319	7,595,280	£5	£15	£40	£85
319/8 9 over 8	*incl. above*	£8	£25	£60	—
320	7,975,440	£5	£15	£38	£85

George III "Northumberland" shilling

GEORGE IV (1820–30)

ATE	MINTAGE	F	VF	EF	UNC
321 First bust, first reverse	2,463,120	£8	£25	£85	£200
321 — — Proof	*incl. above*	—	—	—	£400
323 — Second reverse	693,000	£20	£50	£150	£250
324 — —	4,158,000	£8	£25	£80	£200
325 — —	2,459,160	£15	£30	£70	£200
325/3 — — 5 over 3	*incl. above*		Extremely rare		
325 Second bust, third reverse .	*incl. above*	£3	Extremely rare		
325 — — Roman I	*incl. above*		Extremely rare		
326 — —	6,351,840	£3	£12	£45	£95
326 — — Proof	*incl. above*	—	—	—	£175
327 — —	574,200	£20	£45	£120	£250
329 — —	879,120	£15	£35	£100	£200

WILLIAM IV (1830–37)

ATE	MINTAGE	F	VF	EF	UNC
331Proof only	—	—	—	£140	£250
334	3,223,440	£6	£20	£70	£175
335	1,449,360	£6	£20	£70	£175
336	3,567,960	£6	£20	£60	£160
337	478,160	£8	£25	£90	£300

VICTORIA (1837–1901)

ATE	MINTAGE	F	VF	EF	UNC
OUNG HEAD ISSUES					
rst head					
338 WW on truncation	1,956,240	£6	£20	£70	£150
339 —	5,666,760	£6	£20	£70	£150
econd head					
339 WW on truncation, Proof only	*incl. above*	—	—	—	£250
339 no WW	*incl. above*	£6	£22	£70	£150
340	1,639,440	£7	£22	£80	£200
341	875,160	£6	£22	£80	£200
342	2,094,840	£6	£22	£60	£175
43	1,465,200	£6	£24	£80	£200
44	4,466,880	£6	£22	£70	£160
45	4,082,760	£6	£22	£70	£175
46	4,031,280	£6	£22	£60	£140
48 last 8 of date over 6	1,041,480	£25	£45	£135	£325

DATE	MINTAGE	F	VF	EF	UNC
1849	845,480	£8	£30	£80	£200
1850	685,080	£200	£400	£1000	£1800
1851	470,071	£25	£100	£250	£450
1851/49 51 over 49	*incl. above*	£125	£350	—	—
1852	1,306,574	£6	£22	£65	£160
1853	4,256,188	£6	£22	£65	£160
1853 Proof	*incl. above*	—	—	—	£400
1854	552,414	£70	£140	£300	£700
1854/1 4 over 1	*incl. above*	£125	£350	—	—
1855	1,368,400	£6	£22	£75	£150
1856	3,168,000	£6	£22	£75	£150
1857	2,562,120	£6	£22	£75	£150
1857 error F:G with inverted G	*incl. above*	£100	£250	—	—
1858	3,108,600	£6	£22	£75	£150
1859	4,561,920	£6	£22	£75	£150
1860	1,671,120	£6	£22	£75	£175
1861	1,382,040	£7	£25	£85	£200
1862	954,360	£40	£100	£250	£600
1863	859,320	£80	£200	£400	£800
1863/1 3 over 1				Extremely rare	
Die no. added above date up to 1879					
1864	4,518,360	£6	£22	£55	£115
1865	5,619,240	£6	£22	£55	£115
1866	4,984,600	£6	£22	£55	£115
1866 error BBITANNIAR	*incl. above*	£70	£150	—	—
1867	2,166,120	£6	£22	£55	£110
Third head—with die no					
1867	*incl. above*	£20	£50	£125	£210
1868	3,330,360	£6	£20	£50	£100
1869	736,560	£6	£20	£50	£110
1870	1,467,471	£6	£20	£50	£110
1871	4,910,010	£6	£18	£50	£100
1872	8,897,781	£6	£18	£50	£100
1873	6,489,598	£6	£18	£50	£100
1874	5,503,747	£6	£18	£50	£100
1875	4,353,983	£6	£18	£50	£100
1876	1,057,487	£6	£18	£50	£110
1877	2,989,703	£6	£18	£45	£100
1878	3,127,131	£6	£18	£45	£100
1879	3,611,507	£8	£30	£80	£150
Fourth head—no die no					
1879 no Die no.	*incl. above*	£5	£15	£50	£100
1880	4,842,786	£5	£16	£45	£80
1881	5,255,332	£5	£16	£45	£80
1882	1,611,786	£7	£24	£100	£200
1883	7,281,450	£4	£16	£45	£75
1884	3,923,993	£4	£16	£45	£75
1885	3,336,526	£4	£16	£45	£75
1886	2,086,819	£4	£16	£45	£75
1887	4,034,133	£5	£15	£50	£100
JUBILEE HEAD ISSUES					
1887	*incl. above*	£2	£4	£9	£20
1887 Proof	1,084	—	—	—	£60
1888	4,526,856	£2	£8	£18	£40
1889	7,039,628	£12	£40	£150	—
1889 Large bust (until 1892)	*incl. above*	£3	£8	£32	£60
1890	8,794,042	£3	£8	£32	£60
*1891	5,665,348	£3	£8	£32	£60
1892	4,591,622	£3	£8	£32	£60
OLD HEAD ISSUES					
1893	7,039,074	£3	£7	£22	£40
1893 small lettering	*incl. above*	£3	£7	£22	£40
1893 Proof	1,312	—	—	—	£75
1894	5,953,152	£6	£15	£40	£85
1895	8,880,651	£5	£14	£35	£75
1896	9,264,551	£5	£11	£30	£60
1897	6,270,364	£4	£10	£30	£50
*1898	9,768,703	£4	£10	£30	£50
1899	10,965,382	£4	£10	£30	£55
1900	10,937,590	£4	£10	£30	£50
1901	3,426,294	£4	£10	£30	£50

Victoria Small Jubilee head

Victoria L
Jubilee h

Victoria Old or Veiled head

ATE	MINTAGE	F	VF	EF	UNC
EDWARD VII (1901–10)					
02	7,809,481	£3	£6	£15	£35
02 Proof matt	13,123	—	—	—	£30
03	2,061,823	£6	£30	£80	£300
04	2,040,161	£6	£30	£80	£275
05	488,390	£40	£150	£450	£1000
06	10,791,025	£3	£9	£35	£70
07	14,083,418	£3	£10	£40	£80
08	3,806,969	£5	£20	£80	£200
09	5,664,982	£3	£14	£55	£125
10	26,547,236	£2	£5	£20	£40
GEORGE V (1910–36)					
st issue					
11	20,065,901	£2	£6	£16	£35
11 Proof	6,007	—	—	—	£35
12	15,594,009	£2	£7	£22	£50
13	9,011,509	£3	£8	£25	£65
14	23,415,843	£1	£4	£16	£32
15	39,279,024	£1	£4	£16	£32
16	35,862,015	£1	£4	£16	£32
17	22,202,608	£1	£4	£16	£32
18	34,915,934	£1	£4	£16	£32
19	10,823,824	£1	£5	£16	£32
cond issue *—debased silver*					
20	22,825,142	—	£2	£15	£35
21	22,648,763	—	£2	£15	£35
22	27,215,738	—	£2	£15	£35
23	14,575,243	—	£2	£15	£30
24	9,250,095	£2	£5	£28	£70
25	5,418,764	£2	£5	£28	£70
26	22,516,453	—	£4	£18	£40
ird issue*—Modified bust*					
26	*incl. above*	—	£3	£18	£30
27 —	9,247,344	£1	£3	£18	£30
urth issue *—large lion and crown on rev., date in legend*					
27	*incl. above*	£1	£2	£15	£32
27 Proof	15,000	—	—	—	£25
28	18,136,778	—	£2	£10	£25
29	19,343,006	—	£2	£12	£25
30	3,172,092	—	£2	£15	£35
31	6,993,926	—	£2	£10	£25
32	12,168,101	—	£2	£10	£25
33	11,511,624	—	£2	£10	£25
34	6,138,463	—	£2	£12	£35
35	9,183,462	—	£2	£6	£15
36	11,910,613	—	£2	£4	£10
GEORGE VI (1936–52)					
England rev. (lion standing on large crown). S = Scotland rev. (lion seated on all crown holding sword and mace)					
37 E	8,359,122	—	£1	£2	£5
37 E Proof	26,402	—	—	—	£8
37 S	6,748,875	—	£1	£2	£5
37 S Proof	26,402	—	—	—	£8
38 E	4,833,436	—	£1	£7	£14
38 S	4,797,852	—	£1	£7	£14
39 E	11,052,677	—	£1	£2	£5
39 S	10,263,892	—	£1	£2	£5
40 E	11,099,126	—	—	£2	£5
40 S	9,913,089	—	—	£2	£5

George V First obverse

George V Second obverse

DATE	MINTAGE	F	VF	EF	UNC
1941 E	11,391,883	—	—	£2	£5
1941 S	8,086,030	—	—	£2	£5
1942 E	17,453,643	—	—	£2	£4
1942 S	13,676,759	—	—	£2	£4
1943 E	11,404,213	—	—	£2	£4
1943 S	9,824,214	—	—	£2	£4
*1944 E	11,586,751	—	—	£2	£4
*1944 S	10,990,167	—	—	£2	£4
1945 E	15,143,404	—	—	£2	£5
1945 S	15,106,270	—	—	£2	£5
1946 E	16,663,797	—	—	£2	£5
1946 S	16,381,501	—	—	£2	£5
1947 E	12,120,611	—	—	—	£2
1947 S	12,283,223	—	—	—	£2
1948 E	45,576,923	—	—	—	£2
1948 S	45,351,937	—	—	—	£2
1949 E	19,328,405	—	—	—	£4
1949 S	21,243,074	—	—	—	£4
1950 E	19,243,872	—	—	—	£4
1950 E Proof	17,513	—	—	—	£8
1950 S	14,299,601	—	—	—	£4
1950 S Proof	17,513	—	—	—	£8
1951 E	9,956,930	—	—	—	£4
1951 E Proof	20,000	—	—	—	£8
1951 S	10,961,174	—	—	—	£4
1951 S Proof	20,000	—	—	—	£8

English reverse

Scottish reverse

ELIZABETH II (1952–)

E = England rev. (shield with three lions). S = Scotland rev. (shield with one lion).

DATE	MINTAGE	F	VF	EF	UNC
1953 E	41,942,894	—	—	—	£1
1953 E Proof	40,000	—	—	—	£3
1953 S	20,663,528	—	—	—	£1
1953 S Proof	40,000	—	—	—	£3
*1954 E	30,262,032	—	—	—	£2
*1954 S	26,771,735	—	—	—	£2
1955 E	45,259,908	—	—	—	£2
1955 S	27,950,906	—	—	—	£2
1956 E	44,907,008	—	—	—	£8
1956 S	42,853,639	—	—	—	£8
1957 E	42,774,217	—	—	—	£1
1957 S	17,959,988	—	—	—	£9
1958 E	14,392,305	—	—	—	£9
1958 S	40,822,557	—	—	—	£1
1959 E	19,442,778	—	—	—	£1
1959 S	1,012,988	£1	£2	£4	£15
1960 E	27,027,914	—	—	—	£1
1960 S	14,376,932	—	—	—	£1
1961 E	39,816,907	—	—	—	£1
1961 S	2,762,558	—	—	—	£3
1962 E	36,704,379	—	—	—	£1
1962 S	17,475,310	—	—	—	£1
1963 E	49,433,607	—	—	—	£1
1963 S	32,300,000	—	—	—	£1
1964 E	8,590,900	—	—	—	£1
1964 S	5,239,100	—	—	—	£1
1965 E	9,216,000	—	—	—	£1
1965 S	2,774,000	—	—	—	£2
1966 E	15,002,000	—	—	—	£1
1966 S	15,604,000	—	—	—	£1

English reverse

Scottish reverse

SIXPENCES

ATE	F	VF	EF	UNC
OLIVER CROMWELL				
58 Patterns by Thos. Simon & Tanner All are very Rare 4 Varieties			Extremely Rare	
CHARLES II (1660–85)				
74	£60	£125	£400	—
75	£60	£125	£400	—
75/4 5 over 4	£65	£140	£400	—
76	£60	£140	£400	—
76/5 6 over 5	£75	£150	£425	—
677	£60	£120	£400	—
78/7	£50	£120	£400	—
79	£50	£120	£400	—
80	£70	£160	£500	—
81	£50	£120	£400	—
82/1	£50	£125	£375	—
82	£55	£125	£400	—
83	£55	£125	£400	—
84	£55	£160	£425	—
JAMES II (1685–88)				
86 Early shields	£80	£200	£500	—
87/6 — 7 over 6	£80	£200	£500	—
87 Late shields	£75	£200	£475	—
87/6 — 7 over 6	£75	£200	£475	—
88 —	£75	£180	£550	—
WILLIAM & MARY (1688–94)				
693	£80	£180	£500	—
93 error inverted 3	£80	£200	£500	—
94	£80	£185	£500	—
WILLIAM III (1694–1702)				
Provincially produced sixpences carry privy marks or initials below the bust: B: Bristol. C: Chester. E: Exeter. N: Norwich. Y or y: York.				
95 First bust, early harp in 4th shield on rev.	£18	£60	£150	—
96 — —	£15	£40	£110	—
96 — — French arms at date			Extremely rare	
96 — — Scottish arms at date			Extremely rare	
96 — — DFI for DEI			Extremely rare	
96 — — No stops on obv.	£20	£60	£175	—
96 — — B	£22	£55	£200	—
96 — — — B over E			Extremely rare	
96 — — C	£22	£55	£225	—
96 — — E	£22	£55	£240	—
96 — — N	£22	£55	£225	—
96 — — y	£22	£55	£225	—
96 — — Y	£25	£70	£300	—
96 — Later harp	£35	£100	£350	—
96 — — B	£30	£110	£300	—
96 — — — no stops on obv	£35	£120	£325	—
96 — — C	£45	£175	£600	—
96 — — N	£40	£150	—	—
96 Second bust	£175	£400	—	—
97 First bust, later harp	£20	£40	£140	—
97 — — Arms of France & Ireland transposed			Extremely rare	

DATE	MINTAGE	F	VF	EF	UNC
1697 — — B		£25	£60	£250	—
1697 — — C		£25	£60	£250	—
1697 — — — Irish shield at date				Extremely rare	
1697 — — E		£25	£60	£250	—
1697 — — N		£25	£60	£250	—
1697 — — — error GVLIEMVS				Extremely rare	
1697 — — y		£25	£60	£250	—
1697 — — — Irish shield at date				Extremely rare	
1697 Second bust		£70	£175	£600	—
1697 Third bust		£15	£40	£120	—
1697 — error GVLIEIMVS				Extremely rare	
1697 — B		£22	£70	£250	—
1697 — — IRA for FRA				Extremely rare	
1697 — C		£22	£100	£300	—
1697 — E		£25	£90	£275	—
1697 — Y		£30	£90	£275	—
1698 —		£30	£90	£250	—
1698 — Plumes in angles on rev.		£35	£100	£350	—
1699 —		£40	£150	£475	—
1699 — Plumes in angles on rev.		£40	£150	£400	—
1699 — Roses in angles on rev.		£45	£150	£400	—
1699 — — error GVLIELMVS				Extremely rare	
1700 —		£25	£60	£200	—
1700 — Plume below bust		£600	—	—	—
1701 —		£30	£75	£275	—

ANNE (1702–14)

DATE	MINTAGE	F	VF	EF	UNC
1703 VIGO below bust Before Union with Scotland		£25	£60	£200	—
1705 Plain		£40	£100	£275	—
*1705 Plumes in angles on rev.		£25	£65	£240	—
1705 Roses & Plumes in angles on rev.		£25	£65	£250	—
1707 Roses & Plumes in angles on rev.		£25	£65	£200	—
1707 (Post-Union), Plain		£20	£40	£150	—
1707 E (Edinburgh) below bust		£20	£45	£160	—
1707 Plumes in angles on rev.		£20	£50	£200	—
1708 Plain		£20	£40	£140	—
1708 E below bust		£18	£45	£175	—
1708 E* below bust		£25	£65	£200	—
1708 "Edinburgh" bust E* below		£25	£75	£225	—
1708 Plumes in angles on rev.		£25	£60	£200	—
1710 Roses & Plumes in angles on rev.		£25	£60	£225	—
1711 Plain		£15	£32	£110	—

GEORGE I (1714–27)

DATE	MINTAGE	F	VF	EF	UNC
*1717 Roses & Plumes in angles on rev.		£60	£150	£375	—
1717 Plain edge				Extremely rare	
1720 —		£55	£125	£400	—
1723 SSC in angles on rev.		£12	£40	£125	—
1723 Larger lettering		£12	£40	£125	—
1726 Small Roses & Plumes in angles on rev.		£80	£200	£550	—

GEORGE II (1727–60)

DATE	MINTAGE	F	VF	EF	UNC
1728 Young head, Plain		£40	£100	£325	—
1728 — Proof		—	—	£1250	—
1728 — Plumes in angles on rev.		£30	£80	£250	—
1728 — Roses & Plumes in angles on rev.		£26	£70	£180	—
1731 — —		£26	£55	£180	—
*1732 — —		£26	£55	£180	—
1734 — —		£26	£60	£200	—
1735 — —		£26	£55	£175	
1735/4 5 over 4		£30	£70	£200	—
1736 — —		£26	£55	£175	—
1739 — Roses in angles on rev.		£20	£50	£140	—
1741 —		£28	£50	£140	—

ATE	MINTAGE	F	VF	EF	UNC
43 Old head, Roses in angles on rev.		£12	£40	£110	—
45 — —		£12	£35	£110	—
45 — — 5 over 3		£15	£45	£120	—
45 — Plain, LIMA below bust		£12	£35	£100	—
46 — — —		£12	£35	£100	—
46 — — Proof		—	—	£350	—
50 — —		£16	£40	£120	—
51 — —		£18	£40	£130	—
57 — —		£10	£20	£50	—
58 — —		£10	£20	£50	—

GEORGE III (1760–1820)

87 rev. no semée of hearts on 4th shield		£8	£18	£35	—
87 rev. with semée of hearts		£8	£18	£35	—
EW COINAGE					
16	—	£5	£12	£35	£70
17	10,921,680	£5	£12	£35	£70
18	4,284,720	£6	£16	£50	£100
19	4,712,400	£5	£12	£35	£70
19 very small 8 in date	*incl. above*	£5	£12	£35	£70
20	1,488,960	£5	£12	£35	£70

GEORGE IV (1820–30)

821 First bust, first reverse	863,280	£8	£25	£70	£150
21 error BBRITANNIAR		£50	£200	£550	—
21 — — Proof	*incl. above*	—	—	—	£350
24 — Second (garter) reverse	633,600	£8	£25	£75	£150
25 —	483,120	£8	£25	£75	£150
26 — —	689,040	£15	£45	£110	£250
26 Second bust, third (lion on crown) reverse	*incl. above*	£7	£22	£60	£110
26 — — Proof	*incl. above*	—	—	—	£125
27 — —	166,320	£15	£35	£100	£200
28 — —	15,840	£12	£28	£90	£175
29 — —	403,290	£10	£25	£90	£160

WILLIAM IV (1830–37)

21 error BBRITANNIAR		£50	£150	£500	—
31	1,340,195	£8	£22	£65	£120
31 Proof	*incl. above*	—	—	£90	£175
834	5,892,480	£8	£22	£65	£130
35	1,552,320	£8	£22	£65	£145
36	1,987,920	£10	£30	£100	£170
37	506,880	£10	£32	£110	£200

VICTORIA (1837–1901)

OUNG HEAD ISSUES					
rst head					
38	1,607,760	£7	£20	£45	£100
39	3,310,560	£7	£20	£45	£100
39 Proof	*incl. above*	—	—	—	£150
40	2,098,800	£7	£20	£45	£120
41	1,386,000	£7	£22	£50	£130
42	601,920	£7	£20	£70	£120
43	3,160,080	£7	£22	£50	£120
44	3,975,840	£7	£20	£45	£110
44 Large 44 in date	*incl. above*	£8	£25	£80	£175
45	3,714,480	£7	£22	£50	£120
46	4,226,880	£7	£22	£50	£110
48	586,080	£20	£50	£125	£300
48/6 final 8 over 6	*incl. above*	£25	£65	£170	—
50	498,960	£7	£24	£50	£130

DATE	MINTAGE	F	VF	EF	UNC
1850/3 0 over 3	*incl. above*	£14	£25	£70	£175
1851	2,288,107	£7	£24	£50	£125
1852	904,586	£7	£24	£50	£140
1853	3,837,930	£7	£24	£50	£120
1853 Proof	*incl above*	—	—	£50	£300
1854	840,116	£45	£110	£250	£500
1855	1,129,684	£7	£20	£50	£110
1855/3 last 5 over 3	*incl. above*	£10	£30	£60	£140
1856	2,779,920	£7	£20	£50	£120
1857	2,233,440	£7	£20	£50	£120
1858	1,932,480	£7	£20	£50	£120
1859	4,688,640	£7	£20	£50	£120
1859/8 9 over 8	*incl. above*	£10	£30	£60	£150
1860	1,100,880	£8	£22	£55	£150
1862	990,000	£25	£60	£175	£400
1863	491,040	£25	£60	£175	£400
Die no. added above date from 1864 to 1879					
1864	4,253,040	£7	£22	£50	£110
1865	1,631,520	£7	£22	£50	£110
1866	4,140,080	£7	£22	£50	£110
1866 no Die no.	*incl. above*	£15	£60	£150	£220
Second head					
1867	1,362,240	£7	£20	£50	£100
1868	1,069,200	£7	£20	£50	£100
1869	388,080	£7	£20	£50	£110
1870	479,613	£7	£20	£50	£100
1871	3,662,684	£6	£20	£45	£85
1871 no Die no.	*incl. above*	£6	£20	£45	£85
1872	3,382,048	£6	£20	£45	£85
1873	4,594,733	£6	£20	£45	£85
1874	4,225,726	£6	£20	£45	£85
1875	3,256,545	£6	£20	£45	£85
1876	841,435	£6	£20	£50	£85
1877	4,066,486	£6	£20	£50	£85
1877 no Die no	*incl. above*	£6	£20	£50	£85
1878	2,624,525	£6	£20	£50	£85
1878 Dritanniar Error	*incl. above*	£60	£200	—	—
1879	3,326,313	£6	£18	£50	£85
1879 no Die no	*incl. above*	£5	£18	£50	£85
1880 no Die no	3,892,501	£5	£18	£50	£85
Third head					
1880	*incl above*	£5	£18	£40	£60
1881	6,239,447	£5	£18	£40	£60
1882	759,809	£6	£20	£70	£140
1883	4,986,558	£5	£16	£35	£60
1884	3,422,565	£5	£16	£35	£60
1885	4,652,771	£5	£16	£35	£60
1886	2,728,249	£5	£16	£35	£55
1887	3,675,607	£5	£16	£32	£60
JUBILEE HEAD ISSUES					
*1887 Shield reverse	*incl. above*	£3	£5	£9	£18
1887 — Proof	*incl. above*	—	—	—	£50
1887 Six Pence in wreath reverse	*incl. above*	£2	£4	£9	£18
1888 —	4,197,698	£3	£7	£20	£35
*1889 —	8,738,928	£3	£7	£25	£40
1890 —	9,386,955	£3	£7	£25	£40
1891 —	7,022,734	£3	£7	£25	£40
1892 —	6,245,746	£3	£8	£28	£50
1893 —	7,350,619	£225	£400	£1100	£1800
OLD HEAD ISSUES					
1893	*incl. above*	£3	£8	£18	£35
1893 Proof	1,312	—	—	—	£60
1894	3,467,704	£7	£14	£40	£75
1895	7,024,631	£6	£14	£35	£55
1896	6,651,699	£4	£9	£30	£45
1897	5,031,498	£4	£9	£30	£45
1898	5,914,100	£4	£9	£30	£45
1899	7,996,80	£4	£9	£30	£45
1900	8,984,354	£4	£9	£30	£45
1901	5,108,757	£4	£9	£28	£45

Jubilee head, shield reverse

Jubilee head, wreath reverse

ATE	MINTAGE	F	VF	EF	UNC

EDWARD VII (1901–10)

02	6,367,378	£1	£4	£20	£35
02 "Matt Proof"	15,123	—	—	—	£35
03	5,410,096	£4	£15	£45	£100
04	4,487,098	£6	£25	£65	£160
05	4,235,556	£6	£20	£60	£140
06	7,641,146	£4	£10	£35	£75
07	8,733,673	£4	£10	£40	£80
908	6,739,491	£7	£25	£50	£150
09	6,584,017	£5	£15	£45	£100
10	12,490,724	£1	£5	£20	£40

Edward VII

GEORGE V (1910–36)

rst issue					
11	9,155,310	£1	£3	£10	£35
11 Proof	6,007	—	—	—	£30
12	10,984,129	£1	£3	£20	£40
13	7,499,833	£1	£6	£22	£50
14	22,714,602	£1	£2	£10	£25
915	15,694,597	£1	£3	£12	£35
16	22,207,178	£1	£2	£8	£25
17	7,725,475	£3	£10	£28	£60
18	27,553,743	£1	£2	£12	£25
19	13,375,447	£1	£3	£12	£30
20	14,136,287	£1	£3	£10	£25
***econd issue**—debased silver*					
20	*incl. above*	£1	£3	£10	£25
21	30,339,741	£1	£3	£10	£25
22	16,878,890	£1	£2	£10	£25
23	6,382,793	£3	£7	£30	£70
24	17,444,218	£1	£5	£10	£20
25	12,720,558	£1	£2	£10	£20
25 Broad rim	*incl. above*	£1	£2	£10	£25
26 —	21,809,621	£1	£2	£10	£25
***hird issue**—Modified bust*					
26	incl. above	£1	£2	£10	£25
27	8,924,873	—	£1	£8	£25
***ourth issue**—New design (oakleaves)*					
27 Proof only	15,000	—	—	—	£20
28	23,123,384	—	£1	£7	£18
29	28,319,326	—	£1	£7	£18
30	16,990,289	—	£1	£7	£20
31	16,873,268	—	£1	£7	£18
32	9,406,117	—	£1	£7	£25
33	22,185,083	—	£1	£7	£18
34	9,304,009	£1	£2	£9	£22
35	13,995,621	—	£1	£5	£10
936	24,380,171	—	£1	£5	£10

George V, first reverse above and second reverse below

GEORGE VI (1936–52)

irst type					
937	22,302,524	—	—	£1	£4
937 Proof	26,402	—	—	—	£5
938	13,402,701	—	£1	£3	£11
939	28,670,304	—	—	£1	£5
940	20,875,196	—	—	£1	£5
941	23,086,616	—	—	£1	£5
942	44,942,785	—	—	£1	£4
943	46,927,111	—	—	£1	£4
944	36,952,600	—	—	£1	£4
945	39,939,259	—	—	£1	£3
946	43,466,407	—	—	£1	£3
upro-nickel					
947	29,993,263	—	—	£1	£3
948	88,323,540	—	—	£1	£3
***econd type**—new cypher on rev.*					
949	41,335,515	—	—	£1	£3

George VI first reverse

George VI second reverse

DATE	MINTAGE	F	VF	EF	UNC
1950	32,741,955	—	—	£1	£3
1950 Proof	17,513	—	—	—	£5
1951	40,399,491	—	—	£1	£3
1951 Proof	20,000	—	—	—	£5
1952	1,013,477	£3	£8	£15	£30

ELIZABETH II (1952–)

DATE	MINTAGE	F	VF	EF	UNC
1953	70,323,876	—	—	—	£2
1953 Proof	40,000	—	—	—	£4
1954	105,241,150	—	—	—	£3
1955	109,929,554	—	—	—	£1
1956	109,841,555	—	—	—	£1
1957	105,654,290	—	—	—	£1
1958	123,518,527	—	—	—	£3
1959	93,089,441	—	—	—	£1
1960	103,283,346	—	—	—	£3
1961	115,052,017	—	—	—	£3
1962	166,483,637	—	—	—	25p
1963	120,056,000	—	—	—	25p
1964	152,336,000	—	—	—	25p
1965	129,644,000	—	—	—	25p
1966	175,676,000	—	—	—	25p
1967	240,788,000	—	—	—	25p

GROATS OR FOURPENCES

The earlier fourpences are included in the Maundy oddments section.

WILLIAM IV (1831–37)

DATE	MINTAGE	F	VF	EF	UNC
*1836	—	£6	£12	£28	£50
1837	962,280	£6	£12	£28	£50

VICTORIA (1838–1901)

DATE	MINTAGE	F	VF	EF	UNC
1837	Extremely Rare Proofs or Patterns only				
1837 Last 8 over 8 on its side		£10	£18	£50	£80
1838	2,150,280	£6	£12	£30	£55
1839	1,461,240	£6	£14	£32	£55
1839 Proof	*incl. above*	—	—	—	£125
1840	1,496,880	£6	£12	£30	£55
1840 Small 0 in date	*incl. above*	£6	£12	£30	£55
1841	344,520	£6	£14	£35	£55
1842/1 2 over 1	*incl. above*	£6	£14	£35	£55
1842	724,680	£6	£14	£35	£55
1843	1,817640	£6	£14	£35	£60
1843 4 over 5	*incl. above*	£6	£14	£35	£55
1844	855,360	£6	£14	£35	£60
1845	914,760	£6	£14	£35	£60
1846	1,366,200	£6	£14	£35	£60
1847 7 over 6	225,720	£12	£25	£100	—
1848	712,800	£6	£14	£30	£50
1848/6 8 over 6	*incl. above*	£20	£100	—	—
1848/7 8 over 7	*incl. above*	£8	£20	£50	£80
1849	380,160	£6	£14	£30	£50
1849/8 9 over 8	*incl. above*	£8	£20	£50	£80
*1851	594,000	£18	£50	£160	£225
1852	31,300	£30	£85	£240	—
1853	11,880	£35	£100	£325	—
1853 Proof	*incl. above*	—	—	—	£300
1854	1,096,613	£6	£14	£35	£55
1855	646,041	£6	£14	£35	£55
1888 Jubilee Head	—	£6	£14	£35	£60

THREEPENCES

The earlier threepences are included in the Maundy oddments section.

WILLIAM IV (1830–37)

(issued for use in the West Indies)

DATE	MINTAGE	F	VF	EF	UNC
1834		£6	£12	£35	£60
1835		£6	£12	£35	£60
1836		£6	£12	£35	£60
1837		£6	£12	£40	£70

VICTORIA (1837–1901)

YOUNG HEAD ISSUES

DATE	MINTAGE	F	VF	EF	UNC
1838 BRITANNIAB error				Extremely rare	
1838	—	£6	£18	£40	£60
1839	—	£6	£18	£45	£70
1940	—	£6	£18	£45	£70
1841	—	£6	£18	£50	£75
1842	—	£6	£18	£50	£75
1843	—	£6	£18	£35	£55
1844	—	£6	£18	£60	£90
*1845	1,314,720	£7	£18	£35	£90
1846	47,520	£7	£22	£70	£110
1849	126,720	£7	£20	£55	£100
1850	950,400	£7	£18	£40	£75
1851	479,065	£6	£18	£45	£75
1851 5 over 8	*incl. above*	£10	£20	£80	—
1853	31,680	£20	£50	£100	£200
1854	1,467,246	£6	£18	£45	£70
1855	383,350	£6	£18	£45	£75
1856	1,013,760	£6	£18	£50	£75
1857	1,758,240	£6	£18	£50	£75
1858	1,441,440	£6	£18	£50	£65
1858 BRITANNIAB error	*incl. above*			Extremely rare	
1858/6 final 8 over 6	*incl. above*	£8	£25	£80	—
1858/5 final 8 over 5	*incl. above*	£8	£25	£80	—
1859	3,579,840	£6	£18	£45	£65
1860	3,405,600	£6	£18	£45	£65
1861	3,294,720	£6	£18	£45	£65
1862	1,156,320	£6	£18	£45	£65
1863	950,400	£6	£20	£50	£90
1864	1,330,560	£6	£18	£45	£75
1865	1,742,400	£6	£18	£45	£80
1866	1,900,800	£6	£18	£45	£60
1867	712,800	£6	£18	£45	£70
1868	1,457,280	£6	£18	£45	£65
1868 RRITANNIAR error	*incl. above*	£50	£100	£225	—
1869	—	£25	£50	£140	£200
1870	1,283,218	£5	£16	£40	£55
1871	999,633	£5	£16	£35	£55
1872	1,293,271	£5	£16	£35	£55
1873	4,055,550	£5	£16	£35	£55
1874	4,427,031	£5	£16	£35	£55
1875	3,306,500	£5	£16	£35	£55
1876	1,834,389	£5	£16	£35	£55
1877	2,622,393	£5	£16	£35	£55
1878	2,419,975	£5	£16	£35	£55
1879	3,140,265	£5	£16	£35	£55
1880	1,610,069	£5	£16	£35	£55
1881	3,248,265	£5	£16	£35	£55
1882	472,965	£6	£20	£55	£100
1883	4,369,971	£5	£10	£28	£40
1884	3,322,424	£5	£10	£28	£40
1885	5,183,653	£5	£10	£28	£40
1886	6,152,669	£5	£10	£25	£40
1887	2,780,761	£5	£10	£25	£40

Victoria first type

DATE	MINTAGE	F	VF	EF	UNC
JUBILEE HEAD ISSUES					
1887	*incl. above*	£1	£3	£9	£18
1887 Proof	*incl. above*	—	—	—	£35
1888	518,199	£2	£5	£18	£35
*1889	4,587,010	£2	£5	£18	£35
1890	4,465,834	£2	£5	£18	£35
1891	6,323,027	£2	£5	£18	£35
1892	2,578,226	£2	£5	£18	£35
1893	3,067,243	£8	£25	£100	£140
OLD HEAD ISSUES					
1893	*incl. above*	£1	£3	£15	£25
1893 Proof	*incl. above*	—	—	—	£40
1894	1,608,603	£2	£6	£24	£45
1895	4,788,609	£1	£5	£22	£45
1896	4,598,442	£1	£5	£18	£30
1897	4,541,294	£1	£5	£18	£30
1898	4,567,177	£1	£5	£18	£30
*1899	6,246,281	£1	£5	£18	£30
1900	10,644,480	£1	£5	£18	£30
1901	6,098,400	£1	£5	£14	£28

Victoria
Jubilee head

Victoria
Old or Veiled
head

EDWARD VII (1901–10)

DATE	MINTAGE	F	VF	EF	UNC
1902	8,268,480	£1	£2	£7	£15
1902 "Matt Proof"	*incl. above*	—	—	—	£15
1903	5,227,200	£1	£4	£20	£35
1904	3,627,360	£2	£7	£35	£70
1905	3,548,160	£1	£4	£25	£55
1906	3,152,160	£1	£4	£20	£45
1907	4,831,200	£1	£4	£20	£45
1908	8,157,600	£1	£3	£20	£45
1909	4,055,040	£1	£4	£20	£40
*1910	4,563,380	£1	£3	£15	£30

GEORGE V (1910–36)

DATE	MINTAGE	F	VF	EF	UNC
First issue					
1911	5,841,084	—	—	£3	£10
1911 Proof	*incl. above*	—	—	—	£20
1912	8,932,825	—	—	£3	£10
1913	7,143,242	—	—	£3	£10
1914	6,733,584	—	—	£3	£10
1915	5,450,617	—	—	£3	£10
1916	18,555,201	—	—	£3	£8
1917	21,662,490	—	—	£3	£8
7918	20,630,909	—	—	£3	£8
1919	16,845,687	—	—	£3	£8
1920	16,703,597	—	—	£3	£8
***Second issue**—debased silver*					
1920	*incl. above*	—	—	£3	£8
1921	8,749,301	—	—	£3	£8
1922	7,979,998	—	—	£3	£8
1925	3,731,859	—	—	£5	£20
1926	4,107,910	—	—	£7	£20
***Third issue**—Modified bust*					
1926	*incl. above*	—	—	£7	£18
***Fourth issue**—new design (oakleaves)*					
1927 Proof only	15,022	—	—	—	£38
1928	1,302,106	£2	£6	£20	£45
1930	1,319,412	£1	£3	£8	£22
1931	6,251,936	—	—	£2	£6
*1932	5,887,325	—	—	£2	£6
1933	5,578,541	—	—	£2	£6
1934	7,405,954	—	—	£2	£6
1935	7,027,654	—	—	£2	£6
1936	3,328,670	—	—	£2	£6

George V,
fourth issue
oak leaves
design reverse

GEORGE VI (1936–52)

DATE	MINTAGE	F	VF	EF	UNC
Silver					
*1937	8,148,156	—	—	£1	£3
1937 Proof	26,402	—	—	—	£5
1938	6,402,473	—	—	£1	£3

DATE	MINTAGE	F	VF	EF	UNC
1939	1,355,860	—	—	£3	£8
1940	7,914,401	—	—	£1	£3
1941	7,979,411	—	—	£1	£3
1942	4,144,051	£2	£5	£12	£30
1943	1,397,220	£2	£5	£12	£30
1944	2,005,553	£5	£12	£35	£70
1945	Only one known				
Brass—lareger size, 12 sided, "Thrift" design					
1937	45,707,957	—	—	£1	£3
1937 Proof	26,402	—	—	—	£3
1938	14,532,332	—	—	£1	£10
1939	5,603,021	—	—	£2	£20
1940	12,636,018	—	—	£1	£7
1941	60,239,489	—	—	£1	£4
1942	103,214,400	—	—	£1	£5
1943	101,702,400	—	—	£1	£5
1944	69,760,000	—	—	£1	£6
1945	33,942,466	—	—	£1	£7
1946	620,734	£3	£15	£90	£225
1948	4,230,400	—	—	—	£10
1949	464,000	£4	£18	£80	£250
1950	1,600,000	—	£2	£10	£100
1950 Proof	17,513	—	—	—	£5
1951	1,184,000	—	£2	£10	£125
1951 Proof	20,000	—	—	—	£5
1952	25,494,400	—	—	—	£6

George VI "Thrift" design of the brass 3d

ELIZABETH II (1952–)

DATE	MINTAGE	F	VF	EF	UNC
1953	30,618,000	—	—	—	£1
1953 Proof	40,000	—	—	—	£5
1954	41,720,000	—	—	—	£4
1955	41,075,200	—	—	—	£4
1956	36,801,600	—	—	—	£4
1957	24,294,500	—	—	—	£3
1958	20,504,000	—	—	—	£6
1959	28,499,200	—	—	—	£3
1960	83,078,400	—	—	—	£2
1961	41,102,400	—	—	—	£1
1962	51,545,600	—	—	—	£1
1963	39,482,866	—	—	—	£1
1964	44,867,200	—	—	—	—
1965	27,160,000	—	—	—	—
1966	53,160,000	—	—	—	—
1967	151,780,800	—	—	—	—

TWO PENCES

It is generally accepted that earlier issues of the small silver twopences were only produced for inclusion with the Maundy sets, q.v., except for those listed below.

1797 "Cartwheel"	£18	£40	£200	£550
1797 Copper Proofs	Many varieties from £500+			

VICTORIA (1837–1901)

For use in the Colonies

1838	£4	£10	£18	£30
1848	£4	£12	£20	£35

"Cartwheel" twopence

THREE-HALFPENCES

WILLIAM IV (1830–37)

DATE	F	VF	EF	UNC
For use in the Colonies				
1834	£6	£16	£32	£70
1835 over 4	£6	£16	£32	£70
1836	£8	£18	£35	£75
1837	£12	£35	£100	£175

VICTORIA (1837–1901)

DATE	F	VF	EF	UNC
For use in the Colonies				
1838	£6	£15	£32	£60
1839	£6	£15	£32	£60
1840	£7	£18	£40	£70
1841	£6	£15	£30	£60
1842	£6	£18	£35	£70
1843	£6	£15	£30	£55
1860	£9	£20	£60	£100
1862	£9	£20	£60	£100

PENNIES

The earlier small silver pennies are included in the Maundy oddments section.

"Cartwheel" penny

GEORGE III (1760–1820)

DATE	MINTAGE	F	VF	EF	UNC
*1797 "Cartwheel", 10 laurel leaves	8,601,600	£15	£32	£125	£350
1797 — 11 laurel leaves	*incl. above*	£15	£32	£125	£350
1806 Third type	—	£5	£12	£55	£120
1807	—	£5	£12	£55	£125
1808					Unique

GEORGE IV (1820–30)

DATE	MINTAGE	F	VF	EF	UNC
1825	1,075,200	£9	£32	£90	£250
*1826 (varieties)	5,913,600	£9	£32	£90	£250
1826 Proof	—	—	—	£90	£150
1827	1,451,520	£60	£175	£700	£1800

WILLIAM IV (1830–37)

DATE	MINTAGE	F	VF	EF	UNC
1831(varieties)	806,400	£12	£35	£125	£250
1831 Proof	—	—	—	£100	£200
1834	322,560	£12	£35	£125	£300
1837	174,720	£12	£35	£125	£300

VICTORIA (1837–1901)

YOUNG HEAD ISSUES

DATE	MINTAGE	F	VF	EF	UNC
Copper					
1839 Proof	unrecorded	—	—	—	£175
*1841	913,920	£6	£14	£45	£100
1841 No colon after REG	*incl. above*	£6	£14	£45	£100
1843	483,840	£24	£75	£200	£400
1844	215,040	£7	£16	£50	£130
1845	322,560	£7	£18	£75	£140

ATE	MINTAGE	F	VF	EF	UNC
846	483,840	£8	£18	£75	£130
846 FID: DEF colon spaced	*incl. above*	£8	£18	£75	£130
846 FID:DEF colon close	*incl. above*	£8	£18	£75	£125
847	430,080	£6	£15	£70	£140
848	161,280	£6	£15	£60	£140
848/7 final 8 over 7	*incl. above*	£6	£15	£60	£140
848/6 final 8 over 6	*incl. above*	£10	£20	£80	—
849	268,800	£35	£140	£320	£600
851	268,800	£8	£20	£80	£175
853	1,021,440	£4	£10	£40	£75
853 Proof	—	—	—	—	£300
854	6,720,000	£4	£10	£40	£75
854/3 4 over 3	*incl. above*	£8	£20	£70	—
855	5,273,856	£4	£10	£40	£75
856	1,212,288	£12	£40	£125	£200
857 Plain trident	752,640	£4	£14	£40	£85
857 Ornamental trident	*incl. above*	£4	£14	£40	£85
858/7 final 8 over 7	*incl. above*	£4	£14	£40	£85
858/3 final 8 over 3	*incl. above*	£20	£60	£150	—
858	1,599,040	£4	£12	£40	£80
859	1,075,200	£7	£24	£60	£150
860/59	32,256	£300	£500	£1500	—
ronze					
860 Beaded border	5,053,440	£4	£10	£40	£90
860 Toothed border	*incl. above*	£4	£10	£45	£100
860 — Piedfort flan	—		Extremely rare		
861	36,449,280	£3	£8	£35	£80
862	50,534,400	£3	£8	£35	£80
862 8 over 6	*incl. above*		Extremely rare		
863	28,062,720	£3	£7	£35	£80
863 Die no below date	*incl. above*		Extremely rare		
864 Plain 4	3,440,640	£8	£35	£250	£500
864 Crosslet 4	*incl. above*	£8	£35	£250	£500
865	8,601,600	£4	£12	£35	£100
865/3 5 over 3	*incl. above*	£10	£50	£150	—
866	9,999,360	£4	£12	£35	£100
867	5,483,520	£4	£12	£35	£100
1868	1,182,720	£8	£32	£100	£200
869	2,580,480	£50	£150	£400	£1000
870	5,695,022	£6	£20	£80	£200
871	1,290,318	£25	£100	£250	£750
872	8,494,572	£5	£15	£40	£95
873	8,494,200	£5	£15	£40	£95
874	5,621,865	£5	£15	£40	£95
874 H	6,666,240	£5	£15	£40	£95
874 Later (older) bust	*incl. above*	£8	£22	£50	£120
875	10,691,040	£5	£15	£40	£75
875 H	752,640	£25	£80	£225	£600
876 H	11,074,560	£5	£12	£45	£100
877	9,624,747	£5	£14	£45	£100
878	2,764,470	£5	£14	£45	£100
879	7,666,476	£3	£12	£40	£85
880	3,000,831	£4	£12	£35	£90
881	2,302,362	£5	£12	£40	£90
881 H	3,763,200	£5	£12	£40	£90
882 H	7,526,400	£5	£12	£35	£75
882 no H	—		Extremely Rare		
883	6,237,438	£5	£12	£35	£75
884	11,702,802	£5	£12	£35	£80
885	7,145,862	£4	£11	£40	£75
886	6,087,759	£4	£11	£40	£75
887	5,315,085	£4	£11	£40	£75

Victoria copper penny

Victoria bronze penny

DATE	MINTAGE	F	VF	EF	UNC
1888	5,125,020	£4	£11	£40	£75
1889	12,559,737	£4	£11	£40	£75
1890	15,330,840	£4	£11	£40	£75
1891	17,885,961	£4	£11	£40	£75
1892	10,501,671	£4	£11	£40	£75
1893	8,161,737	£4	£11	£40	£75
1894	3,883,452	£7	£20	£60	£125
OLD HEAD ISSUES					
1895 Trident 2mm from P(ENNY)	5,395,830	£4	£18	£70	£200
1895 Trident 1mm from P	*incl. above*	—	£2	£15	£40
1896	24,147,156	—	£2	£15	£35
*1897	20,756,620	—	£2	£15	£35
1898	14,296,836	—	£2	£16	£35
1899	26,441,069	—	£2	£14	£35
1900	31,778,109	—	£2	£13	£30
1901	22,205,568	—	£2	£7	£15

EDWARD VII (1901–10)

DATE	MINTAGE	F	VF	EF	UNC
1902	26,976,768	—	£1	£8	£22
1902 "Low tide" to sea line	*incl. above*	—	£5	£20	£50
1903	21,415,296	—	£3	£14	£50
1904	12,913,152	—	£3	£14	£50
1905	17,783,808	—	£3	£14	£45
1906	37,989,504	—	£3	£14	£40
1907	47,322,240	—	£3	£14	£40
*1908	31,506,048	—	£3	£14	£45
1909	19,617,024	—	£3	£15	£50
1910	29,549,184	—	£3	£14	£40

GEORGE V (1910–36)

DATE	MINTAGE	F	VF	EF	UNC
1911	23,079,168	—	£3	£12	£32
1912	48,306,048	—	£3	£12	£32
*1912 H	16,800,000	—	£3	£25	£70
1913	65,497,812	—	£3	£12	£40
1914	50,820,997	—	£3	£12	£40
1915	47,310,807	—	£3	£12	£40
1916	86,411,165	—	£3	£12	£40
1917	107,905,436	—	£3	£12	£40
1918	84,227,372	—	£3	£12	£40
1918 H	3,660,800	£1	£8	£80	£240
1918 KN	*incl. above*	£7	£60	£300	£800
1919	113,761,090	—	£2	£12	£40
1919 H	5,209,600	£1	£10	£70	£250
1919 KN	*incl. above*	£8	£70	£350	£1000
1920	124,693,485	—	£2	£12	£25
1921	129,717,693	—	£2	£12	£25
1922	16,346,711	—	£2	£12	£40
1926	4,498,519	—	£6	£20	£75
1926 Modified effigy	incl above	£7	£25	£300	£500
1927	60,989,561	—	£2	£8	£25
1928	50,178,00	—	£2	£8	£25
1929	49,132,800	—	£2	£8	£25
1930	29,097,600	—	£2	£15	£40
1931	19,843,200	—	£2	£8	£30
1932	8,277,600	—	£2	£10	£32
1933		Only 7 examples known			
1934	13,965,600	—	£2	£8	£32
1935	56,070,000	—	—	£2	£9
1936	154,296,000	—	—	£2	£8

GEORGE VI (1936–52)

ATE	MINTAGE	F	VF	EF	UNC
937	88,896,000	—	—	—	£3
937 Proof	26,402	—	—	—	£5
938	121,560,00	—	—	—	£3
939	55,560,000	—	—	—	£4
940	42,284,400	—	—	—	£6
944	42,600,000	—	—	—	£6
945	79,531,200	—	—	—	£5
946	66,855,600	—	—	—	£3
947	52,220,400	—	—	—	£3
948	63,961,200	—	—	—	£3
949	14,324,400	—	—	—	£3
950	240,000	£3	£7	£14	£20
950 Proof	17,513	—	—	—	£14
951	120,000	£5	£9	£18	£26
951 Proof	20,000	—	—	—	—

ELIZABETH II (1952–)

ATE	MINTAGE	F	VF	EF	UNC
1953	1,308,400	—	—	£1	£4
953 Proof	40,000	—	—	—	£6
954	Only one known				
961	48,313,400	—	—	—	£1
962	143,308,600	—	—	—	50p
963	125,235,600	—	—	—	50p
964	153,294,000	—	—	—	50p
965	121,310,400	—	—	—	50p
966	165,739,200	—	—	—	50p
967	654,564,000	—	—	—	—

ater issues are included in the Decimal section.

HALFPENNIES

CHARLES II (1660–85)

ATE	F	VF	EF	UNC
672	£40	£150	£500	—
672 CRAOLVS error	Extremely rare			
673	£40	£150	£500	—
673 CRAOLVS error	Extremely rare			
673 No rev. stop	£70	£250	—	—
673 No stops on obv.	Extremely rare			
675	£40	£120	£475	—
675 No stops on obv.	£50	£175	—	—

JAMES II (1685–88)

ATE	F	VF	EF	UNC
685 (tin)	£100	£225	£1000	—
686 (tin)	£110	£250	£1000	—
687 (tin)	£100	£225	£1000	—

WILLIAM & MARY (1688–94)

Tin

ATE	F	VF	EF	UNC
1689 Small draped busts, edge dated	£300	—	—	—
1690 Large cuirassed busts, edge dated	£110	£275	£1000	—
1691 — date on edge and in exergue	£110	£275	£1000	—
1692 — —	£110	£275	£1000	—

DATE	F	VF	EF	UNC
Copper				
*1694 Large cuirassed busts, date in exergue	£32	£100	£750	—
1694 — — GVLIEMVS error			Extremely rare	
1694 — — MΛRIΛ error			Extremely rare	
1694 — — No stops on rev.			Extremely rare	

WILLIAM III (1694–1702)

DATE	F	VF	EF	UNC
1695 First issue (date in exergue)	£30	£80	£450	—
1695 — No stop after GVLIEMVS on obv.	£50	£100	—	—
1695 — No stop after BRITANNIA on rev.	£50	£100	—	—
1696 —	£30	£100	£475	—
1696 — TERTVS error			Extremely rare	
1697 —	£30	£90	£450	—
1697 — No stop after TERTIVS on obv.	£50	£100	—	—
1698 —	£30	£90	£525	—
1698 Second issue (date in legend)	£30	£120	—	—
1698 — No stop after date	£45	£100	—	—
1699 —	£30	£90	£450	—
1699 — No stop after date	£45	£100	—	—
1699 Third issue (date in exergue) (Britannia with right hand on knee)	£30	£90	£450	—
1699 — No stop after date			Extremely rare	
1699 — BRITΛNNIΛ error	£70	£140	—	—
1699 — TERTVS error			Extremely rare	
1699 — No stop on rev.			Extremely rare	
1699 — No stops on obv.	£70	£140	—	—
1700 —	£30	£90	£450	—
1700 — No stops on obv.	£75	£150	—	—
1700 — No stops after GVLIELMUS	£75	£150	—	—
1700 — BRITVANNIA error			Extremely rare	
1700 — GVIELMS error	£75	£150	—	—
1700 — GVLIEEMVS error	£50	£140	—	—
*1701 —	£30	£90	£450	—
1701 — BRITΛNNIΛ error	£50	£140	—	—
1701 — No stops on obv.			Extremely rare	
1701 — inverted As for Vs	£50	£140	—	—

GEORGE I (1714–27)

DATE	F	VF	EF	UNC
*1717 "Dump" issue	£40	£110	£400	
1718 —	£28	£70	£300	—
1719 Second issue	£25	£70	£300	—
1720 —	£25	£70	£300	—
1721 —	£25	£70	£300	—
1721 — Stop after date	£35	£80	—	—
1722 —	£25	£70	£300	—
1722 —inverted A for V on obv.	£40	£125	—	—
1723 —	£25	£70	£300	—
1723 —No stop on rev.	£30	£80	—	—
1724 —	£25	£67	£300	—

GEORGE II (1727–60)

DATE	F	VF	EF	UNC
1729 Young head	£22	£50	£175	—
1729 — No stop on rev.	£25	£60	£180	—
1730 —	£15	£45	£170	—
1730 — GEOGIVS error	£30	£80	£300	—
1730 — Stop after date	£25	£70	£200	—
1730 — No stop after REX on obv.	£30	£80	£210	—
1731 —	£15	£50	£180	—
1731 — No rev. stop	£25	£70	£200	—
1732 —	£18	£50	£180	—
1732 — No rev. stop	£25	£70	£200	—
1733 —	£15	£50	£180	—

DATE	MINTAGE	F	VF	EF	UNC
1734/3 — 4 over 3		£25	£100	—	—
1734 — No stop on obv.		£30	£100	—	—
1735 —		£18	£40	£175	—
1736 —		£18	£40	£160	—
1737 —		£18	£40	£160	—
1738 —		£18	£40	£160	—
1739 —		£18	£40	£160	—
1740 Old head		£12	£38	£150	—
1742 —		£12	£38	£150	—
1742/0 — 2 over 0		£20	£75	£200	—
1743 —		£12	£40	£150	—
1744 —		£12	£40	£150	—
1745 —		£12	£40	£150	—
1746 —		£12	£40	£150	—
1747 —		£12	£40	£150	—
1748 —		£12	£40	£150	—
1749 —		£12	£40	£150	—
1750 —		£12	£40	£150	—
*1751 —		£12	£40	£150	—
1752 —		£12	£40	£150	—
1753 —		£12	£40	£150	—
1754 —		£12	£40	£150	—

George II old head

GEORGE III (1760–1820)

First type—Royal Mint					
1770		£10	£30	£130	—
1770 No stop on rev.		£20	£55	£140	—
1771		£10	£35	£175	—
1771 No stop on rev.		£20	£60	£175	—
1772 Error GEORIVS		£35	£80	£400	
1772		£9	£28	£130	—
1772 No stop on rev		£20	£60	£150	—
1773		£9	£28	£125	—
1773 No stop after REX		£25	£60	—	—
1773 No stop on rev.		£20	£40	£130	—
1774		£9	£28	£130	—
*1775		£10	£28	£130	—
Second type—Soho Mint					
*1799		£2	£6	£30	£65
Third type					
1806		£2	£6	£30	£65
1807		£2	£6	£30	£65

George III first type

GEORGE IV (1820–30)

1825	215,040	£8	£28	£70	£125
1826 (varieties)	9,031,630	£7	£25	£50	£100
1826 Proof	—	—	—	£80	£120
1827	5,376,000	£8	£25	£70	£120

WILLIAM IV (1830–37)

1831	806,400	£7	£22	£65	£125
1831 Proof	—	—	—	—	£125
1834	537,600	£7	£22	£65	£125
1837	349,440	£7	£22	£66	£125

VICTORIA (1837–1901)

YOUNG HEAD ISSUES

Copper

1838	456,960	£4	£15	£40	£75
1839 Proof	268,800	—	—	—	£120

George III second type

DATE	MINTAGE	F	VF	EF	UNC
1841	1,0745,200	£4	£15	£40	£75
1843	967,680	£15	£40	£90	£175
1844	1,075,200	£4	£15	£40	£75
1845	1,075,200	£25	£70	£250	£500
1846	860,160	£6	£15	£35	£70
1847	725,640	£6	£15	£35	£70
1848	322,560	£6	£15	£35	£70
1848/7 final 8 OVER 7	*incl. above*	£7	£15	£40	£80
1851	215,040	£5	£14	£35	£65
1852	637,056	£5	£12	£35	£65
1853	1,559,040	£4	£7	£20	£50
1853/2 3 over 2	*incl. above*	£10	£20	£40	£100
1853 Proof	—	—	—	—	£200
1854	12,354,048	£4	£8	£30	£50
1855	1,455,837	£4	£8	£30	£50
1856	1,942,080	£6	£14	£45	£100
1857	1,820,720	£5	£12	£30	£60
1858	2,472,960	£4	£10	£30	£60
1858/7 final 8 over 7	*incl. above*	£4	£10	£30	£60
1858/6 final 8 over 6	*incl. above*	£4	£10	£30	£60
1859	1,290,240	£5	£15	£35	£80
1859/8 9 over 8	*incl. above*	£4	£10	£30	£55
1860	*unrecorded*		£600	£1750	—
Bronze					
1860 Beaded border	6,630,400	£3	£9	£30	£55
1860 Toothed border		£4	£12	£40	£70
1861	54,118,400	£3	£9	£30	£55
1862 Die letter A, B or C to left of lighthouse				Extremely rare	
1862	61,107,200	£3	£9	£30	£55
1863	15,948,800	£3	£9	£30	£55
1864	537,600	£3	£10	£40	£80
1865	8,064,000	£4	£15	£50	£85
1865/3 5 over 3	*incl. above*	£15	£30	£75	—
1866	2,508,800	£5	£15	£50	£85
1867	2,508,800	£5	£15	£45	£85
1868	3,046,400	£4	£10	£40	£110
1869	3,225,600	£7	£30	£60	£175
1870	4,350,739	£5	£15	£50	£100
1871	1,075,280	£30	£80	£200	£500
1872	4,659,410	£4	£10	£35	£75
1873	3,404,880	£4	£10	£35	£75
1874	1,347,655	£5	£20	£60	£125
1874 H	5,017,600	£3	£10	£30	£75
1875	5,430,815	£3	£8	£30	£75
1875 H	1,254,400	£4	£10	£35	£75
1876 H	5,809,600	£4	£10	£35	£75
1877	5,209,505	£3	£10	£30	£75
1878	1,425,535	£5	£20	£60	£110
1879	3,582,545	£3	£10	£30	£60
1880	2,423,465	£4	£12	£40	£80
1881	2,007,515	£4	£12	£35	£75
1881 H	1,792,000	£3	£10	£30	£60
1882 H	4,480,000	£3	£10	£30	£70
1883	3,000,725	£3	£10	£30	£50
1884	6,989,580	£3	£10	£30	£50
1885	8,600,574	£3	£10	£30	£50
1886	8,586,155	£3	£10	£25	£50
1887	10,701,305	£3	£10	£25	£50
1888	6,814,670	£3	£10	£25	£50
1889	7,748,234	£3	£10	£25	£50
1889/8 9 over 8	*incl. above*	£10	£30	£75	—
1890	11,254,235	£3	£10	£25	£50

Victoria copper halfpenny

Victoria bronze halfpenny

DATE	MINTAGE	F	VF	EF	UNC
1891	13,192,260	£3	£10	£25	£50
1892	2,478,335	£3	£10	£25	£60
1893	7,229,344	£3	£10	£25	£50
1894	1,767,635	£5	£12	£32	£85
OLD HEAD ISSUES					
1895	3,032,154	£1	£4	£15	£40
1896	9,142,500	£1	£4	£10	£32
1897	8,690,315	£1	£4	£10	£32
1898	8,595,180	£1	£4	£10	£32
1899	12,108,001	£1	£4	£10	£35
1900	13,805,190	£1	£4	£10	£28
1901	11,127,360	£1	£2	£6	£15

EDWARD VII (1901–10)

DATE	MINTAGE	F	VF	EF	UNC
1902	13,672,960	£2	£4	£8	£22
1902 "Low tide"	*incl. above*	£6	£15	£45	£100
*1903	11,450,880	£2	£5	£18	£40
1904	8,131,200	£2	£5	£18	£40
1905	10,124,800	£2	£5	£18	£40
1906	16,849,280	£2	£5	£18	£40
1907	16,849,280	£2	£5	£18	£40
1908	16,620,800	£2	£5	£18	£40
1909	8,279,040	£2	£5	£18	£40
1910	10,769,920	£2	£5	£18	£40

GEORGE V (1910–36)

DATE	MINTAGE	F	VF	EF	UNC
1911	12,570,880	—	£3	£12	£30
1912	21,185,920	—	£2	£12	£30
1913	17,476,480	—	£2	£14	£35
1914	20,289,111	—	£2	£12	£35
1915	21,563,040	£1	£3	£14	£35
1916	39,386,143	—	£2	£12	£35
1917	38,245,436	—	£2	£12	£30
1918	22,321,072	—	£2	£12	£30
1919	28,104,001	—	£2	£12	£30
1920	35,146,793	—	£2	£12	£30
1921	28,027,293	—	£2	£12	£30
*1922	10,734,964	—	£2	£15	£40
1923	12,266,282	—	£2	£12	£30
1924	13,971,038	—	£2	£10	£30
1925	12,216,123	—	£2	£10	£30
1925 Modified effigy	*incl. above*	£2	£5	£20	£50
1926	6,172,306	—	£2	£10	£32
1927	15,589,622	—	£2	£10	£30
1928	20,935,200	—	£2	£8	£25
1929	25,680,000	—	£2	£8	£25
1930	12,532,800	—	£2	£8	£25
1931	16,137,600	—	£2	£8	£25
1932	14,448,000	—	£2	£8	£25
1933	10,560,000	—	£2	£8	£25
1934	7,704,000	—	£2	£12	£30
1935	12,180,000	—	£1	£6	£15
1936	23,008,800	—	£1	£5	£8

GEORGE VI (1936–52)

DATE	MINTAGE	F	VF	EF	UNC
1937	24,504,000	—	—	£1	£2
1937 Proof	26,402	—	—	£1	£5
1938	40,320,000	—	—	£1	£4
1939	28,924,800	—	—	£1	£4

DATE	MINTAGE	F	VF	EF	UNC
1940	32,162,400	—	—	£1	£5
1941	45,120,000	—	—	£1	£5
1942	71,908,800	—	—	£1	£3
1943	76,200,000	—	—	£1	£3
1944	81,840,000	—	—	£1	£3
1945	57,000,000	—	—	£1	£3
1946	22,725,600	—	—	£1	£5
1947	21,266,400	—	—	£1	£3
1948	26,947,200	—	—	£1	£2
*1949	24,744,000	—	—	£1	£2
1950	24,153,600	—	—	£1	£4
1950 Proof	17,513	—	—	£1	£5
1951	14,868,000	—	—	£1	£5
1951 Proof	20,000	—	—	£1	£5
1952	33,78,400	—	—	£1	£2

ELIZABETH II (1952–)

DATE	MINTAGE	F	VF	EF	UNC
1953	8,926,366	—	—	—	£1
1953 Proof	40,000	—	—	—	£3
*1954	19,375,000	—	—	—	£3
1955	18,799,200	—	—	—	£3
1956	21,799,200	—	—	—	£3
1957	43,684,800	—	—	—	£1
1958	62,318,400	—	—	—	£1
1959	79,176,000	—	—	—	£1
1960	41,340,000	—	—	—	£1
1962	41,779,200	—	—	—	£1
1963	45,036,000	—	—	—	20p
1964	78,583,200	—	—	—	20p
1965	98,083,200	—	—	—	20p
1966	95,289,600	—	—	—	20p
1967	146,491,200	—	—	—	10p

Later issues are included in the Decimal section.

FARTHINGS

OLIVER CROMWELL

DATE	F	VF	EF	UNC
Undated (copper) Draped bust, shield rev. Variations			Extremely rare	

CHARLES II (1660–85)

DATE	F	VF	EF	UNC
Copper				
1672	£25	£60	£300	—
*1673	£25	£60	£300	—
1673 CAROLA for CAROLO error	£70	£250	—	—
1673 No stops on obv.			Extremely rare	
1673 No stop on rev.			Extremely rare	
1674	£25	£60	£300	—
1675	£25	£60	£300	—
1675 No stop after CAROLVS			Extremely rare	
1679	£35	£75	£350	—
1679 No stop on rev.	£60	£180	—	—
Tin				
1684 with date on edge	£150	£375	—	—
1685 —	£300	—	—	—

DATE	F	VF	EF	UNC
JAMES II (1685–88)				
1684 (tin) Cuirassed bust		Extremely rare		
1685 (tin) —	£100	£250	£900	—
1686 (tin) —	£100	£250	£900	—
1687 (tin) —		Extremely rare		
1687 (tin) Draped bust	£150	£350	—	—
WILLIAM & MARY (1688–94)				
1689 (tin) Small draped busts	£325	—	—	—
1689 (tin) — with edge date 1690		Extremely rare		
1690 (tin) Large cuirassed busts	£100	£250	£950	—
1690 (tin) — with edge date 1689	£200	—	—	—
1691 (tin) —	£125	£325	—	—
1692 (tin) —	£100	£325	£900	—
1694 (copper) —	£35	£90	£550	—
1694 No stop after MARIΛ		Extremely rare		
1694 No stop on obv.		Extremely rare		
1694 No stop on rev.		Extremely rare		
1694 Unbarred As in BRITANNIA		Extremely rare		
WILLIAM III (1694–1702)				
1695 First issue (date in exergue)	£30	£100	£400	—
1695 — GVLIELMV error		Extremely rare		
1696 —	£30	£100	£400	—
1697 —	£25	£90	£400	—
1697 — GVLIELMS error		Extremely rare		
1698 —	£80	£200	—	—
1698 Second issue (date in legend)	£30	£110	£500	—
1699 First issue	£30	£100	£450	—
1699 Second issue	£30	£100	£475	—
1699 — No stop after date	£40	£100	—	—
1700 First issue	£28	£90	£450	—
1700 — error RRITANNIA		Extremely rare		
ANNE (1702–14)				
*1714	£150	£275	£475	—
GEORGE I (1714–27)				
*1717 First small "Dump" issue	£50	£150	£450	—
1719 Second issue	£25	£75	£250	—
1719 — No stop on rev.	£45	£175	—	—
1719 — No stops on obv.	£45	£175	—	—
1720 —	£25	£75	£250	—
*1721 —	£25	£75	£250	—
1721/0 — Last 1 over 0	£40	£130	—	—
1722 —	£25	£75	£250	—
1723 —	£25	£75	£275	—
1723 — R over sideways R in REX		Extremely rare		
1724 —	£25	£80	£275	—
GEORGE II (1727–60)				
1730 Young head	£14	£40	£175	—
1731 —	£14	£40	£175	—
1732 —	£14	£50	£175	—
1733 —	£14	£45	£175	—
1734 —	£14	£40	£170	—
1734 — No stop on obv.	£25	£80	£225	—

George I, first type

George I second type

DATE	MINTAGE	F	VF	EF	UNC
1735 —		£12	£40	£140	—
1735 — 3 over 5		£20	£70	£220	—
1736 —		£12	£40	£150	—
1737 —		£12	£40	£150	—
1739 —		£12	£40	£140	—
1741 Old Head		£12	£40	£140	—
1744 —		£11	£35	£135	—
1746 —		£11	£30	£135	—
1746 — V over LL in GEORGIVS			Extremely rare		
1749 —		£15	£40	£140	—
1750 —		£12	£30	£140	—
1754 —		£9	£20	£125	—
1754 — 4 over 0		£18	£40	£175	—

George III, third (Soho Mint) issue

GEORGE III (1760–1820)

DATE	MINTAGE	F	VF	EF	UNC
1771 First (London) issue		£18	£45	£175	—
1773 —		£11	£30	£95	—
1773 — No stop on rev.		£18	£40	£95	—
1773 — No stop after REX		£20	£70	£140	
1774 —		£10	£30	£110	—
1775 —		£10	£30	£110	—
1797 Second (Soho Mint) issue				Patterns only	
*1799 Third (Soho Mint) issue		£2	£8	£32	£70
*1806 Fourth (Soho Mint) issue		£2	£8	£32	£70
1807 —		£2	£8	£32	£70

George III, fourth (Soho Mint) issue

GEORGE IV (1820–30)

DATE	MINTAGE	F	VF	EF	UNC
1821 First bust (laureate, draped), first reverse (date in exergue) .	2,688,000	£2	£9	£40	£75
*1822 —	5,924,350	£2	£9	£40	£75
1823 —	2,365,440	£2.50	£10	£40	£75
1823 I for 1 in date	*incl. above*	£15	£60	£140	—
1825 —	4,300.800	£2.50	£10	£40	£70
1826 —	6,666,240	£2.50	£8	£40	£70
1826 Second bust (couped, date below), second reverse (ornament in exergue)	*incl. above*	£2.50	£10	£40	£75
1826 — Proof	—	—	—	£70	£120
1827 —	2,365,440	£2.50	£9	£35	£80
1828 —	2,365,440	£2.50	£9	£35	£80
1829 —	1,505,280	£2.50	£10	£40	£90
1830 —	2,365,440	£2.50	£8	£35	£80

WILLIAM IV (1830–37)

DATE	MINTAGE	F	VF	EF	UNC
1831	2,688,000	£5	£12	£35	£80
1831 Proof	—	—	—	—	£125
1834	1,935,360	£5	£12	£35	£80
1835	1.720,320	£5	£12	£30	£75
1836	1,290.240	£5	£12	£40	£80
1837	3.010,560	£5	£12	£35	£80

VICTORIA (1837–1901)

FIRST YOUNG HEAD (COPPER) ISSUES

DATE	MINTAGE	F	VF	EF	UNC
1838	591,360	£4	£12	£35	£70
1839	4,300,800	£4	£12	£35	£65
1839 Proof	—	—	—	—	£150
1840	3,010,560	£4	£12	£35	£60
1841	1,720,320	£4	£12	£35	£60
1842	1,290,240	£6	£20	£50	£110
1843	4,085,760	£5	£10	£35	£60

DATE	MINTAGE	F	VF	EF	UNC
1843 I for 1 in date		£45	£150	£220	—
1844	430,080	£40	£100	£250	£500
1845	3,225,600	£5	£10	£35	£65
1846	2,580,480	£6	£18	£45	£80
*1847	3,879,720	£5	£10	£35	£65
1848	1,290,240	£5	£10	£35	£65
1849	645,120	£20	£50	£110	£250
1850	430,080	£5	£10	£35	£60
1851	1,935,360	£6	£20	£55	£100
1851 D over sideways D in DEI	*incl. above*	£25	£50	£125	—
1852	822,528	£7	£20	£50	£110
1853	1,028,628	£4	£7	£30	£50
1853 Proof	—	—	—	—	£250
1854	6,504,960	£4	£10	£35	£50
1855	3,440,640	£4	£10	£35	£50
1856	1,771,392	£8	£15	£50	£100
1856 R over E in VICTORIA	*incl. above*	£20	£50	£100	—
1857	1,075,200	£4	£10	£35	£55
1858	1,720,320	£3	£8	£35	£50
1859	1,290,240	£9	£25	£60	£140
1860	*unrecorded*	£750	£1800	—	—

Victoria Young Head first (copper) issue

SECOND YOUNG OR "BUN" HEAD (BRONZE) ISSUES

DATE	MINTAGE	F	VF	EF	UNC
1860 Toothed border	2,867,200	£2	£5	£22	£50
1860 Beaded border	*incl. above*	£3	£7	£30	£60
1860 Toothed/Beaded border mule	*incl. above*			Extremely rare	
1861	8,601,600	£2	£5	£25	£60
1862	14,336,000	£1	£5	£25	£50
1862 Large 8 in date	*incl. above*			Extremely rare	
1863	1,433,600	£20	£50	£150	£250
1864	2,508,800	£1	£5	£25	£50
1865	4,659,200	£1	£5	£25	£55
1865 5 over 2	incl. above	£8	£15	£35	—
1866	3,584,000	£1	£5	£20	£50
1867	5,017,600	£1	£5	£25	£55
1868	4,851,210	£1	£5	£25	£55
1869	3,225,600	£1	£8	£30	£65
1872	2,150,400	£1	£5	£25	£55
1873	3,225,620	£1	£5	£25	£50
1874 H	3,584,000	£1	£5	£25	£60
1874 H both Gs over sideways G	*incl. above*	£75	£170	£325	—
1875	712,760	£3	£10	£35	£75
1875 H	6,092,800	£1	£5	£20	£50
1876 H	1,175,200	£2	£10	£35	£70
*1878	4,008,540	£1	£4	£18	£40
1879	3,977,180	£1	£4	£18	£40
1880	1,842,710	£1	£4	£18	£45
1881	3,494,670	£1	£4	£18	£45
1881 H	1,792,000	£1	£4	£18	£40
1882 H	1,792,000	£1	£5	£18	£40
1883	1,128,680	£4	£15	£45	£75
1884	5,782,000	£1	£4	£16	£30
1885	5,442,308	£1	£4	£16	£30
1886	7.707,790	£1	£4	£16	£30
1887	1,340,800	£1	£4	£16	£30
1888	1,887,250	£1	£4	£16	£30
1890	2,133,070	£1	£4	£16	£30
1891	4,959,690	£1	£4	£16	£30
1892	887,240	£2	£7	£30	£60
1893	3,904,320	£1	£4	£16	£30
1894	2,396,770	£1	£4	£16	£30
1895	2,852,852	£10	£25	£60	£120

Victoria Young Head second (bronze) issue

DATE	MINTAGE	F	VF	EF	UNC
OLD HEAD ISSUES					
1895 Bright finish	*incl. above*	£1	£2	£14	£22
1896 —	3,668,610	£1	£2	£14	£20
1897 —	4,579,800	£1	£2	£14	£20
1897 Dark finish	*incl. above*	£1	£2	£14	£20
1898 —	4,010,080	£1	£2	£14	£20
1899 —	3,864,616	£1	£2	£14	£20
1900 —	5,969,317	£1	£2	£14	£20
*1901 —	8,016,460	£1	£2	£6	£14

EDWARD VII (1901–10)

1902	5,125,120	50p	£1	£7	£12
1903	5,331,200	50p	£1	£8	£15
1904	3,628,800	£1	£2	£10	£20
1905	4,076,800	50p	£1	£8	£20
1906	5,340,160	50p	£1	£8	£15
*1907	4,399,360	50p	£1	£7	£15
1908	4,264,960	50p	£1	£7	£14
1909	8,852,480	50p	£1	£7	£14
1910	2,298,400	£1	£6	£14	£40

GEORGE V (1910–36)

1911	5,196,800	25p	50p	£5	£10
1912	7,669,760	25p	50p	£4	£10
1913	4,184,320	25p	50p	£5	£10
1914	6,126,988	25p	50p	£4	£10
1915	7,129,255	25p	50p	£4	£10
1916	10,993,325	25p	50p	£4	£10
*1917	21,434,844	25p	50p	£4	£10
1918	19,362,818	25p	50p	£4	£10
1919	15,089,425	25p	50p	£4	£10
1920	11,480,536	25p	50p	£4	£8
1921	9,469,097	25p	50p	£4	£8
1922	9,956,983	25p	50p	£4	£8
1923	8,034,457	25p	50p	£4	£8
1924	8,733,414	25p	50p	£4	£8
1925	12,634,697	25p	50p	£4	£8
1926 Modified effigy	9,792,397	25p	50p	£4	£8
1927	7,868,355	25p	50p	£4	£8
1928	11,625,600	25p	50p	£4	£8
1929	8,419,200	25p	50p	£4	£8
1930	4,195,200	25p	50p	£4	£8
1931	6,595,200	25p	50p	£4	£8
1932	9,292,800	25p	50p	£4	£8
1933	4,560,000	25p	50p	£4	£8
1934	3,052,800	25p	50p	£4	£8
1935	2.227,200	£1	£2	£8	£20
1936	9,734,400	25p	50p	£3	£6

GEORGE VI (1936–52)

1937	8,131,200	—	—	50p	£1
1937 Proof	26,402	—	—	£1	£4
1938	7,449,600	—	—	£1	£5
1939	31,440,000	—	—	50p	£1
1940	18,360,000	—	—	50p	£1
1941	27,312,000	—	—	50p	£1
1942	28,857,600	—	—	50p	£1
1943	33,345,600	—	—	50p	£1
1944	25,137,600	—	—	50p	£1
1945	23,736,000	—	—	50p	£1

ATE	MINTAGE	F	VF	EF	UNC
946	24,364,800	—	—	50p	£1
947	14,745,600	—	—	50p	£1
948	16,622,400	—	—	50p	£1
1949	8,424,000	—	—	50p	£1
950	10,324,800	—	—	50p	£1
950 Proof	17,513	—	—	50p	£3
951	14,016,000	—	—	50p	£1
951 Proof	20,000	—	—	50p	£3
952	5,251,200	—	—	50p	£1

ELIZABETH II (1952–)

953	6,131,037	—	—	—	£1
953 Proof	40,000	—	—	—	£2
1954	6,566,400	—	—	—	£1
955	5,779,200	—	—	—	£1
956	1,996,800	—	50p	£1	£2

HALF FARTHINGS

)ATE	MINTAGE	F	VF	EF	UNC

GEORGE IV (1820–30)

828 (two different obverses) (issued for Ceylon)	7,680,000	£9	£20	£45	£80
830 (large or small date) (issued for Ceylon)	8,766,320	£9	£20	£45	£80

WILLIAM IV (1830–37)

837 (issued for Ceylon)	1,935,360	£20	£55	£140	£220

VICTORIA (1837–1901)

839	2,042,880	£5	£10	£30	£65
842	*unrecorded*	£4	£8	£25	£65
843	3,440,640	£3	£6	£20	£40
844	6,451,200	£3	£6	£15	£40
844 E over N in REGINA	*incl. above*	£10	£45	£100	—

DATE	MINTAGE	F	VF	EF	UNC
1847	3,010,560	£6	£12	£30	£60
1851	*unrecorded*	£5	£12	£35	£60
1851 5 over 0		£8	£20	£60	£125
1852	989,184	£5	£12	£40	£65
1853	955,224	£5	£15	£45	£85
1853 Proof	*incl. above*	—	—	—	£175
1854	677,376	£8	£25	£70	£125
1856	913,920	£8	£25	£70	£125
1868		—	—	—	Rare
1868		—	—	—	Rare

THIRD FARTHINGS

DATE	MINTAGE	F	VF	EF	UNC
GEORGE IV (1820–30)					
1827 (issued for Malta)	*unrecorded*	£5	£14	£35	£70
WILLIAM IV (1830–37)					
1835 (issued for Malta)	*unrecorded*	£7	£16	£40	£85
VICTORIA (1837–1901)					
1844 (issued for Malta)	1,301,040	£10	£24	£70	£140
1844 RE for REG	*incl. above*	£30	£60	£250	—
1866	576,000	£6	£14	£30	£55
1868	144,000	£6	£14	£30	£55
1876	162,000	£6	£14	£30	£55
1878	288,000	£6	£14	£30	£55
1881	144,000	£6	£14	£30	£50
1884	144,000	£6	£14	£30	£50
1885	288,000	£6	£14	£30	£50
EDWARD VII (1902–10)					
1902 (issued for Malta)	288,000	£3	£7	£20	£30
GEORGE V (1911–36)					
1913 (issued for Malta)	288,000	£3	£7	£20	£30

QUARTER FARTHINGS

DATE	MINTAGE	F	VF	EF	UNC
VICTORIA (1837–1901)					
1839 (issued for Ceylon)	3,840,000	£10	£25	£50	£100
1851 (issued for Ceylon)	2,215,680	£10	£25	£50	£100
1852 (issued for Ceylon)	*incl. above*	£10	£25	£50	£100
1853 (issued for Ceylon)	*incl. above*	£10	£25	£50	£100
1853 Proof	—	—	—	—	£400

EMERGENCY ISSUES

GEORGE III (1760–1820)

o alleviate the shortage of circulating coinage during the 'apoleonic Wars the Bank of England firstly authorised the ɔuntermarking of other countries' coins, enabling them to ass as English currency. The coins, countermarked with unches depicting the head of George III, were mostly panish American 8 reales of Charles III. Although this had nited success it was later decided to completely overstrike e coins with a new English design on both sides— oecimens that still show traces of the original host coin's ate are avidly sought after by collectors. This overstriking ontinued for a number of years although all the known oins are dated 1804. Finally, in 1811 the Bank of England sued silver tokens which continued up to 1816 when a ompletely new regal coinage was introduced.

ATE	F	VF	EF	UNC
OLLAR				
)val countermark of George III				
)n "Pillar" type 8 reales	£165	£650	£1000	—
On "Portrait" type	£200	£350	£750	—
)ctagonal countermark of George III				
n "Portrait" type	£200	£600	£850	—
ALF DOLLAR				
)val countermark of George III				
)n "Portrait" type 4 reales .	£200	£400	£850	—
IVE SHILLINGS OR ONE DOLLAR				
'hese coins were overstruck on Spanish-American coins				
1804	£100	£250	£450	—
– With details of original coin still visible add from 10%.				
ANK OF ENGLAND TOKENS				
HREE SHILLINGS				
811 Draped bust	£35	£45	£100	—
812 —	£35	£50	£125	—
812 Laureate bust	£35	£45	£100	—
813 —	£35	£45	£100	—
814 —	£35	£45	£100	—
815 —	£35	£45	£100	—
816 —	£125	£250	£850	—
ONE SHILLING AND SIXPENCE				
811 Draped bust	£20	£45	£75	£145
812 —	£20	£45	£75	£145
1812 Laureate bust	£20	£45	£75	£145
812 Proof in platinum				Unique
813 —	£20	£35	£65	£125
813 Proof in platinum				Unique
814 —	£20	£35	£65	£125
815 —	£20	£35	£65	£125
816 —	£20	£35	£65	£125
INEPENCE				
812 Pattern only	—	—	Very Rare	

MAUNDY SETS

CHARLES II (1660–85)

DATE	F	VF	EF	UNC
Undated	£130	£175	£400	—
1670	£110	£150	£375	—
1671	£100	£145	£345	—
1672	£100	£140	£345	—
1673	£100	£140	£345	—
1674	£105	£150	£355	—
1675	£100	£145	£345	—
1676	£110	£150	£350	—
1677	£100	£145	£345	—
1678	£150	£210	£420	—
1679	£110	£160	£360	—
1680	£105	£150	£350	—
1681	£120	£170	£370	—
1682	£110	£150	£350	—
1683	£110	£155	£350	—
1684	£170	£220	£425	—

JAMES II (1685–88)

DATE	F	VF	EF	UNC
1686	£130	£190	£360	—
1687	£130	£190	£375	—
1688	£160	£200	£425	—

WILLIAM & MARY (1688–94)

DATE	F	VF	EF	UNC
1689	£400	£600	£850	—
1691	£250	£320	£500	—
1692	£260	£350	£550	—
1693	£220	£290	£485	—
1694	£200	£260	£415	—

WILLIAM III (1694–1702)

DATE	F	VF	EF	UNC
1698	£140	£210	£415	—
1699	£220	£300	£500	—
1700	£150	£215	£425	—
1701	£145	£205	£405	—

ANNE (1702–14)

DATE	F	VF	EF	UNC
1703	£125	£210	£400	—
1705	£115	£195	£385	—
1706	£125	£190	£375	—
1708	£215	£295	£480	—
1709	£135	£210	£395	—
1710	£140	£220	£410	—
1713	£125	£210	£395	—

GEORGE I (1714–27)

DATE	F	VF	EF	UNC
1723	£125	£205	£385	—
1727	£120	£195	£375	—

GEORGE II (1727–60)

DATE	MINTAGE	F	VF	EF	UNC
1729		£100	£160	£325	—
1731		£100	£160	£325	—
1732		£90	£150	£290	—
1735		£90	£150	£290	—
1737		£90	£150	£290	—
1739		£90	£150	£290	—
1740		£90	£150	£290	—
1743		£120	£175	£325	—
1746		£90	£140	£275	—
1760		£95	£155	£290	—

GEORGE III (1760–1820)

DATE	MINTAGE	F	VF	EF	UNC
1763		£85	£120	£220	—
1766		£85	£120	£230	—
1772		£90	£130	£245	—
1780		£85	£120	£220	—
1784		£85	£125	£230	—
1786		£85	£125	£240	—
1792 Wire		£110	£160	£250	£37
1795		£50	£75	£100	£16
1800		£50	£75	£100	£17
New Coinage					
1817		£80	£100	£150	£24
1818		£75	£95	£140	£21
1820		£75	£95	£140	£23

GEORGE IV (1820–30)

DATE	MINTAGE	F	VF	EF	UNC
1822		—	£80	£145	£22
1823		—	£80	£145	£22
1824		—	£80	£145	£22
1825		—	£75	£140	£21
1826		—	£75	£140	£21
1827		—	£75	£140	£22
1828		—	£80	£140	£21
1829		—	£75	£140	£21
1830		—	£75	£140	£21

WILLIAM IV (1830–37)

DATE	MINTAGE	F	VF	EF	UNC
1831		—	£85	£150	£24
1831 Proof		—	—	—	£42
1832		—	£85	£150	£24
1833		—	£85	£150	£24
1834		—	£85	£150	£24
1835		—	£85	£150	£24
1836		—	£85	£150	£24

VICTORIA (1837–1901)

YOUNG HEAD ISSUES

DATE	MINTAGE	F	VF	EF	UNC
1838	4,158	—	—	£105	£17
1839	4,125	—	—	£115	£18
1839 Proof	unrecorded	—	—	£200	£40
1840	4,125	—	—	£135	£19
1841	2,574	—	—	£140	£20
1842	4,125	—	—	£140	£20
1843	4,158	—	—	£110	£18
1844	4,158	—	—	£140	£20
1845	4,158	—	—	£100	£17
1846	4,158	—	—	£140	£22
1847	4,158	—	—	£200	£28
1848	4,158	—	—	£200	£28
1849	4,158	—	—	£160	£21
1850	4,158	—	—	£115	£18
1851	4,158	—	—	£120	£18
1852	4,158	—	—	£205	£30
1853	4,158	—	—	£210	£30

ATE	MINTAGE	EF	UNC
853 Proof	unrecorded	—	£475
854	4,158	£110	£185
855	4,158	£110	£185
856	4,158	£100	£170
857	4,158	£105	£170
858	4,158	£95	£170
859	4,158	£95	£160
860	4,158	£105	£175
861	4,158	£105	£190
862	4,158	£110	£180
863	4,158	£110	£180
864	4,158	£100	£170
865	4,158	£100	£180
866	4,158	£105	£175
867	4,158	£100	£180
868	4,158	£95	£170
869	4,158	£110	£190
870	4,458	£100	£160
871	4,488	£90	£150
872	4,328	£90	£150
873	4,162	£85	£145
874	4,488	£85	£145
875	4,154	£85	£145
876	4,488	£85	£125
877	4,488	£80	£120
878	4,488	£80	£120
879	4,488	£80	£120
880	4,488	£80	£120
881	4,488	£80	£120
882	4,146	£85	£130
883	4,488	£70	£110
884	4,488	£70	£110
885	4,488	£70	£110
886	4,488	£70	£110
887	4,488	£80	£125
UBILEE HEAD ISSUES			
888	4,488	£75	£105
889	4,488	£70	£100
890	4,488	£75	£100
891	4,488	£70	£100
892	4,488	£70	£100
LD HEAD ISSUES			
893	8,976	£60	£80
894	8,976	£65	£85
895	8,976	£60	£80
896	8,976	£60	£80
897	8,976	£60	£80
898	8,976	£60	£80
899	8,976	£60	£80
900	8,976	£60	£75
901	8,976	£60	£75

EDWARD VII (1902–110)

902	8,976	£45	£65
902 Matt proof	15,123	—	£75
903	8,976	£45	£65
904	8,976	£55	£80
905	8,976	£55	£80
906	8,800	£50	£70
907	8,760	£45	£70
908	8,769	£45	£70
909	1,983	£65	£120
910	1,440	£75	£130

GEORGE V (1911–136)

DATE	MINTAGE	EF	UNC
911	1,786	£60	£95
911 Proof	6,007	—	£105
912	1,246	£65	£105
913	1,228	£65	£105
1914	982	£70	£120
1915	1,293	£65	£105
1916	1,128	£60	£100
1917	1,237	£60	£100
1918	1,375	£60	£100
1919	1,258	£60	£100
1920	1,399	£60	£100
1921	1,386	£65	£110
1922	1,373	£60	£100
1923	1,430	£65	£105
1924	1,515	£65	£105
1925	1,438	£60	£100
1926	1,504	£60	£100
1927	1,647	£65	£105
1928	1,642	£65	£105
1929	1,761	£65	£105
1930	1,724	£60	£95
1931	1,759	£60	£95
1932	1,835	£60	£95
1933	1,872	£60	£95
1934	1,887	£60	£95
1935	1,928	£65	£105
1936	1,323	£75	£105

GEORGE VI (1936–52)

1937	1,325	£55	£85
1937 Proof	20,900	£55	£80
1938	1,275	£60	£100
1939	1,234	£60	£100
1940	1,277	£60	£100
1941	1,253	£65	£100
1942	1,231	£60	£100
1943	1,239	£60	£100
1944	1,259	£60	£100
1945	1,355	£60	£100
1946	1,365	£60	£100
1947	1,375	£65	£105
1948	1,385	£65	£105
1949	1,395	£65	£105
1950	1,405	£65	£105
1951	1,468	£65	£105
1952	1,012	£75	£120

ELIZABETH II (1952–)

1953	1,025	—	£375
1954	1,020	—	£90
1955	1,036	—	£90
1956	1,088	—	£90
1957	1,094	—	£90
1958	1,100	—	£90
1959	1,106	—	£90
1960	1,112	—	£90
1961	1,118	—	£90
1962	1,125	—	£90
1963	1,131	—	£90
1964	1,137	—	£90
1965	1,143	—	£90
1966	1,206	—	£90
1967	986	—	£95
1968	964	—	£95
1969	1,002	—	£90
1970	980	—	£90

Later issues are listed in the Decimal section.
Sets in contemporary dated boxes are usually worth a higher premium. For example approximately £10 can be added to sets from Victoria to George VI in contemporary undated boxes and above £15 for dated boxes.

MAUNDY ODDMENTS SINGLE COINS

It is nowadays considered that the early small denomination silver coins 4d–1d were originally struck for the Maundy ceremony although undoubtedly many subsequently circulated as small change—therefore they are listed here under "Maundy silver single coins".

FOUR PENCE

CHARLES II (1660–85)

DATE	F	VF	EF
Undated	£30	£48	£95
1670	£38	£55	£100
1671	£25	£40	£80
1672	£25	£40	£80
1673	£25	£40	£80
1674	£25	£40	£80
1675	£25	£40	£80
1676	£25	£40	£80
*1677	£23	£37	£80
1678	£25	£40	£80
1679	£22	£35	£70
1680	£24	£37	£75
1681	£25	£40	£80
1682	£25	£40	£85
1683	£26	£40	£85
1684	£24	£40	£90

JAMES II (1685–88)

DATE	F	VF	EF
1686	£30	£45	£90
1687	£30	£30	£100
1688	£30	£44	£85

WILLIAM & MARY (1688–94)

DATE	F	VF	EF
*1689	£27	£42	£90
1690	£35	£50	£100
1691	£37	£55	£100
1692	£45	£60	£110
1693	£45	£65	£125
1694	£42	£55	£110

WILLIAM III (1694–1702)

DATE	F	VF	EF
1698	£40	£52	£110
1699	£38	£50	£110
1700	£42	£54	£105
1701	£40	£52	£115
1702	£35	£47	£90

ANNE (1702–14)

DATE	F	VF	EF
1703	£37	£55	£110
1704	£28	£50	£95
1705	£35	£50	£100
1706	£32	£50	£100
1708	£30	£50	£100
1709	£32	£55	£105
1710	£27	£42	£75
*1713	£30	£50	£95

GEORGE I (1714–27)

DATE	F	VF	EF
1717	£30	£50	£90
1721	£27	£50	£85
1723	£38	£55	£100
1727	£35	£50	£95

GEORGE II (1727–60)

ATE	F	VF	EF	UNC
729	£30	£45	£70	—
731	£30	£45	£70	—
732	£28	£42	£70	—
735	£28	£47	£75	—
737	£28	£40	£70	—
739	£28	£40	£70	—
740	£28	£40	£75	—
743	£40	£65	£110	—
746	£25	£38	£70	—
760	£28	£40	£75	—

GEORGE III (1760–1820)

763 Young head	£22	£40	£60	—
765	£275	£525	£775	—
766	£25	£45	£75	—
770	£60	£100	£150	—
772	£40	£60	£100	—
780	£25	£40	£70	—
784	£25	£40	£70	—
786	£25	£40	£75	—
792 Older head, Thin 4	—	£50	£70	£120
795	—	£20	£37	£55
300	—	£19	£35	£50
817 New coinage	—	£22	£35	£50
318	—	£30	£38	£60
320	—	£25	£35	£50

GEORGE IV (1820–30)

322	—	—	£30	£50
323	—	—	£30	£45
324	—	—	£30	£50
326	—	—	£30	£50
327	—	—	£30	£50
328	—	—	£30	£50
329	—	—	£30	£50
330	—	—	£30	£45

WILLIAM IV (1830–37)

331–37	—	—	£30	£45

VICTORIA (1837–1901)

338–87 (Young Head)	—	—	£12	£17
341 & 1857	—	—	£18	£25
388–92 (Jubilee Head)	—	—	£10	£17
393–1909 (Old Head	—	—	£8	£14

EDWARD VII (1901–10)

902–08	—	—	£9	£14
909 & 1910	—	—	£12	£18

GEORGE V (1910–36)

911–36	—	—	£12	£17

GEORGE VI (1936–52)

937–52	—	—	£12	£18

ELIZABETH II (1952–)

953	—	—	£55	£85
954–85	—	—	£15	£20
986–2002	—	—	£18	£23

THREEPENCE

CHARLES II (1660–85)

DATE	F	VF	EF	UNC
Undated	£30	£42	£90	—
1670	£25	£38	£80	—
1671	£25	£38	£80	—
1672	£25	£37	£80	—
1673	£25	£37	£76	—
1674	£27	£35	£80	—
1675	£28	£37	£85	—
1676	£28	£40	£85	—
1677	£26	£35	£80	—
1678	£22	£36	£85	—
1679	£20	£30	£75	—
1680	£22	£38	£83	—
1681	£26	£40	£85	—
1682	£27	£40	£85	—
1683	£27	£38	£85	—
1684	£28	£39	£90	—

JAMES II (1685–88)

DATE	F	VF	EF	UNC
1685	£28	£40	£85	—
1686	£28	£42	£90	—
1687	£22	£35	£80	—
1688	£35	£65	£110	—

WILLIAM & MARY (1688–94)

DATE	F	VF	EF	UNC
1689	£28	£40	£90	—
1690	£39	£50	£110	—
1691	£130	£190	£250	—
1692	£45	£60	£120	—
1693	£85	£140	£200	—
1694	£45	£65	£120	—

WILLIAM III (1694–1702)

DATE	F	VF	EF	UNC
1698	£38	£50	£100	—
1699	£35	£50	£90	—
1700	£40	£60	£110	—
1701	£35	£47	£90	—

ANNE (1702–14)

DATE	F	VF	EF	UNC
1703	£35	£45	£90	—
1704	£27	£38	£75	—
1705	£30	£45	£85	—
1706	£27	£40	£85	—
1707	£25	£36	£75	—
1708	£26	£40	£80	—
1709	£28	£42	£80	—
1710	£22	£40	£75	—
1713	£28	£45	£90	—

GEORGE I (1714–27)

DATE	F	VF	EF	UNC
1717	£30	£40	£80	—
1721	£30	£40	£80	—
1723	£38	£48	£90	—
1727	£38	£50	£95	—

GEORGE II (1727–60)

DATE	F	VF	EF	UNC
1729	£30	£40	£75	—
1731	£30	£40	£75	—
1732	£30	£40	£75	—

ATE	F	VF	EF	UNC
735	£30	£45	£80	—
737	£30	£40	£75	—
739	£30	£40	£75	—
740	£27	£38	£70	—
743	£27	£37	£65	—
746	£25	£37	£65	—
760	£30	£40	£75	—

GEORGE III (1760–1820)

762	£12	£20	£35	—
763	£12	£20	£35	—
765	£200	£315	£525	—
766	£25	£35	£65	—
770	£27	£38	£65	—
772	£22	£35	£60	—
780	£25	£35	£60	—
784	£25	£40	£65	—
786	£25	£35	£60	—
792	—	£35	£50	£80
795	—	£20	£30	£45
800	—	£18	£28	£45
817	—	£20	£30	£45
818	—	£16	£28	£35
820	—	£20	£30	£47

GEORGE IV (1820–30)

822	—	—	£40	£80
823	—	—	£35	£75
824	—	—	£40	£80
925–30	—	—	£35	£75

WILLIAM IV (1830–37)

831–1836	—	—	£45	£85
837	—	—	£55	£100

VICTORIA (1837–1901)

838	—	—	£50	£100
839	—	—	£65	£125
840	—	—	£70	£135
841	—	—	£75	£145
842	—	—	£75	£145
843	—	—	£55	£100
844	—	—	£70	£140
845	—	—	£45	£90
846	—	—	£85	£160
847	—	—	£150	£225
848	—	—	£150	£225
849	—	—	£70	£145
850	—	—	£55	£85
851	—	—	£55	£95
852	—	—	£150	£235
853	—	—	£165	£245
854	—	—	£60	£100
855	—	—	£65	£120
856	—	—	£50	£90
957	—	—	£70	£120
858	—	—	£60	£110
859	—	—	£50	£95
860	—	—	£65	£125
861	—	—	£60	£120
862	—	—	£65	£125
863	—	—	£70	£135
864	—	—	£60	£115
865	—	—	£65	£125

DATE	F	VF	EF	UNC
1866	—	—	£60	£115
1867	—	—	£70	£125
1868	—	—	£50	£105
1869	—	—	£70	£130
1870	—	—	£55	£100
1871	—	—	£55	£110
1872	—	—	£50	£95
1873	—	—	£45	£85
1874	—	—	£40	£75
1875	—	—	£40	£75
1876	—	—	£40	£75
1877	—	—	£40	£75
1878	—	—	£40	£75
1879	—	—	£45	£80
1880	—	—	£40	£75
1881	—	—	£40	£75
1882	—	—	£60	£120
1883	—	—	£40	£75
1884	—	—	£35	£70
1885	—	—	£35	£70
1886	—	—	£35	£70
1887	—	—	£45	£90
1888–1892 (Jubilee Head)	—	—	£25	£45
1893–1901 (Old Head)	—	—	£15	£35

EDWARD VII (1901–10)

1902	—	—	£15	£35
1903	—	—	£18	£35
1904	—	—	£25	£45
1905	—	—	£30	£55
1906	—	—	£25	£45
1907	—	—	£25	£45
1908	—	—	£20	£40
1909	—	—	£25	£50
1910	—	—	£30	£60

GEORGE V (1910–36)

1911–34	—	—	£15	£30
1935	—	—	£25	£45
1936	—	—	£30	£55

GEORGE VI (1936–52)

1937–52	—	—	£20	£40

ELIZABETH II (1952–)

1953	—	—	£60	£90
1954–85	—	—	£18	£35
1986–2003	—	—	£20	£38

TWOPENCE

CHARLES II (1660–85)

Undated	£30	£40	£90	—
1668	£35	£45	£105	—
1670	£25	£40	£80	—
1671	£25	£40	£80	—
1672	£25	£38	£80	—
1673	£27	£40	£85	—
1671	£25	£40	£85	—
1675	£25	£37	£85	—
1676	£25	£37	£80	—
1677	£23	£37	£80	—

ATE	F	VF	EF	UNC
678	£25	£38	£80	—
679	£20	£32	£70	—
680	£22	£35	£75	—
681	£22	£37	£80	—
682	£25	£37	£85	—
683	£25	£37	£85	—
684	£27	£40	£90	—

JAMES II (1685–88)

1686	£28	£38	£80	—
687	£32	£45	£90	—
688	£25	£37	£80	—

WILLIAM & MARY (1688–94)

689	£20	£35	£75	—
691	£25	£37	£80	—
692	£47	£80	£120	—
693	£34	£45	£85	—
694	£27	£38	£80	—

WILLIAM III (1694–1702)

698	£38	£55	£100	—
699	£29	£45	£85	—
700	£30	£45	£90	—
701	£35	£50	£95	—

ANNE (1702–14)

703	£30	£45	£90	—
704	£24	£36	£65	—
705	£28	£45	£85	—
706	£28	£45	£85	—
707	£22	£36	£75	—
708	£22	£37	£80	—
709	£30	£47	£95	—
710	£19	£35	£70	—
713	£38	£60	£110	—

GEORGE I (1714–27)

717	£20	£32	£60	—
721	£17	£28	£50	—
723	£16	£35	£65	—
726	£18	£35	£60	—
727	£25	£40	£75	—

GEORGE II (1727–60)

729	£19	£28	£45	—
731	£19	£28	£45	—
732	£20	£30	£48	—
735	£19	£30	£45	—
737	£19	£30	£45	—
739	£20	£30	£45	—
740	£20	£30	£50	—
743	£20	£30	£50	—
746	£20	£30	£45	—
756	£18	£25	£40	—
759	£18	£25	£40	—
760	£22	£34	£50	—

GEORGE III (1760–1820)

763	£18	£30	£45	—
765	£210	£350	£625	—

DATE	F	VF	EF	UNC
1766	£18	£26	£42	—
1772	£18	£25	£40	—
1780	£18	£26	£40	—
1784	£18	£27	£42	—
1786	£17	£25	£38	—
1792	—	£30	£40	£65
1795	—	£15	£20	£30
1800	—	£13	£20	£28
1817	—	£15	£30	£38
1818	—	£13	£18	£27
1820	—	£13	£18	£27

GEORGE IV (1820–30)

1822–30	—	—	£18	£30

WILLIAM IV (1830–37)

1831–37	—	—	£20	£32

VICTORIA (1837–1901)

1838–87 (Young Head)	—	—	£12	£18
1888–92 (Jubilee Head)	—	—	£10	£16
1893–1901 (Old Head	—	—	£8	£14

EDWARD VII (1901–10)

1902–08	—	—	£8	£14
1909	—	—	£9	£17
1910	—	—	£11	£20

GEORGE V (1910–36)

1911–34	—	—	£11	£18
1935	—	—	£13	£20
1936	—	—	£15	£25

GEORGE VI (1936–52)

1937–47	—	—	£11	£18
1948–52	—	—	£13	£22

ELIZABETH II (1952–)

1953	—	—	£45	£70
1954–85	—	—	£15	£20
1986–2003	—	—	£15	£22

PENNY

CHARLES II (1660–85)

Undated	£30	£45	£90	—
1670	£25	£45	£85	—
1671	£25	£45	£85	—
1672	£27	£45	£85	—
1673	£27	£45	£85	—
*1674	£27	£45	£85	—
1675	£27	£45	£85	—
1676	£30	£50	£95	—
1677	£25	£45	£85	—
1678	£90	£160	£210	—
1679	£40	£65	£110	—
1680	£25	£45	£85	—
1681	£50	£80	£130	—
1682	£30	£50	£95	—
1683	£30	£50	£95	—
1684	£120	£170	£225	—

Charles II

JAMES II (1685–88)

ATE	F	VF	EF	UNC
1685	£30	£45	£80	—
686	£30	£45	£85	—
687	£40	£50	£105	—
688	£38	£45	£80	—

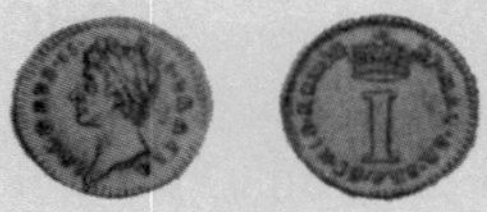

James II

WILLIAM & MARY (1688–94)

689	£300	£400	£550	—
690	£45	£65	£100	—
691	£45	£70	£110	—
692	£85	£125	£225	—
693	£50	£70	£105	—
694	£45	£65	£100	—

WILLIAM III (1694–1702)

698	£45	£60	£100	—
699	£150	£200	£270	—
700	£47	£65	£100	—
701	£45	£60	£95	—

ANNE (1702–14)

703	£37	£50	£100	—
705	£35	£50	£90	—
706	£35	£45	£80	—
708	£135	£185	£250	—
709	£35	£42	£80	—
710	£80	£130	£195	—
713	£40	£55	£85	—

GEORGE I (1714–27)

716	£25	£35	£50	—
718	£25	£35	£50	—
720	£25	£35	£50	—
723	£35	£45	£85	—
725	£25	£35	£50	—
726	£25	£35	£50	—
727	£35	£47	£85	—

GEORGE II (1727–60)

729	£30	£45	£70	—
731	£30	£40	£55	—
732	£20	£32	£50	—
735	£20	£32	£45	—
737	£20	£32	£45	—
739	£20	£32	£45	—
740	£25	£32	£45	—
743	£20	£35	£45	—
746	£25	£40	£55	—
750	£18	£27	£40	—
752	£18	£27	£40	—
753	£18	£27	£40	—
754	£18	£27	£40	—
755	£20	£30	£45	—
756	£18	£27	£40	—
757	£18	£27	£40	—
758	£18	£29	£45	—
759	£18	£28	£40	—
760	£25	£35	£50	—

George II

DATE	F	VF	EF	UNC
GEORGE III (1760–1820)				
1763	£20	£32	£42	—
1766	£18	£26	£35	—
1772	£20	£28	£38	—
1780	£18	£26	£35	—
1781	£17	£25	£35	—
1784	£15	£25	£35	—
1786	£16	£25	£35	—
1792	—	£28	£38	£46
1795	—	£17	£22	£30
1800	—	£16	£21	£28
*1817	—	£15	£19	£26
1818	—	£15	£19	£25
1820	—	£15	£19	£26
GEORGE IV (1820–30)				
1822–30	—	—	£15	£25
WILLIAM IV (1830–37)				
1831–37	—	—	£16	£27
VICTORIA (1837–1901)				
1838–87 (Young Head)	—	—	£9	£16
1888–92 (Jubilee Head)	—	—	£8	£15
1893–1901 (Old Head)	—	—	£7	£14
EDWARD VII (1901–10)				
1902–08	—	—	£7	£12
1909	—	—	£10	£18
1910	—	—	£13	£25
GEORGE V (1910–36)				
1911–14	—	—	£10	£18
1915	—	—	£12	£22
1916–19	—	—	£10	£18
1920	—	—	£12	£22
1921–28	—	—	£10	£18
1929	—	—	£13	£22
1930–34	—	—	£10	£18
1935	—	—	£13	£23
1936	—	—	£15	£25
GEORGE VI (1936–52)				
1937–40	—	—	£12	£20
1941	—	—	£14	£25
1942–47	—	—	£12	£22
1948–52	—	—	£14	£24
ELIZABETH II (1952–)				
1953	—	—	£80	£150
1965–85	—	—	£15	£25
1986–2003	—	—	£17	£28

DECIMAL COINAGE

Since the introduction of the Decimal system in the UK, many coins have been issued for circulation purposes in vast quantities. In addition, from 1982 sets of coins to non-proof standard, and including examples of each denomination found in circulation, have been issued each year. For 1982 and 1983 they were to "circulation" standard and described as "Uncirculated". Individual coins from these sets are annotated "Unc" on the lists that follow. From 1984 to the present day they were described as "Brilliant Uncirculated" (BU on the lists), and from around 1986 these coins are generally distinguishable from coins intended for circulation. They were from then produced by the Proof Coin Division of the Royal Mint (rather than by the Coin Production Room which produces circulation-standard coins). For completeness however, we have included the annotations Unc and BU back to 1982, the start year for these sets.

It is emphasised that the abbreviations Unc and BU in the left-hand columns adjacent to the date refer to an advertising description or to an engineering production standard, not the preservation condition or grade of the coin concerned. Where no such annotation appears adjacent to the date, the coin is circulation-standard for issue as such.

In general we have only included the mintage figures of coins struck in precious metals where these are available, but have at this stage excluded them for such versions of circulation coins. Where a coin is available in uncirculated grade at, or just above, face value no price has been quoted.

Base metal Proof issues of circulation coinage (£2 or £1 to one or ½ penny) of the decimal series were only issued, as with Unc or BU, as part of Year Sets, but many of these sets have been broken down into individual coins, hence the appearance of the latter on the market.

The lists do not attempt to give details of die varieties, except where there was an obvious intention to change the appearance of a coin, e.g. 1992 20p.

FIVE POUNDS (Sovereign series)

This series is all minted in gold, and, except where stated, have the St George reverse. BU coins bear a U in a circle.

DATE	Mintage	UNC
1980 Proof	10,000	£450
1981 Proof	5,400	£450
1982 Proof	2,500	£480
1984 BU	15,104	£400
1984 Proof	905	£475
1985 New portrait BU	13,626	£400
1985 — Proof	6,130	£480
1986 BU	7,723	£400
1987 Uncouped portrait BU	5,694	£400
*1988 BU	3,315	£400
1989 500th Anniversary of the Sovereign. Enthroned portrayal obverse and Crowned shield reverse BU	2,937	£550
1989 — Proof	5000	£625
1990 BU	1,226	£400
1990 Proof	1,721	£500
1991 BU	976	£400
1991 Proof	1,336	£550
1992 BU	797	£400
1992 Proof	1,165	£550
1993 BU	906	£400
1993 Proof	1,078	£550
1994 BU	1,000	£400
1994 Proof	918	£550
1995 BU	1,000	£400
1995 Proof	1,250	£550
1996 BU	1,000	£400
1996 Proof	1,250	£550
1997 BU	1,000	£400
1997 Proof	1,000	£600
1998 New portrait BU	1,000	£425
1998 Proof	1,500	£650
1999 BU	1,000	£425
1999 Proof	1,000	£650
2000 ("Bullion")	10,000	£350
2000 BU	994	£450
2000 Proof	3,000	£650
2001 BU	1,000	£450
2001 Proof	3,500	£650
2002 Shield rev. ("Bullion")	—	£350
2002 BU	—	£450
2002 Proof	3,000	£650
2003 BU	—	—
2003 Proof	—	—

The obverse of the 1989 gold coins portray HM the Queen enthroned

FIVE POUNDS (Crown series)

This series commenced in 1990 when the "Crown" was declared legal tender at £5, instead of 25p as all previous issues continued to be. Mintage is in cupro-nickel unless otherwise stated. BU includes those in individual presentation folders, and those in sets sold with stamp covers and/or banknotes.

1990 Queen Mother's 90th Birthday.	2,761,431	£8
1990 — BU	48,477	£10
1990 — Silver Proof	56,800	£32
1990 — Gold Proof	2,500	£525

DATE	Mintage	UNC
1993 Coronation 40th Anniversary	1,834,655	£8
1993 — BU	—	£10
1993 — Proof	—	£15
1993 — Silver Proof	100,000	£32
1993 — Gold Proof	2,500	£525
1996 HM the Queen's 70th Birthday	2,396,100	£8
1996 — BU	—	£10
1996 — Proof	—	£15
1996 — Silver Proof	70,000	£32
1996 — Gold Proof	2,750	£650
1997 Royal Golden Wedding	1,733,000	£8
1997 — BU	—	£10
1997 — — with £5 note	5,000	£55
1997 — Proof	—	£20
1997 — Silver Proof	75,000	£32
1997 — Gold Proof	2,750	£650
1998 Prince of Wales 50th birthday	1,407,300	£7
1998 — BU	—	£12
1998 — Proof	—	£20
1998 — Silver Proof	—	£40
1998 — Gold Proof	—	£650
1999 Princess of Wales Memorial.	1,600,000	£9
1999 — BU	—	£12
1999 — Proof	—	£20
1999 — Silver Proof	350,000	£40
1999 — Gold Proof	7,500	£650
1999 Millennium	3,796,300	£8
1999 — BU	—	£15
1999 — Proof	—	£22
1999 — Silver Proof	100,000	£40
1999 — Gold Proof	2,500	£600
*2000 —	—	£8
2000 — BU	—	£15
2000 — — with special Millennium Dome mintmark	—	£12
2000 — Proof	—	£22
2000 — Silver Proof with gold highlight	27,435	£40
2000 — Gold Proof	1,487	£575
2000 Queen Mother's 100th Birthday	3,147,010	£7
2000 — BU	—	£12
2000 — Silver Proof	100,000	£40
2000 — — — Piedfort	14,850	£175
2000 — Gold Proof	3,000	£550
*2001 Victorian Era.	848,400	£7
2001 — BU	—	£12
2001 — Proof	—	£20
2001 — Silver Proof	100,000	£40
2001 — Gold Proof	3,000	£550
2001 — — with frosted relief	750	£850
*2002 Golden Jubilee	—	£7
2002 — BU	—	£12
2002 — Proof	—	£20
2002 — Silver Proof	75,000	£40
2002 — Gold Proof	5,502	£550
2002 Queen Mother Memorial	—	£7
2002 — BU	—	£12
2002 — Silver Proof	25,000	£40
2002 — Gold Proof	3,000	£550
2003 Coronation Jubilee	—	—
2003 — BU	—	—
2003 — Proof	—	—

DOUBLE SOVEREIGN

As with the Sovereign series Five Pound coins, those listed under this heading bear the St George reverse, except where otherwise stated, and are minted in gold. They are, and always have been, legal tender at £2, and have a diameter indentical to that of the base metal Two Pound coins listed further below under a different heading. The denomination does not appear on Double Sovereigns.

DATE	Mintage	UNC
1980 Proof	10,000	£200
1982 Proof	£2,500	£200
1983 Proof	12,500	£180
1985 New Portrait Proof	5,849	£200
1987 Proof	14,301	£200
1988 Proof	12,743	£200
1989 500th Anniversary of the Sovereign. Enthroned portrayal obverse and Crowned shield reverse Proof	14,936	£240
1990 Proof	4,374	£200
1991 Proof	3,108	£220
1992 Proof	2,608	£220
1993 Proof	2,155	£220
1996 Proof	3,167	£220
1998 New Portrait Proof	4,500	£225
2000 Proof	2,250	£275
2002 Shield reverse Proof	8,000	£300

TWO POUNDS

This series commenced in 1986 with nickel-brass commemorative coins, with their associated base metal and precious metal BU and proof coins. From 1997 (actually issued in 1998) a thinner bi-metal version commenced with a reverse theme of the advance of technology, and from this date the coin was specifically intended to circulate. This is true also for the parallel issues of anniversary and commemorative Two Pound issues in 1999 and onwards. All have their BU and proof versions, as listed below.

DATE	UNC
*1986 Commonwealth Games	£6
1986 — BU	£7
1986 — Proof	£10
1986 — Silver BU	£15
1986 — — Proof	£18
1986 — Gold Proof	£250
1989 Tercentenary of Bill of Rights.	£7
1989 — BU (issued in folder with Claim of Right)	£20
1989 — Proof (issued as pair with Claim of Right)	£28
1989 — Silver Proof (Pair as above)	£40
1989 — — — Piedfort (Pair as above)	£60
*1989 Tercentenary of Claim of Right (issued in Scotland)	£12
1989 — BU (see above)	£20
1989 — Proof (see above)	£28
1989 — Silver Proof (see above)	£40
1989 — — — Piedfort (see above)	£60
*1994 Tercentenary of the Bank of England	£5
1994 — BU	£7
1994 — Proof	£10
1994 — Silver Proof	£28
1994 — — — Piedfort	£65
1994 — Gold Proof	£400
1994 — — — with Double Sovereign obverse (no denomination)	£575

DATE	UNC
1995 50th Anniversary of End of WWII.	£5
1995 — BU	£6
1995 — Proof	£10
1995 — Silver Proof	£35
1995 — — — Piedfort	£55
1995 — Gold Proof	£450
1995 50th Anniversary of The United Nations	£5
1995 — BU	£6
1995 — Proof	£10
1995 — Silver Proof	£35
1995 — Silver Proof Piedfort	£60
1995 — Gold Proof	£450
1996 European Football Championships.	£5
1996 — BU	£6
1996 — Proof	£8
1996 — Silver Proof	£32
1996 — — — Piedfort	£55
1996 — Gold Proof	£450
1997	£4
1997 BU	£8
1997 Proof	£12
1997 Silver Proof	£25
1997 — — Piedfort	£45
1997 Gold Proof (red (outer) and yellow (inner) 22ct)	£355
1998 New Portrait	£3
1998 — BU	£7
1998 Proof	£10
1998 Silver Proof	£32
1999	£3
1999 Rugby World Cup	£3
1999 — BU	£4
1999 — Silver Proof (gold plated ring)	£32
1999 — — — Piedfort (Hologram)	£85
1999 — Gold Proof	£355
2000	£3
2000 BU	£4
2000 Proof	£10
2000 Silver Proof	£32
2000 Gold Proof	£355
2001	—
2001 BU	£3
2001 Proof	£10
2001 Marconi	£3
2001 — BU	£4
2001 — Proof	£10
2001 — Silver Proof (gold plated ring)	£30
2001 — — — Piedfort	£85
2001 — Gold Proof	£355
2002	—
2002 BU	£3
2002 Proof	£10
2002 Commonwealth Games (4 versions) each	£3
2002 — — BU (issued in set of 4)	£4
2002 — — Proof (issued in set of 4)	£10
2002 — Silver Proof (issued in set of 4)	£32
2002 — — — Piedfort (painted) (issued in set of 4)	£85
2002 — Gold (issued in set of 4)	£300
2003	—
2003 BU	—
2003 Proof	£10
2003 DNA Double Helix	—
2003 — BU	—
2003 — Proof	£10
2003 — Silver Proof (Gold-plated ring)	£30
2003 — — Piedfort	—
2003 — Gold Proof	£300

SOVEREIGN

All are minted in gold, bear the St George reverse except where stated, and are legal tender at one pound.

DATE	MINTAGE	UNC
1974	5,002,566	£55
1976	4,150,000	£55
1978	6,550,000	£55
1979	9,100,000	£55
1979 Proof	50,000	£75
1980	5,100,000	£55
1980 Proof	91,200	£75
1981	5,000,000	£55
1981 Proof	32,960	£75
1982	2,950,000	£55
1982 Proof	22,500	£75
1983 Proof	21,250	£75
1984 Proof	19,975	£85
1985 New portrait Proof	17,242	£85
1986 Proof	17,579	£85
1987 Proof	22,479	£85
1988 Proof	18,862	£90
1989 500th Anniversary of the Sovereign—details as Five Pounds (Sov. Series). Proof	23,471	£180
1990 Proof	8,425	£130
1991 Proof	7,201	£130
1992 Proof	6,854	£150
1993 Proof	6,090	£150
1994 Proof	7,165	£150
1995 Proof	9,500	£150
1996 Proof	10,000	£150
1997 Proof	9,750	£165
1998 New Portrait Proof	13,500	£165
1999 Proof	11,903	£170
2000 (first Unc issue since 1982)	124,182	£55
2000 Proof	12,159	£125
2001	100,000	£55
2001 Proof	10,000	£125
2002 Shield Rev. ("bullion")	—	£60
2002 Proof	20,500	£125
2003 ("bullion")	—	—
2003 Proof	—	—

HALF SOVEREIGN

Legal Tender at 50 pence, otherwise the notes for the Sovereign apply

DATE	MINTAGE	UNC
1980 Proof only	86,700	£40
1982	2,500,000	£40
1982 Proof	21,590	£45
1983 Proof	19,710	£50
1984 Proof	19,505	£50
1985 New portrait Proof	15,800	£45
1986 Proof	17,075	£45
1987 Proof	20,687	£45
1988 Proof	18,266	£50
1989 500th Anniversary of the Sovereign		
(details as Five Pounds (Sov. Series) Proof	21,824	£80
1990 Proof	7,889	£55
1991 Proof	6,076	£55
1992 Proof	5,915	£65
1993 Proof	4,651	£65
1994 Proof	7,167	£70
1995 Proof	7,500	£70
1996 New Portrait Proof	10,500	£70
1997 Proof	9,750	£70
1998 Proof	11,000	£70
1999 Proof	9,750	£70
2000	142,304	£40
2000 Proof	9,708	£70
2001	—	£40
2001 Proof	7,500	£70
2002 Shield reverse ("bullion")	18,000	£70
2002 Proof	—	£40
2003 ("bullion")	—	—
2003 Proof	—	—

ONE POUND

Introduced into circulation in 1983 to replace the £1 note, all are minted in nickel-brass unless otherwise stated. The reverse changes yearly, the Royal coat of arms being the "definitive" version. Unc or BU may come either in a presentation folder or from a set.

DATE	UNC
1983 Royal coat of arms	£5
1983 — Unc	£7
1983 — Proof	£10
1983 — Silver Proof	£30
1983 — — — Piedfort	£120
1984 Scottish Thistle	£4
1984 — BU	£6
1984 — Proof	£7
1984 — Silver Proof	£32
1984 — — — Piedfort	£60
1985 New portrait. Welsh Leek	£3
1985 — BU	£6
1985 — Proof	£7
1985 — Silver Proof	£30
1985 — — — Piedfort	£50

1983, 1993, 1998, 2003

1984, 1989

DATE	UNC
1986 Northern Ireland Flax	£3
1986 — BU	£6
1986 — Proof	£8
1986 — Silver Proof	£35
1986 — — — Piedfort	£55
1987 English Oak	£3
1987 — BU	£6
1987 — Proof	£10
1987 — Silver Proof	£30
1987 — — — Piedfort	£50
1988 Crowned Royal Arms	£2
1988 — BU	£6
1988 — Proof	£10
1988 — Silver Proof	£32
1988 — — — Piedfort	£55
1989 Scottish Thistle	£2
1989 — BU	£6
1989 — Proof	£8
1989 — Silver Proof	£28
1989 — — — Piedfort	£50
1990 Welsh Leek	£2
1990 — BU	£5
1990 — Proof	£8
1990 — Silver Proof	£28
1991 Northern Ireland Flax	£2
1991 — BU	£6
1991 — Proof	£8
1991 — Silver Proof	£32
1992 English Oak	£2
1992 — BU	£5
1992 — Proof	£8
1992 — Silver Proof	£32
1993 Royal Coat of Arms	£2
1993 — BU	£5
1993 — Proof	£10
1993 — Silver Proof	£34
1993 — — Piedfort Proof	£65
1994 Scottish Lion	£2
1994 — BU	£6
1994 — Proof	£8
1994 — Silver Proof	£32
1994 — — — Piedfort	£65
1995 Welsh Dragon	£2
1995 — BU	£6
1995 — — (Welsh)	£8
1995 — Proof	£10
1995 — Silver Proof	£34
1995 — — — Piedfort	£65
1996 Northern Ireland Celtic-style Cross	£3
1996 — BU	£6
1996 — Proof	£8
1996 — Silver Proof	£33
1996 — — — Piedfort	£65
1997 English Lions	£3
1997 — BU	£6
1997 — Proof	£8
1997 — Silver Proof	£35
1997 — — — Piedfort	£70
1998 New portrait. Royal Coat of Arms. BU	£7
1998 — Proof	£8
1998 — Silver Proof	£30
1998 — — — Piedfort	£45
1999 Scottish Lion. BU	£6
1999 — Proof	£8
1999 — Silver Proof	£35
1999 — — — Reverse Frosting	£45
1999 — — — Piedfort	£75

1985, 1990

1986, 1991

1987, 1992

1988

1994, 1999

1995, 2000

1996, 2001

DATE	UNC
2000 Welsh Dragon	£2
2000 — BU	£6
2000 — Proof	£8
2000 — Silver Proof	£35
2000 — — — Reverse Frosting	£40
2000 — — — Piedfort	£45
2001 Northern Ireland Celtic-style Cross.	£2
2001 — BU	£6
2001 — Proof	£8
2001 — Silver Proof	£35
2001 — — — Piedfort	£45
2002 English Lions	£2
2002 — BU	£6
2002 — Proof	£8
2002 — Silver Proof	£32
2002 — — — Piedfort	£50
2002 — Gold Proof	£160
2003 Royal Coat of Arms	—
2003 — BU	—
2003 — Proof	—
2003 — Silver Proof	—
2003 — — Piedfort	—

1997, 2002

FIFTY PENCE

Introduced as legal tender for 10 shillings to replace the banknote of that value prior to decimalisation, coins of the original size are no longer legal tender. Unless otherwise stated, i.e. for commemoratives, the reverse design is of Britannia. The reverse legend of NEW PENCE became FIFTY PENCE from 1982.

DATE	UNC
*1969	£3
1970	£4
1971 Proof	£8
1972 Proof	£8
1973 Accession to EEC	£3
1973 — Proof	£5
1973 — Silver Proof Piedfort	£750
1974 Proof	£5
1975 Proof	£5
1976	£3
1976 Proof	£5
1977	£3
1977 Proof	£5
1978	£3
1978 Proof	£5
1979	£3
1979 Proof	£5
1980	£3
1980 Proof	£5
1981	£2
1981 Proof	£5
*1982	£1
1982 Unc	£2
1982 Proof	£5
1983	£1
1983 Unc	£3
1983 Proof	£5
1984 BU	£3
1984 Proof	£5
1985 New portrait	£1
1985 BU	£3
1985 Proof	£5

DATE	UNC
1986 BU	£4
1986 Proof	£5
1987 BU	£4
1987 Proof	£5
1988 BU	£4
1988 Proof	£5
1989 BU	£4
1989 Proof	£5
1990 BU	£4
1990 Proof	£5
1991 BU	£5
1991 Proof	£6
1992 BU	£9
1992 — Proof	£15
*1992 Presidency of EC Council and EC accession 20th anniversary (includes 1993 date)	£8
1992 — BU	—
1992 — Proof	—
1992 — Silver Proof	£30
1992 — — — Piedfort	£50
1992 — Gold Proof	£400
1993 BU	£5
1993 Proof	—
*1994 50th Anniversary of the Normandy Landings	£5
1994 — BU (also in presentation folder)	£6
1994 — Proof	£8
1994 — Silver Proof	£30
1994 — — — Piedfort	£60
1994 — Gold Proof	£425
1995 BU	£5
1995 Proof	£8
1996 BU	£5
1996 Proof	£7
1996 Silver Proof	£22
1997 BU	£8
1997 Proof	£10
1997 Silver Proof	£28
1997 *new reduced size*	£4
1997 BU	—
1997 Proof	£6
1997 Silver Proof	£28
1997 — — Piedfort	£40
1998 New portrait	£2
1998 BU	—
1998 Proof	£5
*1998 Presidency and 25th anniversary of EU entry	£2
1998 — BU	£4
1998 — Proof	£7
1998 — Silver Proof	£25
1998 — — — Piedfort	£65
1998 — Gold Proof	£275
*1998 50th Anniversary of the National Health Service	£2
1998 — BU	£4
1998 — Silver Proof (believed not issued as Cu-Ni proof)	£25
1998 — — — Piedfort	£75
1998 — Gold Proof	£275
1999	£2
1999 BU	£4
1999 Proof	£5
2000	£1
2000 BU	£2
2000 Proof	£5
*2000 150th Anniversary of Public Libraries	£1
2000 — BU	£3
2000 — Proof	£8
2000 — Silver Proof	£30
2000 — — — Piedfort	£45
2000 — Gold proof	£250

DATE	UNC
2001	£1
2001 BU	£2
2001 Proof	£5
2002	—
2002 BU	£1
2002 Proof	£5
2002 Gold Proof	£125
2003	—
2003 BU	—
2003 Proof	£5
2003 Centenary of Votes for Women	—
2003 — BU	—
2003 — Proof	—
2003 — Silver Proof Piedfort	—

TWENTY-FIVE PENCE (CROWN)

This series is a continuation of the pre-decimal series, there having been four crowns to the pound. The coins below have a legal tender face value of 25p to this day, and are minted in cupro-nickel except where stated otherwise.

DATE	MINTAGE	UNC
1972 Royal Silver Wedding	7,452,100	£2
1972 — Proof	150,000	£6
1972 — Silver Proof	100,000	£20
1977 Silver Jubilee	37,061,160	£2
1977 — in Presentation folder	*Incl. above*	£3
1977 — Proof	193,000	£5
1977 — Silver Proof	377,000	£15
1980 Queen Mother 80th Birthday	9,306,000	£1.50
1980 — in Presentation folder	*Incl. above*	£3
1980 — Silver Proof	83,670	£28
*1981 Royal Wedding	26,773,600	£2
1981 — in Presentation folder	*Incl. above*	£3
1981 — Silver Proof	218,140	£25

TWENTY PENCE

DATE	UNC
1982	£1
1982 Unc	£2
1982 Proof	£5
1982 Silver Proof Piedfort	£40
1983	£1
1983 Unc	£2
1983 Proof	£5
1984	£1
1984 BU	£2
1984 Proof	£5
1985 New portrait	£1
1985 BU	£2
1985 Proof	£6
1986 BU	£4
1986 Proof	£5
1987	£1
1987 BU	£2
1987 Proof	£4
1988	£1
1988 BU	£2

DATE	UNC
1988 Proof	£4
1989	£1
1989 BU	£2
1989 Proof	£4
1990	£1
1990 BU	£1
1990 Proof	£4
1991	£1
1991 BU	£2
1991 Proof	£5
1992	£4
1992 Enhanced effigy	£2
1992 — BU	£2
1992 — Proof	£4
1993	£1
1993 BU	£2
1993 Proof	£4
1994	£1
1994 BU	£2
1994 Proof	£4
1995	£1
1995 BU	£2
1995 Proof	£4
1996	£1
1996 BU	£2
1996 Proof	£4
1996 Silver Proof	£15
1997	£1
1997 BU	£2
1997 Proof	£4
1998 New portrait	£1
1998 BU	£2
1998 Proof	£4
1999	£1
1999 BU	£2
1999 Proof	£4
2000	£1
2000 BU	£2
2000 Proof	£4
2000 Silver Proof	£25
2001	£1
2001 BU	£2
2001 Proof	£4
2002	£1
2002 BU	£2
2002 Proof	£4
2002 Gold Proof	£125
2003	—
2003 BU	£1
2003 Proof	£5

TEN PENCE

The series commenced before decimalisation with the legend NEW PENCE, this changed to TEN PENCE from 1982. These "florin-sized" coins up to 1992 are no longer legal tender.

DATE	UNC
1968	£1
1969	£2
1970	£2
1971	£2
1971 Proof	£2
1972 Proof	£3
1973	£2
1973 Proof	£4
1974	£2
1974 Proof	£4
1975	£2
1975 Proof	£4
1976	£2
1976 Proof	£4
1977	£2
1977 Proof	£4
1978 Proof	£5
1979	£2
1979 Proof	£4
1980	£2
1980 Proof	£3
1981	£2
1981 Proof	£3
1982 Unc	£4
1982 Proof	£5
1983 Unc	£3
1983 Proof	£2
1984 BU	£2
1984 Proof	£3
1985 New portrait BU	£4
1985 Proof	£3
1986 BU	£4
1986 Proof	£3
1987 BU	£4
1987 Proof	£5
1988 BU	£4
1988 Proof	£5
1989 BU	£6
1989 Proof	£5
1990 BU	£6
1990 Proof	£5
1991 BU	£6

DATE	UNC
1991 Proof	£5
1992 BU	£5
1992 Proof	£6
1992 Silver Proof	£17
1992 Size reduced (24.5mm diam)	£1
1992 — BU	£2
1992 — Proof	£4
1992 — Silver Proof	£17
1992 — — — piedfort	£40
1993 BU	£2
1993 Proof	£3
1994 BU	£2
1994 Proof	£3
1995	£1
1995 BU	£2
1995 Proof	£3
1996	£1
1996 BU	£2
1996 Proof	£3
1996 Silver Proof	£22
1997	£1
1997 BU	£2
1997 Proof	£3
1998 New portrait BU	£4
1998 Proof	£3
1999 BU	£3
1999 Proof	£3
2000	£1
2000 BU	£2
2000 Proof	£3
2000 Silver Proof	£24
2001	£1
2001 BU	£2
2001 Proof	£3
2002	£1
2002 BU	£2
2002 Proof	£3
2002 Gold Proof	£150
2003	—
2003 BU	£1
2003 Proof	£3

FIVE PENCE

This series commenced simultaneously with the Ten Pence (qv). They were the same size and weight as their predecessor, the shilling, and such coins up to 1990 are no longer legal tender.

DATE	UNC
1968	50p
1969	50p
1970	55p
1971	50p
1971 Proof	£4
1972 Proof	£5
1973 Proof	£5
1974 Proof	£5
1975	50p
1975 Proof	£3
1976 Proof	£5
1977	50p
1977 Proof	£4
1978	£1
1978 Proof	£3
1979	£1
1979 Proof	£3
1980	£1
1980 Proof	£2
1981 Proof	£3
1982 Unc	£3
1982 Proof	£3
1983 Unc	£4
1983 Proof	£3
1984 BU	£3
1984 Proof	£4
1985 New Portrait. BU	£2
1985 Proof	£4
1986 BU	£2
1986 Proof	£4
1987	—
1987 BU	£1
1987 Proof	£3
1988	—
1988 BU	£1
1988 Proof	£2
1989	—
1989 BU	£1
1989 Proof	£4
1990 BU	£2
1990 Proof	£5
1990 Silver Proof	£15
1990 *Size reduced to 18mm*	—
1990 — BU	£1

DATE	UNC
1990 Proof	£2
1990 Silver Proof	£15
1990 — — Piedfort	£3
1991	—
1991 BU	£1
1991 Proof	£3
1992	—
1992 BU	£1
1992 Proof	£3
1993 BU	50p
1993 Proof	£4
1994	—
1994 BU	£1
1994 Proof	£3
1995	—
1995 BU	£1
1995 Proof	£3
1996	—
1996 BU	£1
1996 Proof	£3
1996 Silver proof	£15
1997	—
1997 BU	£1
1997 Proof	£3
1998 New portrait	—
1998 BU	£1
1998 Proof	£3
1999	—
1999 BU	£1
1999 Proof	£3
2000	—
2000 BU	£1
2000 Proof	£3
2000 Silver Proof	£20
2001	—
2001 BU	—
2001 Proof	£3
2002	—
2002 BU	—
2002 Proof	£3
2002 Gold Proof	£85
2003	—
2003 BU	—
2003 Proof	—

TWO PENCE

Dated from 1971, and legal tender from Decimal Day that year, early examples are found in the blue Specimen decimal set wallets of 1968. They were minted in bronze up to 1991, and mainly in copper-plated steel from 1992. However details of where this rule does not totally apply (1992, 1996, 1998–2000 and 2002) are given below. As with other denominations, "NEW" was replaced by the quantity of pence in word from 1982.

DATE	UNC
1971	50p
1971 Proof	£2
1972 Proof	£3
1973 Proof	£3
1974 Proof	£2
1975	£1
1975 Proof	£2
1976	50p
1976 Proof	£2
1977	50p
1977 Proof	£2
1978	50p
1978 Proof	£2
1979	50p
1979 Proof	£2
1980	50p
1980 Proof	£2
1981	50p
1981 Proof	£2
1982 Unc	£2
1982 Proof	£2
1983 Unc	£2
1983 Error NEW instead of TEN	£250
1983 Proof	£3
1984 BU	£1
1984 Proof	£1
1985 New portrait	50p
1985 BU	—
1985 Proof	£1
1986	25p
1986 BU	50p
1986 Proof	£1
1987	25p
1987 BU	50p
1987 Proof	£1
1988	25p
1988 BU	50p
1988 Proof	£1
1989	25p
1989 BU	50p
1989 Proof	£1
1990	25p
1990 BU	50p
1990 Proof	£1

DATE	UNC
1991	25p
1991 BU	50p
1991 Proof	£1
1992 *Copper plated steel*	£1
1992 *Bronze* BU	£3
1992 — Proof	£1
1993	50p
1993 BU	£1
1993 Proof	£2
1994	25p
1994 BU	50p
1994 Proof	£2
1995	—
1995 BU	50p
1995 Proof	£2
1996	—
1996 BU	50p
1996 Proof	£2
1996 Silver Proof	£18
1997	—
1997 BU	50p
1997 Proof	£2
1998 New portrait	—
1998 BU	50p
1998 Proof	£4
1998 *Bronze*	£1
1999	£1
1999 *Bronze* BU	£4
1999 — Proof	£5
2000	—
2000 BU	50p
2000 Proof	£4
2000 Silver Proof	£15
2001	—
2001 BU	50p
2001 Proof	£4
2002	—
2002 BU	—
2002 Proof	£4
2002 Gold Proof	£85
2003	—
2003 BU	—
2003 Proof	—

ONE PENNY

The history of this coin is very similar to that of the Two Pence coin (qv) except that all 1998 examples were of copper-plated steel.

DATE	UNC	DATE	UNC
1971	25p	1990	25p
1971 Proof	£1	1990 BU	50p
1972 Proof	£2	1990 Proof	£2
1973	£1	1991	25p
1973 Proof	£2	1991 BU	50p
1974	£1	1991 Proof	£2
1974 Proof	£2	1992 *Copper-plated steel*	£1
1975	£1	1992 *Bronze* BU	£2
1975 Proof	£2	1992 — Proof	£2
1976	£1	1993	25p
1976 Proof	£2	1993 BU	50p
1977	50p	1993 Proof	£1
1977 Proof	£1	1994	25p
1978	£1	1994 BU	50p
1978 Proof	£2	1994 Proof	£1
1979	£1	1995	25p
1979 Proof	£2	1995 BU	50p
1980	£1	1995 Proof	£1
1980 Proof	£2	1996	—
1981	£1	1996 BU	50p
1981 Proof	£2	1996 Proof	£1
1982 Legend changed to ONE PENNY	50p	1996 Silver Proof	£16
1982 Unc	£1	1997	—
1982 Proof	£2	1997 BU	50p
1983	50p	1997 Proof	£1
1983 Unc	£1	1998 New portrait	25p
1983 Proof	£1	1998 — BU	50p
1984	50p	1998 Proof	£2
1984 BU	£1	1999	£2
1984 Proof	£1	1999 *Bronze* BU	£3
1985 New portrait	25p	1999 *Bronze* Proof	£1
1985 BU	50p	2000	—
1985 Proof	£1	2000 BU	50p
1986	25p	2000 Proof	£2
1986 BU	50p	2000 Silver Proof	£20
1986 Proof	£1	2001	—
1987	25p	2001 BU	—
1987 BU	50p	2001 Proof	£2
1987 Proof	£1	2002	—
1988	25p	2002 BU	—
1988 BU	50p	2002 Proof	£3
1988 Proof	£3	2002 Gold Proof	£65
1989	25p	2003	—
1989 BU	50p	2003 BU	£1
1989 Proof	£2	2003 Proof	£3

HALF PENNY

No longer legal tender, its history tracks that of the Two Pence and One Penny

DATE	UNC
1971	25p
1971 Proof	£1
1972 Proof	£5
1973	50p
1973 Proof	£3
1974	50p
1974 Proof	£2
1975	50p
1975 Proof	£2
1976	50p
1976 Proof	£2
1977	50p
1977 Proof	£2
1978	75p
1978 Proof	£2
1979	£1
1979 Proof	£2

DATE	UNC
1980	50p
1980 Proof	£1
1981	£1
1981 Proof	£2
1982 Legend changed to HALF PENNY	50p
1982 Unc	£1
1982 Proof	£3
1983	25p
1983 Unc	£1
1983 Proof	£4
1984	£4
1984 BU	£5
1984 Proof	£5

MAUNDY SETS

DATE AND PLACE OF ISSUE	MINTAGE	UNC
1971 Tewkesbury Abbey	1,018	£90
1972 York Minster	1,026	£95
1973 Westminster Abbey	1,004	£90
1974 Salisbury Cathedral	1,042	£90
1975 Peterborough Cathedral	1,050	£90
1976 Hereford Cathedral	1,158	£90
1977 Westminster Abbey	1,138	£95
1978 Carlisle Cathedral	1,178	£90
1979 Winchester Cathedral	1,188	£90
1980 Worcester Cathedral	1,198	£90
1981 Westminster Abbey	1,178	£90
1982 St David's Cathedral	1,218	£90
1983 Exeter Cathedral	1,228	£90
1984 Southwell Minster	1,238	£90
1985 Ripon Cathedral	1,248	£90
1986 Chichester Cathedral	1,378	£90
1987 Ely Cathedral	1,390	£95
1988 Lichfield Cathedral	1,402	£95
1989 Birmingham Cathedral	1,353	£95
1990 Newcastle Cathedral	1,523	£100
1991 Westminster Abbey	1,384	£100
1992 Chester Cathedral	1,424	£100
1993 Wells Cathedral	1,440	£100
1994 Truro Cathedral	1,433	£100
1995 Coventry Cathedral	1,466	£100
1996 Norwich Cathedral	1,629	£110
1997 Birmingham Cathedral	1,786	£110
1998 Portsmouth Cathedral	1,654	£110
1999 Bristol Cathedral	1,676	£110
2000 Lincoln Cathedral	1,684	£120

DATE AND PLACE OF ISSUE	MINTAGE	UNC
2000 Proof	13,180	£125
2001 Westminster Abbey	1,706	£125
2002 Canterbury Cathedral		£125
2002 Gold Proof	2,002	£500
2003 Gloucester Cathedral		£130

In keeping with ancient tradition the Royal Maundy sets are made up of four silver coins of 4p, 3p, 2p and 1p. The designs for the reverse of the coins are a crowned numeral in a wreath of oak leaves—basically the same design that has been used for Maundy coins since Charles II.

PROOF AND SPECIMEN SETS

The following listings are an attempt to include all officially marketed products from the Royal Mint of two coins or more, but excluding those which included non-UK coins. It is appreciated that not all have been advertised as new to the public, but it is assumed that at some time they have been, or will be, available. In a few cases, therefore, the prices may be conjectural but are, nevertheless, attempts at listing realistic value, in some instances based on an original retail price. In the case of Elizabeth II sets, if no metal is stated in the listing, the coins in the sets are of the same metal as the circulation coin equivalent.

DATE	FDC
GEORGE IV	
1826 £5–farthing (11 coins)	£18,000
WILLIAM IV	
1831 Coronation £2–farthing (14 coins)	£16,000
VICTORIA	
1839 "Una and the Lion" £5–farthing (15 coins)	£30,000
1853 Sovereign–quarter farthing, including "Gothic"crown (16 coins)	£27,500
1887 Golden Jubilee £5– 3d (11 coins)	£6500
1887 Golden Jubilee Crown–3d (7 coins)	£1250
1893 £5–3d (10 coins)	£7500
1893 Crown–3d (6 coins)	£1250
EDWARD VII	
1902 Coronation £5–Maundy penny matt proofs (13 coins)	£1550
1902 Coronation Sovereign–Maundy penny matt proofs (11 coins)	£650
GEORGE V	
1911 Coronation £5–Maundy penny (12 coins)	£2550
1911 Sovereign–Maundy penny (10 coins)	£800
1911 Coronation Halfcrown–Maundy penny (8 coins)	£425
1927 New types Crown–3d (6 coins)	£300

DATE	FDC
GEORGE VI	
1937 Coronation £5–half sovereign (4 coins)	£1550
1937 Coronation Crown–farthing including Maundy money (15 coins)	£150
1950 Mid-century Halfcrown–farthing (9 coins)	£60
1951 Festival of Britain, Crown–farthing (10 coins)	£80
ELIZABETH II	
1953 Proof Coronation Crown–farthing (10 coins)	£55
1953 Currency (plastic) set halfcrown–farthing (9 coins)	£12
1968 Specimen decimal set 10p, 5p and 1971-dated bronze in blue wallet (5 coins)	£2.50
1970 Proof Last £sd coins (issued from 1972) Halfcrown–halfpenny (8 coins)	£18
1971 Proof (issued 1973) 50p–½p (6 coins)	£12
1972 Proof (issued 1976) 50p–½p (7 coins including Silver Wedding crown)	£15
1973 Proof (issued 1976) 50p–½p (6 coins)	£14
1974 Proof (issued 1976) 50p–½p (6 coins)	£16
1975 Proof (issued 1976) 50p–½p (6 coins)	£16
1976 Proof 50p–½p (6 coins)	£16
1977 Proof 50p–½p (7 coins including Silver Jubilee crown)	£15
1978 Proof 50p–½p (6 coins)	£15
1979 Proof 50p–½p (6 coins)	£16
1980 Proof gold sovereign series (4 coins)	£700
1980 — 50p–½p (6 coins)	£14
1981 Proof £5, sovereign, Royal Wedding Silver crown, 50p–½p (9 coins)	£650
1981 — 50p–½p (6 coins)	£17
1982 Proof gold sovereign series (4 coins)	£700
1982 — 50p–½p (7 coins)	£16
1982 Uncirculated 50p–½p (7 coins)	£11
1983 Proof gold double-sovereign to half sovereign (3 coins)	£350
1983 — £1–½p (8 coins)	£20
1983 Uncirculated £1–½p (8 coins) (includes Benson & Hedges and Martini sets)	£25
1983 — 50p –½p (7 coins) (H. J. Heinz sets)	£10
1984 Proof gold five pounds, sovereign and half-sovereigns (3 coins)	£600
1984 — £1 (Scottish rev.)–½p (8 coins)	£16
1984 BU £1 (Scottish rev.)–½p (8 coins)	£15
1985 New portrait proof gold sovereign series (4 coins)	£750
1985 Proof £1–1p in de luxe case (7 coins)	£25
1985 — in standard case	£18
1985 BU £1–1p (7 coins) in folder	£15
1986 Proof gold Commonwealth Games £2, sovereign and half sovereign (3 coins)	£400
1986 — Commonwealth Games £2–1p, de luxe case (8 coins)	£25
1986 — — in standard case (8 coins)	£23
1986 BU £2–1p in folder (8 coins)	£15
1987 Proof gold Britannia set (4 coins)	£750
1987 — — — £25 and £10 (2 coins)	£150
1987 — — double- to half sovereign (3 coins)	£325
1987 — £1–1p in de luxe case (7 coins)	£28
1987 — £1–1p in standard case (7 coins)	£20
1987 BU £1–1p in folder (7 coins)	£12
1988 Proof gold Britannia set (4 coins)	£750
1988 — — — £25 and £10 (2 coins)	£150
1988 — — double- to half sovereign (3 coins)	£325
1988 — £1–1p in de luxe case (7 coins)	£30
1988 — £1–1p in standard case (7 coins)	£25
1988 BU £1–1p in folder (7 coins)	£12
1989 Proof gold Britannia set (4 coins)	£760
1989 — — — £25 and £10 (2 coins)	£150
1989 — — 500th anniversary of the sovereign series set (4 coins)	£950
1989 — — — double- to half sovereign (3 coins)	£600
1989 — Silver Bill of Rights £2, Claim of Right £2 (2 coins)	£42
1989 — — Piedfort as above (2 coins)	£85
1989 BU £2 in folder (2 coins)	£15
1989 Proof £2 (both)–1p in de luxe case (9 coins)	£35
1989 — in standard case (9 coins)	£30

DATE	FDC
1989 BU £1–1p in folder (7 coins)	£18
1990 Proof gold Britannia set (4 coins)	£800
1990 — — sovereign series set (4 coins)	£875
1990— — double- to half sovereign (3 coins)	£400
1990 — silver 5p, 2 sizes (2 coins)	£20
1990 — £1–1p in de luxe case (8 coins)	£32
1990 — £1–1p standard case (8 coins)	£25
1990 BU £1–1p in folder (8 coins)	£16
1991 Proof gold Britannia set (4 coins)	£775
1991 — — sovereign series set (4 coins)	£1000
1991 — — double- to half sovereign (3 coins)	£450
1991 — £1–1p in de luxe case (7 coins)	£30
1991 — £1–1p in standard case (7 coins)	£25
1991 BU £1–1p in folder (7 coins)	£16
1992 Proof gold Britannia set (4 coins)	£775
1992 — — sovereign series set (4 coins)	£900
1992 — — double- to half sovereign (3 coins)	£450
1992 — £1–1p including two each 50p and 10p in de luxe case (9 coins)	£35
1992 — £1–1p as above in standard case (9 coins)	£30
1992 BU £1–1p as above in folder (9 coins)	£15
1992 Proof silver 10p, two sizes (2 coins)	£35
1993 Proof gold Britannia set 1 (4 coins)	£900
1993 — — sovereign series set (4 coins plus silver Pistrucci medal)	£1000
1993 — — double- to half sovereign (3 coins)	£500
1993 — Coronation anniversary £5–1p in de luxe case (8 coins)	£38
1993 — — in standard case (8 coins)	£35
1993 BU £1–1p including 1992 EU 50p (8 coins)	£15
1994 Proof gold Britannia set (4 coins)	£825
1994 — — sovereign series set (4 coins)	£1000
1994 — — £2 to half sovereign (3 coins)	£550
1994 — Bank of England Tercentenary £2–1p in de luxe case (8 coins)	£35
1994 — — in standard case (8 coins)	£32
1994 BU £1–1p in folder (7 coins)	£16
1994 Proof gold 1992 and 1994 50p (2 coins)	£145
1994 — "Family silver" set £2–50p (3 coins)	£45
1995 Proof gold Britannia set (4 coins)	£810
1995 — — sovereign series (4 coins)	£1,250
1995 — — £2 to half sovereign (3 coins)	£525
1995 — 50th Anniversary of WWII £2–1p in de luxe case (8 coins)	£35
1995 — — as above in standard case (8 coins)	£32
1995 BU as above in folder (8 coins)	£15
1995 Proof "Family Silver" set £2 (two) and £1 (3 coins)	£50
1996 Proof gold Britannia set (4 coins)	£950
1996 — — sovereign series set (4 coins)	£1000
1996 — — double- to half sovereign (3 coins)	£525
1996 — Royal 70th Birthday £5–1p in de luxe case (9 coins)	£45
1996 — — as above in standard case (9 coins)	£38
1996 BU Football £2–1p in folder (8 coins)	£15
1996 Proof gold Britannia £10 and half-sovereign (2 coins)	£450
1996 — — sovereign and silver £1 (2 coins)	£165
1996 — — "Family silver" set £5–£1 (3 coins)	£45
1996 — silver 25th Anniversary of Decimal currency £1–1p (7 coins)	£130
1996 Circulation and BU 25th Anniversary of Decimalisation 2*s* 6*d*–½d (misc.) and £1–1p in folder (14 coins)	£45
1997 Proof gold Britannia set (4 coins)	£1000
1997 — — sovereign series set (4 coins)	£950
1997 — — — £2 to half sovereign (3 coins)	£520
1997 — — Silver Britannia set (4 coins)	£100
1997 — Golden Wedding £5–1p in red leather case	£50
1997 — — as above in standard case (10 coins)	£38
1997 BU £2 to 1p in folder (9 coins)	£20
1997 Proof silver 50p set, two sizes (2 coins)	£35
1997/1998 Proof silver £2 set, both dates (2 coins)	£18
1998 Proof gold Britannia set (4 coins)	£1000
1998 — — sovereign series set (4 coins)	£1000

DATE	FDC
1998 — — — double- to half sovereign (3 coins)	£500
1998 Proof silver Britannia set (4 coins)	£95
1998 — Prince of Wales £5–1p (10 coins) in red leather case	£42
1998 — — as above in standard case (10 coins)	£36
1998 BU £2–1p in folder (9 coins)	£15
1998 Proof silver European/NHS 50p set (2 coins)	£50
1998 BU Britannia/EU 50p set (2 coins)	£5
1999 Proof gold Britannia set (4 coins)	£1000
1999 — — sovereign series set (4 coins)	£1000
1999 — — — £2 to half sovereign (3 coins)	£500
1999 — Princess Diana £5–1p in red leather case (9 coins)	£50
1999 — — as above in standard case (9 coins)	£38
1999 BU £2–1p (8 coins) in folder	£15
1999 Proof "Family Silver" set. Both £5, £2 and £1 (4 coins)	£45
1999 Britannia Millennium set. Bullion £2 and BU £5 (2 coins)	£25
1999/2000 Reverse frosted proof set, two x £1 (2 coins)	£65
2000 Proof gold Britannia set (4 coins)	£1000
2000 — — sovereign series set (4 coins)	£1000
2000 — — — double- to half sovereign (3 coins)	£500
2000 — Millennium £5–1p in red leather case (10 coins)	£50
2000 — — as above in de luxe case (10 coins)	£40
2000 — — as above in standard case (10 coins)	£35
2000 — Silver set Millennium £5 to 1p plus Maundy (13 coins)	£135
2000 BU £2–1p set in folder (9 coins)	£12
2000 Millennium "Time Capsule" BU £5 to 1p (9 coins)	£25
2001 Proof gold Britannia set (4 coins)	£825
2001 — — sovereign series set (4 coins)	£1000
2001 — — — £2–half sovereign (3 coins)	£500
2001 — silver Britannia set (4 coins)	£100
2001 — Victoria £5–1p in Executive case (10 coins)	£75
2001 — — as above in red leather case (10 coins)	£50
2001 — — as above in "Gift" case (10 coins)	£45
2001 — — as above in standard case (10 coins)	£35
2001 BU £2–1p in folder (9 coins)	£15
2002 Proof gold Britannia set (4 coins)	£825
2002 — — sovereign series set, all Shield rev. (4 coins)	£1000
2002 — — — double- to half sovereign (3 coins)	£450
2002 — — Golden Jubilee set £5–1p plus Maundy (13 coins)	£2500
2002 — Golden Jubilee £5–1p in Executive case (9 coins)	£65
2002 — — as above in red leather de luxe case (9 coins)	£45
2002 — — as above in "Gift" case (9 coins)	£40
2002 — — as above in standard case (9 coins)	£30
2002 BU £2–1p (8 coins) in folder	£15
2002 Proof Gold Commonwealth Games £2 set (4 coins)	£1200
2002 — Silver Piedfort Commonwealth Games £2 set (4 coins)	£200
2002 — — Commonwealth Games £2 set (4 coins)	£100
2002 — Commonwealth Games £2 set (4 coins)	£25
2002 BU Commonwealth Games £2 set (4 coins) in folder	£15
2003 Proof gold Britannia set (4 coins)	£950
2003 — — — £50–£10 (3 coins)	£400
2003 — — — type set, one of each £100 reverse (4 coins)	£1350
2003 — — sovereign series set (4 coins)	£1000
2003 — — — series £2–half sovereign (3 coins)	£425
2003 — silver Britannia set (4 coins)	£100
2003 — — — type set (one of each £2 reverse) (4 coins)	£75
2003 — £5 to 1p, two of each £2 and 50p in Executive case (11 coins)	£75
2003 — — as above in red leather case (11 coins)	£45
2003 — — as above in standard case (11 coins)	£40
2003 BU £2 (two)–1p in folder (10 coins)	£15
2003 Proof silver Piedfort set. DNA £2, £1 and Suffragette 50p (3 coins)	£150

In addition to the above the Royal Mint also produce special Wedding and "Baby" gift packs each year also the following trial pattern coin of historical interest:

1999 (dated 1994) Bi-metal £2, plus three unprocessed or part-processed elements.

PETER MORRIS

Coins • Banknotes • Antiquities • Tokens • Medals

Ask for our latest Coin, Token or Banknote List via our FREE POST Service or visit our web-site:
www.petermorris.co.uk
or
e-mail: info@petermorris.co.uk

Retail:
1 STATION CONCOURSE
BROMLEY NORTH
BR STATION, KENT
Tel: 020 8313 3410
Fax: 020 8466 8502

Postal:
P.O. BOX 223
BROMLEY, KENT
BR1 4EQ

Monday - Friday
10am - 1pm, 2pm - 6pm
Closed Wednesdays
Saturdays 9am - 2pm

Dealer in Coins & Medals

BNTA

A. D. HAMILTON & CO.

(Estd. 1890)

7 ST. VINCENT PLACE, GLASGOW G1 2DW
Telephone: 0141-221 5423
Fax: 0141–248 6019

NEW WEBSITE: www.antiquesglasgow.co.uk
E-mail address: jefffineman@hotmail.com

SPECIALISTS IN EARLY SCOTTISH AND ENGLISH

WE HAVE A
LARGE & VARIED SELECTION OF QUALITY BRITISH COINS & BANKNOTES ALWAYS IN STOCK

WE WILL PAY TOP PRICES FOR GOOD QUALITY COINS—CALL FOR AN ACCURATE VALUATION

OPEN MONDAY–SATURDAY 10.00am–5.00pm

Format *of* Birmingham

Buying & selling English & World Coins, Tokens, Medallions, Banknotes etc

Regular Lists Issued

Format of Birmingham Ltd
18 Bennetts Hill,
Birmingham B2 5QJ
Tel: 0121 643 2058
Fax: 0121 643 2210

BNTA

SCOTLAND

The coins illustrated are pennies representative of the reign, unless otherwise stated.

DAVID I (1124–53)

Berwick, Carlisle, Edinburgh and Roxburgh Mints

	F	VF
Penny	£550	£1350

David I

HENRY (1136–52)

Bamborough, Carlisle and Corbridge Mints for the Earl of Huntingdon and Northumberland

	F	VF
Penny	£1200	£3000

MALCOLM IV (1153–65)

Berwick and Roxburgh Mints

	F	VF
Penny (5 different types)	£3500	£9500

Henry

WILLIAM THE LION (1165–1214)

Berwick, Edinburgh, Dun (Dunbar?), Perth and Roxburgh Mints

	F	VF
Penny	£100	£200

William the Lion

ALEXANDER II (1214–49)

Berwick and Roxburgh Mints

	F	VF
Penny	£750	£1500

Alexander II

ALEXANDER III (1249–86)

FIRST COINAGE (1250–80)

Pennies struck at the Mints at

	F	VF
Aberdeen	£100	£300
Ayr	£100	£325
Berwick	£85	£185
"Dun" (Dumfries?)	£145	£375
Edinburgh	£55	£165
Forfar	£145	£425
Forres	£150	£400
Glasgow	£165	£435
Inverness	£165	£385
Kinghorn	£185	£450
Lanark	£165	£385
Montrose	£275	£500
Perth	£85	£185
Renfrew	£185	£500
Roxburgh	£85	£200
St Andrews	£115	£265
Stirling	£150	£355

Alexander III

SECOND COINAGE (1280–86)

	F	VF
Penny	£50	£100
Halfpenny	£100	£225
Farthing	£175	£450

JOHN BALIOL (1292–1306)

FIRST COINAGE *(Rough Surface issue)*

	F	VF
Penny	£125	£275
Halfpenny	*Extremely rare*	

SECOND COINAGE *(Smooth Surface issue)*

	F	VF
Penny	£175	£350
Halfpenny	£235	£550

John Baliol

ROBERT BRUCE (1306–29)

Berwick Mint

	F	VF
*Penny	£300	£850
Halfpenny	£350	£950
Farthing	*Extremely Rare*	

Robert Bruce

DAVID II (1329–71)

Aberdeen and Edinburgh Mints

	F	VF
Noble	*Extremely Rare*	
Groat	£85	£250
Halfgroat	£75	£185
Penny	£55	£125
Halfpenny	£165	£375
Farthing	£550	£1550

David II

ROBERT II (1371–90)

Dundee, Edinburgh and Perth Mints

	F	VF
Groat	£85	£200
Halfgroat	£100	£225
Penny	£85	£200
Halfpenny	£150	£400

Robert II

ROBERT III (1390–1406)

Aberdeen, Dumbarton, Edinburgh, Perth Mints

	F	VF
*Lion or crown	£450	£1000
Demy lion or halfcrown	£350	£800
Groat	£65	£175
Halfgroat	£120	£325
Penny	£155	£350
Halfpenny	£350	£1000

JAMES I (1406–37)

Aberdeen, Edinburgh, Inverness, Linlithgow, Perth, Stirling Mints

	F	VF
Demy	£350	£750
Half demy	£450	£850
Groat	£125	£265
Penny	£100	£275
Halfpenny	£125	£400

Robert III Lion

JAMES II (1437–60)

Aberdeen, Edinburgh, Linlithgow, Perth, Roxburgh, Stirling Mints

	F	VF
Demy	£400	£850
Lion	£460	£1500
Half lion	*Extremely rare*	
*Groat	£175	£550
Halfgroat	£400	£950
Penny (billon)	£200	£575

JAMES III (1460–88)

Aberdeen, Berwick and Edinburgh Mints

	F	VF
Rider	£750	£1750
Half rider	£900	£2000
Quarter rider	£900	£2000
Unicorn	£750	£1700
Groat	£155	£355
Halfgroat	£350	£850
Penny (silver)	£120	£350
Plack (billon)	£75	£175
Half plack	*Extremely rare*	
Penny (billon)	£75	£200
Farthing (copper)	£155	£325

James III Groat, Berwick Mint

JAMES IV (1488–1513)

Edinburgh Mint	F	VF
Jnicorn	£675	£1500
Half unicorn	£550	£1100
.ion or crown	£800	£1750
Half lion	£1500	£3500
Groat	£320	£750
Halfgroat	£320	£650
Penny (silver)	£400	£1000
Plack	£45	£120
Half plack	£100	£200
Penny (billon)	£55	£150

James IV

JAMES V (1513–42)

Edinburgh Mint	F	VF
Jnicorn	£750	£1800
Half Unicorn	£1450	£4000
Crown	£500	£1250
Ducat or Bonnet piece	£1500	£3250
'wo-thirds ducat	£1850	£3200
One -third ducat	£2000	£4000
Groat	£100	£210
One-third groat	£145	£375
Plack	£45	£145
Bawbee	£35	£115
Half bawbee	£75	£175
Quarter bawbee	*Extremely rare*	

James V Edinburgh Groat

MARY (1542–67)

Edinburgh and Stirling Mints

FIRST PERIOD (1542–58)	F	VF
Crown	£850	£2350
wenty shillings	£1750	£3000
ions (Forty-four shillings)	£800	£1950
Half lions (Twenty-two shillings)	£450	£1500
Ryals (Three pounds)	£1750	£4500
Half ryal	£2750	£6000
'ortrait testoon	£1000	£4000
Non-portrait testoon	£175	£485
Half testoon	£165	£455
awbee	£55	£115
Half bawbee	£85	£200
'enny (facing bust)	£175	£500
enny (no bust)	*Extremely rare*	
ion	£35	£100
lack	£35	£100
SECOND PERIOD (Francis and Mary, 1558–60)		
ucat (Sixty shillings)	*Extremely rare*	
on-portrait testoon	£165	£475
alf testoon	£185	£525
2 penny groat	£100	£250
ion	£45	£100
HIRD PERIOD (Widowhood, 1560–65)		
ortrait testoon	£750	£2350
alf testoon	£850	£2500
OURTH PERIOD (Henry and Mary, 1565–67)		
ortrait ryal	*Extremely rare*	
on-portrait ryal	£200	£550
wo-third ryal	£225	£650

Mary First Period Testoon

	F	VF
One-third ryal	£450	£1000
Testoon	£225	£850

FIFTH PERIOD (Second widowhood, 1567)

	F	VF
Non-portrait ryal	£250	£650
Two thirds ryal	£225	£600
One-third ryal	£275	£750

James VI Fourth coinage thirty shillings

JAMES VI
(Before accession to the English throne) (1567–1603)

FIRST COINAGE (1567–71)

	F	VF
Ryal	£185	£550
Two-thirds ryal	£180	£500
One-third ryal	£185	£500

SECOND COINAGE (1571–80)

	F	VF
Twenty pounds	*Extremely rare*	
Noble	£85	£350
Half noble	£80	£275
Two merks or Thistle dollar	£900	£1700
Merk	£850	—

THIRD COINAGE (1580–81)

	F	VF
Ducat	*Extremely rare*	
Sixteen shillings	£900	£2500
Eight shillings	£850	£2200
Four shillings	*Extremely rare*	
Two shillings	*Extremely rare*	

FOURTH COINAGE (1582–88)

	F	VF
Lion noble	£2000	£6000
Two-third lion noble	£2500	£6500
One-third lion noble	£3000	£7750
Forty shillings	£2500	£7600
*Thirty shillings	£185	£850
Twenty shillings	£135	£450
Ten shillings	£125	£350

FIFTH COINAGE (1588)

	F	VF
Thistle noble	£1450	£3250

SIXTH COINAGE (1591–93)

	F	VF
"Hat" piece	£2500	£6000
"Balance" half merk	£175	£400
"Balance" quarter merk	£265	£600

SEVENTH COINAGE (1594–1601)

	F	VF
Rider	£425	£900
Half rider	£350	£750
Ten shillings	£100	£275
Five shillings	£110	£300
Thirty pence	£85	£275
Twelve pence	£65	£250

EIGHTH COINAGE (1601–04)

	F	VF
Sword and sceptre piece	£275	£500
Half sword and sceptre piece	£225	£400
Thistle-merk	£55	£200
Half thistle-merk	£45	£175
Quarter thistle-merk	£45	£175
Eighth thistle-merk	£50	£185

	F	VF
illon and copper issues		
lack	£50	£145
alf plack	£880	£400
ardhead	£35	£100
altire plack	£100	£500
wopence	*Very rare*	
enny	*Very rare*	

JAMES VI
(After accession to the English throne)
(1603–25)

	F	VF
nit	£385	£750
ouble crown	£450	£1200
ritish crown	£325	£1000
alfcrown	£275	£500
nistle crown	£275	£500
ixty shillings	£285	£650
'hirty shillings	£85	£275
velve shillings	£75	£225
ix shillings	£125	£550
vo shillings	£55	£250
ne shilling	£85	£300
opper twopence	£35	£100
opper penny	£35	£100

James VI after accession thirty shillings

CHARLES I (1625–49)

IRST COINAGE (1625–36)

	F	VF
nit	£450	£850
ouble crown	£1200	£2500
ritish crown	*Extremely rare*	
ixty shillings	£265	£750
nirty shillings	£65	£250
velve shillings	£60	£180
x shillings	£125	£425
vo shillings	£75	£325
ne shilling	*Extremely rare*	

ECOND COINAGE (1636)

	F	VF
alf merk	£55	£200
orty penny piece	£45	£175
venty penny piece	£65	£300

HIRD COINAGE (1637–42)

	F	VF
nit	£450	£1250
alf unit	£575	£1750
ritish crown	£425	£1200
ritish half crown	£355	£1000
xty shillings	£285	£950
'hirty shillings	£70	£200
velve shillings	£70	£200
x shillings	£65	£185
alf merk	£55	£165
rty pence	£35	£100
venty pence	£30	£85
nree shillings	£50	£150
vo shillings	£50	£155
vopence (copper)	£30	£85
enny	*Extremely rare*	
vopence (CR crowned)	£30	£85
vopence (Stirling turner)	£25	£75

Charles I Third coinage thirty shillings

CHARLES II (1660–85)

Charles II two merks

	F	VF
FIRST COINAGE		
Four merks		
1664 Thistle above bust	£285	£675
1664 Thistle below bust	£300	£750
1665	*Extremely rare*	
1670	£200	£565
1673	£200	£565
1674 F below bust	£325	£755
1675	£200	£550
Two merks		
1664 Thistle above bust	£200	£550
1664 Thistle below bust	£225	£650
1670	£165	£500
1673	£165	£500
1673 F below bust	£285	£950
1674	£255	£950
1674 F below bust	£225	£850
1675	£165	£475
Merk		
1664	£50	£175
1665	£50	£175
1666	£85	£355
1668	£50	£175
1669	£50	£175
1670	£85	£285
1671	£70	£185
1672	£70	£185
1673	£70	£220
1674	£70	£220
1674 F Below bust	£65	£215
*1675 F below bust	£65	£215
1675	£85	£285
Half merk		
1664	£60	£200
1665	£60	£200
1666	£75	£250
1667	£60	£185
1668	£60	£185
1669	£80	£225
1670	£100	£350
1671	£65	£185
1672	£65	£185
1673	£55	£165
1675 F below bust	£50	£165
1675	£65	£200
SECOND COINAGE		
Dollar		
1676	£185	£450
1679	£185	£425
1680	£250	£1000
1681	£155	£450
1682	£145	£300
Half Dollar		
1675	£175	£450
1676	£185	£475
1681	£175	£450
Quarter Dollar		
1675	£75	£220
1676	£85	£255
1677	£125	£350

	F	VF
679	£75	£325
680	£65	£275
681	£80	£350
682	£100	£250
ighth Dollar		
676	£55	£155
677	£55	£155
678/7		*Rare*
679	£155	£650
680	£75	£175
682	£125	£500
ixteenth Dollar		
677	£40	£125
678/7	£75	£175
679/7		*Rare*
680	£80	£250
681	£45	£135
wopence CR crowned	£35	£125
awbees.	£45	£150
urners.	£35	£125

James VII ten shillings

JAMES VII (1685–89)

	F	VF
ixty shillings		
688 proof only	—	£1000
orty shillings		
687	£115	£350
688	£155	£450
en shillings		
687	£100	£275
688	£100	£300

WILLIAM & MARY (1689–94)

	F	VF
ixty shillings		
691	£155	£575
692	£140	£500
orty shillings		
689	£100	£300
690	£100	£285
691	£75	£245
692	£85	£285
693	£110	£425
694	£100	£425
wenty shillings		
693	£100	£385
694	£200	£500
en shillings		
689	*Extremely rare*	
690	£100	£300
691	£75	£225
692	£50	£150
694	£175	£400
ive shillings		
691	£725	£265
694	£70	£220
awbee		
691–94	£45	£125
odle		
691–94	£40	£85

William & Mary ten shillings

WILLIAM II (1694–1702)

	F	VF
Pistole	£1550	£4000
Half pistole	£1500	£3500
Forty shillings		
1695	£85	£350
1696	£65	£275
1697	£85	£355
1698	£60	£265
1699	£135	£675
1700	£215	£875
Twenty shillings		
1695	£55	£225
1696	£55	£225
1697	£125	£450
1698	£125	£375
1699	£100	£350
Ten shillings		
*1695	£85	£265
1696	£95	£300
1697	£100	£325
1698	£100	£325
1699	£125	£375
Five shillings		
1695	£75	£300
1696	£75	£300
1697	£55	£145
1699	£55	£265
1700	£55	£255
1701	£60	£285
1702	£75	£325
Bawbee		
1695–97	£35	£150
Bodle		
1695–97	£45	£155

William II ten shillings

ANNE (1702–14)

PRE-UNION 1702–7

	F	VF
Ten shillings		
1705	£75	£275
1706	£125	£450
Five shillings		
1705	£35	£125
*1706	£45	£150

Anne five shillings

POST-UNION 1707–14

See listing in English section.

JAMES VIII (The Old Pretender) (1688–1766)

A number of Guineas and Crowns in various metals were struck in 1828 using original dies prepared by Norbert Roettiers, all bearing the date 1716. These coins are extremely rare and are keenly sought after.

ISLE OF MAN

)ATE	F	VF	EF	UNC
'ENNY				
1709 Cast	£30	£75	£175	—
709 Silver cast Proof	—	—	—	£1250
709 Brass	£30	£82	£175	—
1733 "Quocunque"	£25	£40	£150	£225
733 "Ouocunoue"	£25	£50	£185	£375
733 Bath metal "Quocunque"	£15	£35	£150	—
733 Silver Proof	—	—	—	£475
733 Bronze Proof	—	—	—	£285
733 Proof	—	—	—	£425
733 Cap frosted	£15	£35	£150	£225
733 Brass, cap frosted	£25	£45	£175	£335
733 Silver Proof cap frosted	—	—	—	£350
733 Bronze annulets instead of pellets	£35	£65	£225	£475
758	£16	£30	£125	£250
758 Proof	—	—	—	£350
758 Silver Proof	—	—	—	£645
1786 Engrailed edge	£18	£32	£140	£300
786 Engrailed edge Proof	—	—	—	£350
786 Plain edge Proof	—	—	—	£675
786 Pellet below bust	£18	£45	£165	£350
1798	£18	£45	£135	£275
798 Proof	—	—	—	£245
798 Bronze Proof	—	—	—	£245
798 Copper-gilt Proof	—	—	—	£1150
798 Silver Proof	—	—	—	£1650
813	£20	£40	£100	£200
813 Proof	—	—	—	£250
813 Bronze Proof	—	—	—	£200
813 Copper-gilt Proof	—	—	—	£1650
839	£15	£30	£85	£165
839 Proof	—	—	—	£275

HALF PENCE

1709 Cast	£35	£50	£155	—
709 Brass	£40	£150	£330	—
1723 Silver	£525	£1000	£2000	—
1723 Copper	£230	£475	£1150	£1650
733 Copper	£18	£40	£150	£225
1733 Bronze	£25	£40	£150	£225
1733 Silver Proof plain cap	—	—	—	£325
1733 Silver Proof frosted cap	—	—	—	—
1733 Bronze Proof	—	—	—	£275
1733 Bath metal plain cap	£25	£35	£140	—
1733 Bath metal frosted cap	£25	£35	£145	—
*1758	£25	£35	£150	£200
1758 Proof	—	—	—	£500
1786 Engrailed edge	£15	£30	£75	£200
1786 Proof engrailed edge	—	—	—	£245
1786 Plain edge	£25	£50	£165	£225
1786 Proof plain edge	—	—	—	£450
1786 Bronze Proof	—	—	—	£250
1798	£18	£30	£75	£200
1798 Proof	—	—	—	£225
1798 Bronze Proof	—	—	—	£200

DATE	F	VF	EF	UNC
1798 Copper-gilt Proof	—	—	—	£750
1798 Silver Proof	—	—	—	£1000
1813	£15	£30	£75	£155
1813 Proof	—	—	—	£225
1813 Bronze Proof	—	—	—	£200
1813 Copper-gilt Proof	—	—	—	£775
1839	£15	£30	£50	£100
1839 Bronze Proof	—	—	—	£200

FARTHING

*1839 Copper	£15	£30	£55	£100
1839 Bronze Proof	—	—	—	£250
1839 Copper-gilt Proof	—	—	—	£1500

The last issue of coins made in the Isle of Man had been in 1839 but in 1970 Spink & Son Ltd was commissioned to produce a modern coinage for the Isle of Man Government which was struck at the Royal Mint. From 1973 onwards the Pobjoy Mint took over the contract and has been a very prolific producer of definitive and commemorative issues. It is not proposed to give a complete listing of all these coins but the Crown and 25p, which from the collector's point of view are the most interesting in the series, have been selected.Additionally a special 50p coin is issued to celebrate Christmas each year.

The listings that follow are of the ordinary uncirculated cupro-nickel crown-size coins. The Island has also issued most of the coins listed in other metals, including silver, gold and platinum in non proof and proof form and in 1984 some were also issued in silver clad cupro-nickel in proof form.

DATE	UNC
1970 Manx Cat	£6
1972 Royal Silver Wedding	£5
1974 Centenary of Churchill's birth	£4
1975 Manx Cat	£5
1976 Bi-Centenary of American Independence	£4
1976 Centenary of the Horse Drawn Tram	£4
1977 Silver Jubilee	£4
1977 Silver Jubilee Appeal	£4
1978 25th Anniversary of the Coronation	£4
1979 300th Anniversary of Manx Coinage	£4
1979 Millennium of Tynwald (5 coins)	£12
1980 Winter Olympics	£4
1980 Derby Bicentennial	£4
1980 22nd Olympics (3 coins)	£10
1980 80th Birthday of Queen Mother	£4
1981 Duke of Edinburgh Award Scheme (4 coins)	£10
1981 Year of Disabled (4 coins)	£10
1981 Prince of Wales' Wedding (2 coins)	£6
1982 12th World Cup—Spain (4 coins)	£12
1982 Maritime Heritage (4 coins)	£12
1983 Manned Flight (4 coins)	£12
1984 23rd Olympics (4 coins)	£12
1984 Quincentenary of College of Arms (4 coins)	£12
1984 Commonwealth Parliamentary Conference (4 coins)	£12
1985 Queen Mother (6 coins)	£12
1986 13th World Cup—Mexico (6 coins)	£12
1986 Prince Andrew Wedding (2 coins)	£8
1987 200th Anniversary of the United States Constitution	£4

DATE	UNC
1987 America's Cup Races (5 coins)	£12
1988 Bicentenary of Steam Navigation (6 coins)	£15
1988 Australia Bicentennial (6 coins)	£15
1988 Manx Cat	£5
1989 Royal Visit	£5
1989 Bicentenary of the Mutiny on the Bounty (4 coins)	£12
1989 Persian Cat	£6
1989 Bicentenary of Washington's Inauguration (4 coins)	£12
1990 150th Anniversary of the Penny Black	£10
1990 World Cup—Italy (4 coins)	£12
1990 25th Anniversary of Churchill's Death (2 coins)	£8
1990 Alley Cat	£6
1990 Queen Mother's 90th Birthday	£6
1991 Norwegian Forest Cat	£6
1991 Centenary of the American Numismatic Association	£5
1991 1992 America's Cup	£6
1991 10th Anniversary of Prince of Wales' Wedding (2 coins)	£8
1992 Discovery of America (4 coins)	£14
1992 Siamese Cat	£7
1992 1992 America's Cup	£5
1993 Maine Coon Cat	£5
1993 Preserve Planet Earth—Dinosaurs (2 coins)	£9
1994 Preserve Planet Earth—Mammoth	£6
1994 Year of the Dog	£6
1994 World Football Cup (6 coins)	£24
1994 Japanese Bobtail Cat	£6
1994 Normandy Landings (8 coins)	£35
1994 Preserve Planet Earth—Endangered Animals (3 coins)	£17
1995 Man in Flight—Series i (8 coins)	£50
1995 Man in Flight—Series ii (8 coins)	£50
*1995 Queen Mother's 95th Birthday	£7
1995 Year of the Pig	£7
1995 Turkish Cat	£7
1995 Preserve Planet Earth—Egret and Otter	£9
1995 America's Cup	£7
*1995 Aircraft of World War II (19 coins)	£85
1995 Famous World Inventions—Series i (12 coins)	£52
1996 Year of the Rat	£7
1996 70th Birthday of HM the Queen	£10
1996 The Flower Fairies—Series i (4 coins)	£32
1996 Famous World Inventions—Series ii (6 coins)	£32
*1996 Olympic Games (6 coins)	£27
1996 Preserve Planet Earth—Killer Whale and Razorbill	£10
1996 Burmese Cat	£9
1996 Robert Burns (4 coins)	£20
1996 King Arthur & the Knights of the Round Table (5 coins)	£28
1996 European Football Championships (8 coins)	£45
1996 Football Championships Winner	£10
1996 Explorers (2 coins)	£17
1997 Year of the Ox	£10
*1997 The Flower Fairies—Series ii (4 coins)	£21
1997 Royal Golden Wedding (2 coins)	£12
1997 Explorers—Eriksson and Nansen (2 coins)	£12
1997 Long-haired Smoke Cat	£8
1997 10th Anniversary of the "Cats on Coins" series (silver only)	£31
1997 90th Anniversary of the TT Races (4 coins)	£25
1998 The Millennium (16 coins to be issued in the next 3 years)	—
1998 Year of the Tiger	£10
1998 FIFA World Cup (4 coins)	£22
1998 Birman Cat	£10
1998 The Flower Fairies—Series iii (4 coins)	£24
1998 18th Winter Olympics, Nagano (4 coins)	£25
1998 Explorers—Vasco da Gama and Marco Polo (2 coins)	£14

DATE	UNC
1998 125th Anniversary of Steam Railway (8 coins)	£50
1998 International Year of the Oceans (4 coins)	£28
1999 50th Birthday of HRH the Prince of Wales	£8
1999 Year of the Rabbit	£8
1999 27th Olympics in Sydney (5 coins)	£30
1999 Rugby World Cup (6 coins)	£35
1999 Wedding of HRH Prince Edward and Sophie Rhys-Jones	£9
1999 Queen Mother's 100th Birthday (4 coins)	£22
1999 The Millennium (4 coins)	£22
1999 Titanium Millennium crown	£7
*2000 Year of the Dragon	£7
2000 Scottish Fold cat	£7
2000 Millennium—own a piece of time	£7
2000 Explorers, Francisco Piarro and Wilem Brents (2 coins)	£12
2000 Life and times of the Queen Mother (4 coins)	£22
2000 Queen Mother's 100th Birthday	£7
2000 60th Anniversary of the Battle of Britain	£7
2000 BT Global Challenge	£7
2000 18th Birthday of H.R.H. Prince William	£7
2001 Year of the Snake	£7
2001 The Somali cat	£7
2001 Life and times of the Queen Mother (2 coins)	£12
2001 Explorers, Martin Frobisher and Roald Amundsen (2 coins)	£12
2001 75th Birthday of HM the Queen	£7
2001 Joey Dunlop	£7
2001 Harry Potter (6 coins)	£47
2002 Year of the Horse	£8
2002 The XIX Winter Olympiad, Salt Lake City (2 coins)	£14
2002 World Cup 2002 in Japan/Korea (4 coins)	£30
2002 The Bengal Cat	£10
*2002 The Queen's Golden Jubilee—i (1 coin)	£12
*2002 Introduction of the Euro	£10
2002 The Queen's Golden Jubilee —ii (4 coins)	£40
2002 The Queen's Golden Jubilee (Emporium Hamburg) (5 coins)	£50
2002 A Tribute to Diana Princess of Wales—5 years on	£15
2003 Year of the Goat	£8
*2003 The Balinese Cat	£10
2003 Anniversary of the "Star of India"	£12

GUERNSEY

DATE	F	VF	EF	UNC
TEN SHILLINGS				
*1966	—	£2	£3	£5
1966 Proof	—	—	—	£10
THREEPENCE				
1956	50p	£1	£2	£3
1956 Proof	—	—	—	£8
1959	50p	£1	£2	£3
1966 Proof	—	—	—	£8
EIGHT DOUBLES				
1834	£4	£8	£30	£90
*1858 5 berries	£3	£7	£30	£90
1858 4 berries	£3	£7	£30	£90
1864 1 stalk	£2	£3	£20	£48
1864 3 stalks	£2	£3	£18	£55
1868	£4	£7	£18	£45
1874	£3	£4	£8	£35
1885H	£3	£4	£7	£25
1889H	£2	£3	£5	£22
1893H small date	£2	£3	£5	£22
1893H large date	£2	£3	£5	£22
1902H	£2	£3	£5	£20
1903H	£2	£3	£5	£20
1910	£2	£3	£5	£22
1911H	£2	£3	£6	£28
1914H	50p	£2	£4	£18
1918H	50p	£2	£4	£15
1920H	50p	£2	£4	£15
1934H	60p	£2	£4	£20
1934H Proof	—	—	—	£85
1938H	60p	£2	£4	£15
1945H	50p	£1	£3	£8
1947H	40p	£1	£3	£8
1949H	40p	£1	£3	£8
1956	30p	50p	£2	£6
1956	30p	50p	£2	£6
1959	30p	50p	£2	£6
1966 Proof	—	—	—	£15
FOUR DOUBLES				
1830	£3	£8	£35	£70
1830 Mule with obv. St Helena ½d	—	£650	—	—
1858	£5	£10	£40	£70
1864 Single stalk	£1	£5	£10	£40
1864 3 stalks	31	£5	£12	£45
1868	£2	£6	£18	£55
1874	£1	£5	£15	£50
1885H	£1	£5	£12	£25
1889H	£1	£2	£9	£20
1893H	£1	£2	£9	£20
1902H	£1	£2	£6	£17
1903H	£1	£2	£9	£20
1906H	£1	£2	£6	£17
1908H	£1	£2	£6	£17
1910H	£1	£2	£6	£17
1911H	£1	£2	£5	£15
1914H	£1	£2	£9	£28
1918H	£1	£2	£8	£25
1920H	£1	£2	£6	£17
1945H	£1	£2	£6	£15
1949H	£1	£2	£8	£25
1956	50p	£1	£3	£8
1966 Proof	—	—	—	£10

DATE	F	VF	EF	UNC
TWO DOUBLES				
1858	£5	£8	£35	£120
1868 Single stick	£5	£10	£40	£125
1868 3 stalks	£6	£12	£60	£130
1874	£3	£8	£35	£80
1885H	£2	£5	£8	£25
1889H	£2	£3	£6	£18
1899H	£2	£4	£12	£30
1902H	£2	£3	£10	£25
1902H	£2	£3	£10	£25
1906H	£2	£3	£10	£25
1908H	£2	£4	£10	£25
1911H	£2	£4	£13	£28
1914H	£2	£4	£13	£28
1917H	£6	£16	£51	£115
1918H	£2	£3	£7	£18
*1920H	£2	£3	£7	£17
1929H	£1	£2	£5	£10
ONE DOUBLE				
*1830	£2	£3	£15	£30
1868	£3	£9	£25	£75
1868/30	£4	£6	£20	£65
1885H	£1	£2	£4	£12
1889H	50p	£1	£3	£12
1893H	50p	£1	£3	£12
1899H	50p	£1	£3	£12
1902	50p	£1	£3	£12
1903H	50p	£1	£3	£12
1911H	50p	£1	£5	£12
1911 (new shield)	50p	£1	£3	£12
1914H	50p	£1	£5	£12
1929H	50p	£1	£3	£12
1933H	50p	£1	£3	£12
1938H	50p	£1	£3	£12

DECIMAL COINAGE

Ordinary circulating coinage from 1986 onwards is usually available in uncirculated condition at a small premium above face value thus it is not listed here. The coins listed are cupro-nickel unless otherwise stated.

	UNC
ONE HUNDRED POUNDS—*Gold*	
1994 50th Anniversary of Normandy Landings. Proof	£500
1995 Anniversary of the Liberation. Proof	£500
FIFTY POUNDS—*Gold*	
1994 50th Anniversary of Normandy Landings. Proof	£250
1995 Anniversary of the Liberation. Proof	£250
TWENTY-FIVE POUNDS—*Gold*	
1994 50th Anniversary of Normandy Landings	£175
1994 — Proof	£150
1995 Anniversary of the Liberation. Proof	£165
1996 European Football Championships. Proof	£165
1997 Royal Golden Wedding. Proof	£225
1998 Royal Air Force. Proof	£165
2000 Queen Mother 100th Birthday. Proof	£175
2001 Queen Victoria centennial	£185
2001 HM the Queen's 75th Birthday	£175
2002 Princess Diana memorial	£200
2002 Duke of Wellington	£200
TEN POUNDS	
1994 50th Anniversary of Normandy Landings. Gold proof	£50
1995 Anniversary of the Liberation. Gold proof	£50
2000 Century of Monarchy. Silver proof	£75
2001 19th Century Monarchy. Silver proof	£75
2002 18th Century Monarchy. Silver proof	£75

DATE	UNC
FIVE POUNDS	
1995 Queen Mother's 95th birthday	£15
1995 — Silver proof	£40
1995 — Small size gold	£100
1996 HM the Queen's 70th birthday	£12
1996 — Silver proof	£35
1996 European Football Championships	£15
1996 — Silver proof	£40
1997 Royal Golden Wedding	£15
1997 — Silver proof	£40
1997 — Small size gold. BU	£52
1997 Castles of the British Isles—Castle Cornet, Guernsey	£12
1997 — Silver proof	£42
1997 Castles of the British Isles—Caernarfon Castle. Silver proof	£42
1997 Castles of the British Isles—Leeds Castle. Silver proof	£44
1998 Royal Air Force.	£6
1998 Royal Air Force. Silver proof	£44
1999 Millennium. Brass	£15
1999 — Silver proof	£34
1999 Wedding of HRH Prince Edward and Sophie Rhys-Jones	£15
1999 — Silver proof	£50
1999 Queen Mother	£15
1999 — Silver proof	£50
1999 Winston Churchill	£8
1999 — Gold	£650
2000 Queen Mother's 100th Birthday	£6
2000 — Silver proof	£40
2000 — Small size gold. Proof	£50
*2000 Centuries of the British Monarchy	£15
2000 — Silver proof	£45
2000 — Small size gold. Proof	£45
2001 The Reign of Queen Victoria	£6
2001 — Proof	£12
2001 — Silver proof	£35
2001 HM the Queen's 75th Birthday	£5
2001 — Silver proof	£35
2001 — Small size gold. Proof	£45
2001 19th Century Monarchy	£8
2001 — Silver proof	£35
2001 — Small size gold. Proof	£45
2002 Golden Jubilee (two types)	£5
2002 — Silver proof	£40
2002 Princess Diana memorial	£6
2002 — Proof	£30
2002 — Gold proof	£550
2002 Century of Monarchy	£6
2002 — Silver proof	£35
2002 — Small size gold. Proof	£45
2002 Queen Mother Memoriam	£8
2002 — Proof	£15
2002 — Silver proof	£35
2002 — Small size gold. Proof	£45
2003 Duke of Wellington	—
2003 — Silver proof	—
2003 — Gold proof	—
TWO POUNDS	
1985 40th anniversary of Liberation	£8
1985 — Proof	£20
1985 — Silver proof	£30
1986 Commonwealth Games, in plastic case	£10
1986 — in special folder	£10
1986 — .500 Silver	£19
1986 — .925 Silver proof	£30
*1987 900th anniv. of death of William the Conqueror, in folder	£9
1987 — Silver proof	£30
1987 — Gold proof	£900

DATE	UNC
1988 William II, in presentation folder	£9
1988 — Silver proof	£30
1989 Henry I, in presentation folder	£9
1989 — Silver proof	£30
1989 Royal Visit	£9
1989 — Silver proof	£30
1990 Queen Mother's 90th birthday	£9
1990 — Silver proof	£35
1991 Henry II, in presentation folder	£9
1991 — Silver proof	£35
1993 40th Anniversary of the Coronation	£9
1993 — Silver proof	£34
*1994 Anniversary of the Normandy Landings	£9
1994 — Silver proof	£35
1995 50th Anniversary of Liberation	£9
1995 — Silver proof	£34
1995 — Silver Piedfort proof	£66
1997 Conserving Nature i	£5
1997 — Silver proof	£35
1998 Conserving Nature ii	£5
ONE POUND	
1981	£4
1981 Gold proof	£87
1981 Gold piedfort	£255
1983 New specification, new reverse	£4
1985 New design (in folder)	£4
1995 Queen Mother's 95th Birthday. Silver proof	£28
1996 Queen's 70th Birthday. Silver proof	£28
1997 Royal Golden Wedding. Silver BU	£12
1997 — Silver proof	£28
1997 Castles of the British Isles—Tower of London. Silver proof only	£22
1998 Royal Air Force. Silver proof	£24
1999 Wedding of Prince Edward. Silver proof	£28
1999 Queen Mother. Silver proof	£28
1999 Winston Churchill. Silver proof	£25
2000 Millennium. Silver proof (gold plated)	£32
2000 Queen Mother's 100th Birthday. Silver proof	£20
2001 HM the Queen's 75th Birthday. Silver proof	£20
FIFTY PENCE	
1969	£2
1970	£4
1971 Proof	£6
1981	£2
1982	£2
1985 New design	—
*2000 60th Anniversary of the Battle of Britain. Silver proof	£35
2000 — Gold proof	£250
TWENTY-FIVE PENCE	
1972 Royal Silver Wedding	£6
1972 — Silver proof	£15
1977 Royal Silver Jubilee	£2
1977 — Silver proof	£15
1978 Royal Visit	£2
1978 — Silver proof	£14
1980 Queen Mother's 80th birthday	£3
1980 — Silver proof	£15
1981 Royal Wedding	£2
1981 — Silver proof	£14

JERSEY

DATE	F	VF	EF	UNC
FIVE SHILLINGS				
1966	—	£2	£4	£6
1966 Proof	—	£2	£6	£12
ONE QUARTER OF A SHILLING				
1957	—	£1	£2	£5
1960 Proof	—	—	£2	£8
1964	—	—	£1	£4
1966	—	—	£1	£4
ONE TWELFTH OF A SHILLING				
1877H	£1	£2	£12	£36
1877H Proof in nickel	—	—	—	£1000
1877 Proof only	—	—	—	£375
1877 Proof in nickel	—	—	—	£1000
1881	£2	£2	£10	£45
1888	£1	£2	£8	£35
1894	£1	£2	£8	£35
1909	£1	£2	£10	£25
1911	£1	£2	£4	£20
1913	£1	£2	£4	£20
1923 Spade shield	£1	£2	£4	£20
1923 Square shield	£1	£2	£4	£20
1926	£1	£2	£5	£30
1931	£1	£2	£4	£8
1933	£1	£2	£4	£8
1935	£1	£2	£4	£8
1937	£1	£2	£4	£8
1946	£1	£2	£4	£6
1947	25p	£2	£4	£7
"1945" GVI	10p	25p	50p	£4
"1945" QE2	10p	25p	50p	£4
1957	10p	35p	50p	£3
*1960 1660–1960 300th anniversary	10p	20p	40p	£3
1960 Mule	—	—	—	£100
1966 "1066–1966"	—	—	50p	£2
ONE THIRTEENTH OF A SHILLING				
1841	£3	£7	£32	£125
1844	£3	£8	£32	£125
1851	£4	£12	£48	£125
1858	£3	£8	£36	£125
1861	£4	£12	£48	£125
1865 Proof only	—	—	—	£575
1866 with LCW	£1	£4	£30	£70
1866 without LCW Proof only	—	—	—	£300
1870	£3	£7	£32	£70
1871	£3	£7	£32	£70
ONE TWENTY-FOURTH OF A SHILLING				
1877H	£2	£3	£7	£35
1877 Proof only	—	—	—	£225
1888	£2	£3	£7	£30
1894	£2	£3	£7	£30
1909	£2	£3	£7	£30
1911	£1	£2	£5	£25
1913	£1	£2	£5	£25

DATE	F	VF	EF	UNC
1923 Spade shield	£1	£2	£6	£25
1923 Square shield	£1	£2	£5	£25
1926	£1	£2	£5	£15
1931	75p	£1.50	£5	£15
*1933	75p	£1.50	£5	£15
1935	75p	£1.50	£5	£15
1937	50p	£1	£3	£10
1946	50p	£1	£3	£10
1947	50p	£1	£3	£10

ONE TWENTY-SIXTH OF A SHILLING

DATE	F	VF	EF	UNC
1841	£3	£6	£25	£60
1844	£3	£6	£20	£55
1851	£2.50	£5	£18	£55
1858	£3	£10	£40	£125
1861	£2.50	£5	£18	£50
*1866	£2	£5	£20	£60
1870	£2	£5	£15	£40
1871	£2	£5	£15	£40

ONE FORTY-EIGHTH OF A SHILLING

DATE	F	VF	EF	UNC
1877H	£5	£10	£45	£85
1877 Proof only	—	—	—	£275

ONE FIFTY-SECOND OF A SHILLING

DATE	F	VF	EF	UNC
1841	£8	£20	£50	£125
1861 Proof only	—	—	—	£500

DECIMAL COINAGE

Ordinary circulating coinage from 1986 onwards is usually available in uncirculated condition at a small premium above face value thus it is not listed here.

(Reduced)

ONE HUNDRED POUNDS—*Gold*

1995 50th Anniversary of Liberation. Gold proof	£450

FIFTY POUNDS—*Gold*

1995 50th Anniversary of Liberation. Gold proof	£350

TWENTY-FIVE POUNDS—*Gold*

1972 25th Royal Wedding anniversary. Gold	£100
1972 — Gold proof	£185
1990 50th Anniversary of Battle of Britain. Gold proof	£200
1995 50th Anniversary of Liberation. Gold proof	£185
2002 Princess Diana memorial. Gold proof	£200

(Enlarged)

TEN POUNDS—*Gold*

1972 25th Royal Wedding anniversary. Gold	£45
1972 — Gold proof	£55
*1990 50th Anniversary of the Battle of Britain. Gold proof	£165
1995 50th Anniversary of Liberation. Gold proof	£165

FIVE POUNDS

1972 25th Royal Wedding anniversary. Gold	£25
1972 — Gold proof	£45
*1990 50th Anniversary of the Battle of Britain. Silver Proof (5 ounces)	£100
1997 Royal Golden Wedding	£15
1997 — Silver proof	£45
*2000 Millennium. Silver proof	£35
2002 Princess Diana memorial	£8
2002 — Silver proof	£30
2002 — Gold proof	£600

TWO POUNDS FIFTY PENCE

1972 Royal Silver Wedding	£10
1972 — Silver proof	£20

DATE	UNC
TWO POUNDS	
(note all modern Proof coins have frosted relief)	
1972 Royal Silver Wedding	£10
1972 — Silver proof	£15
1981 Royal Wedding, nickel silver (crown size)	£5
1981— in presentation pack	£8
1981 — Silver proof	£20
1981 — Gold proof	£325
1985 40th Anniversary of Liberation (crown size)	£5
1985 — in presentation pack	£6
1985 — Silver proof	£25
1985 — Gold proof	£985
1986 Commonwealth Games	£8
1986 — in presentation case	£8
1986 — .500 silver	£25
1986 — .925 silver proof	£30
1987 World Wildlife Fund 25th Anniversary	£8
1987 — Silver proof	£28
1989 Royal Visit	£8
1989 — Silver proof	£30
1990 Queen Mother's 90th Birthday	£8
1990 — Silver proof	£4
1990 — Gold proof	£425
1990 50th Anniversary of the Battle of Britain, silver proof	£40
1993 40th Anniversary of the Coronation	£8
1993 — Silver proof	£45
*1995 50th Anniversary of Liberation	£9
1995 — Silver Proof	£45
1996 HM the Queen's 70th Birthday	£8
1996 — Silver proof	£38
1997 Bimetal	£10
1997 — Silver proof	£35
1997 — new portrait	£8
ONE POUND	
1972 Royal Silver Wedding	£6
1972 — Silver proof	£7
1981	£7
1981 Silver proof	£15
1981 Gold proof	£180
1983 New designs and specifications on presentation card (St Helier)	£5
1983 — Silver proof	£25
1983 — gold proof	£350
1984 Presentation wallet (St Saviour)	£7
1984 — Silver proof	£28
1984 — Gold proof	£325
1984 Presentation wallet (St Brelade)	£7
1984 — Silver proof	£25
1984 — Gold proof	£350
1985 Presentation wallet (St Clement)	£58
1985 — Silver proof	£25
1985 — Gold proof	£350
1985 Presentation wallet (St Lawrence)	£8
1985 — Silver proof	£25
1985 — Gold proof	£350
1986 Presentation wallet (St Peter)	£8
1986 — Silver proof	£25
1986 — Gold proof	£350
1986 Presentation wallet (Grouville)	£8
1986 — Silver proof	£25
1986 — Gold proof	£350
1987 Presentation wallet (St Martin)	£8

DATE	UNC
1987 — Silver proof	£25
1987 — Gold proof	£350
1987 Presentation wallet (St Ouen)	£5
1987 — Silver proof	£25
1987 — Gold proof	£350
1988 Presentation wallet (Trinity)	£6
1988 — Silver proof	£26
1988 — Gold proof	£350
1988 Presentation wallet (St John)	£7
1988 — Silver proof	£25
1988 — Gold proof	£350
1989 Presentation wallet (St Mary)	£7
1989 — Silver proof	£25
1989 — Gold proof	£350
1991 Ship Building in Jersey Series	
1991 "Tickler" Silver proof	£40
1991 — Gold proof	£350
1991 "Percy Douglas" Silver proof	£30
1991 — Gold proof	£350
1992 "The Hebe" Silver proof	£25
1992 — Gold proof	£350
1992 "Coat of Arms" Silver proof	£25
1992 — Gold proof	£350
1993 "The Gemini" Silver proof	£25
1993 — Gold proof	£350
1993 "The Century" Silver proof	£25
1993 — Gold proof	£350
*1994 "Resolute" Silver proof	£30
1994 — Gold proof	£350
FIFTY PENCE	
1969	£3
1972 Royal Silver Wedding	£5
1972 — Silver proof	£5
1983 New design	£3
1985 40th Anniversary of Liberation	£5
TWENTY-FIVE PENCE	
1977 Royal Jubilee	£3
1977 — Silver proof	£12
TWENTY PENCE	
1982 Date on rocks on rev. (cased)	£3
1982 — Silver proof piedfort	£40
1983 New obv. with date, rev. no date on rocks	—
SOVEREIGN—*Gold sovereign size*	
*1999 The Millennium	£98

ALDERNEY

DATE	UNC
ONE HUNDRED POUNDS	
1994 50th Anniversary of D-Day Landings. Gold proof	£470
FIFTY POUNDS	
1994 50th Anniversary of D–Day Landing. Gold proof	£260
TWENTY FIVE POUNDS	
1993 40th Anniversary of Coronation. Gold proof	£170
1994 50th Anniversary of D-Day Landings. Gold proof	£170
1997 Royal Golden Wedding. Gold proof	£170
1997 — Silver proof	£20
*2000 60th Anniversary of the Battle of Britain. Gold proof	£180
2002 Princess Diana memorial	£225
2002 Duke of Wellington	£225
TEN POUNDS	
1994 50th Anniversary of D–Day Landing. Gold proof	£60
FIVE POUNDS	
1995 Queen Mother	£12
1995 — Silver proof	£35
1995 — Silver piedfort	£65
1995 — Gold proof	£650
1996 HM the Queen's 70th Birthday	£8
1996 — Silver proof	£40
1996 — Silver piedfort	£65
1996 — Gold proof	£650
*1999 Eclipse of the Sun	£12
1999 — Silver proof with colour centre	£30
1999 Winston Churchill. Gold proof	£650
2000 60th Anniversary of the Battle of Britain	£10
2000 — Silver proof	£40
2002 Golden Jubilee. Silver proof	£35
2002 50 Years of Reign. Silver proof	£35
2002 Diana memorial	£6
2002 — Silver proof	£30
2002 — Gold proof	£600
2002 Duke of Wellington	£8
2002 — Silver proof	£35
2002 — Gold proof	£600
TWO POUNDS	
1989 Royal Visit	£8
1989 — Silver proof	£35
1989 — Silver piedfort	£65
1989 — Gold proof	£930
*1990 Queen Mother's 90th Birthday	£8
1990 — Silver proof	£35
1990 — Silver piedfort	£68
1990 — Gold proof	£930
*1992 40th Anniversary of Accession	£8
1992 — Silver proof	£35
1992 — Silver piedfort	£68
1992 — Gold proof	£930
1993 40th Anniversary of Coronation	£8
1993 — Silver proof	£35
1993 — Silver piedfort	£68
1994 50th Anniversary of D-Day Landings	£8
1994 — Silver proof	£38

DATE	UNC
1994 — Silver piedfort	£68
1995 50th Anniversary of Return of Islanders	£8
1995 — Silver proof	£35
1995 — Silver piedfort	£68
1995 — Gold proof	£750
*1997 WWF Puffin	£10
1997 — Silver proof	£35
1997 Royal Golden Wedding	£8
1997 — Silver proof	£45
1999 Eclipse of the Sun. Silver	£8
1999 — Silver proof	£35
1999 — Gold proof	£850
2000 Millennium. Silver proof	£35

ONE POUND

1993 40th Anniversary of Coronation Silver proof	£35
*1995 50th Anniversary of VE Day Silver proof	£28
1995 — Gold proof	£330

IRELAND

As in the English hammered section (q.v.) the prices given here are for the most common coins in the series. For a more specialised listing the reader is referred to *Coincraft's Standard Catalogue of Scotland, Ireland, Channel Islands & Isle of Man,* or other specialised publications. Collectors should be aware that with most of the coins of the Irish series there are many varieties struck at different mints. The coins listed are all silver unless mentioned otherwise. Another important factor to consider when collecting early Irish coins is that few examples exist in high grades.

HIBERNO-NORSE ISSUES (995–1155)

	F	VF
Penny, imitating English silver pennies, many various types	£125	£200

A typical Hiberno-Norse period example.

JOHN, Lord of Ireland (1185–99)

	F	VF
Halfpenny, profile	Extremely rare	
Halfpenny, facing	£50	£100
Farthing	£250	£500

JOHN de COURCY, Lord of Ulster (1177–1205)

	F	VF
Halfpenny	Extremely rare	
Farthing	£450	£1000

John Lord of Ireland halfpenny.

JOHN as King of England and Lord of Ireland (c. 1199–1216)

	F	VF
Penny	£50	£100
Halfpenny	£100	£200
Farthing	£450	£1000

HENRY III (1216–72)

	F	VF
Penny	£40	£100

Henry III penny.

EDWARD I (1272–1307)

	F	VF
Penny	£45	£100
Halfpenny	£45	£100
Farthing	£100	£250

No Irish coins were struck for Edward II (1307–27).

EDWARD III (1327–77)

	F	VF
Halfpenny	Extremely rare	

No Irish coins were struck for Richard II (1377–99), Henry IV (1399–1413) or Henry V (1413–22).

Edward III halfpenny.

HENRY VI (1422–61)

	F	VF
Penny	Extremely rare	

EDWARD IV (1461–83)

	F	VF
"Anonymous crown" groat	£300	£650
— Penny	£600	—
"Titled crown" groat	£950	—
— Halfgroat		Extremely rare
— Penny		Extremely rare
Cross on rose/Sun groat	£950	—
Bust/Rose on sun double groat	£1500	£3500
— groat	£1750	—
— halfgroat		Extremely rare
— penny		Extremely rare
Bust/Cross & pellets groat—*First issue*	£65	£150
— halfgroat	£375	£700
— penny	£60	£125
— halfpenny		Extremely rare
— *Second (light) issue*	£65	£150
— halfgroat	£375	£700
— penny	£60	£125
— halfpenny		Extremely rare
Bust/Rose on cross groat	£350	£750
— penny	£50	£100
Billon/Copper issues		
Small crown/Cross farthing (1460–61)	£850	—
— half farthing ("Patrick")	£700	—
Large crown/Cross farthing (1462)		Extremely rare
Patricius/Salvator farthing (1463–65)	£200	£1000
— half farthing		Extremely rare
Shield/Rose on sun farthing	£100	£500

Edward IV groat. "Anonymous crown" issue.

Edward IV penny. "Anonymous crown" issue.

RICHARD III (1483–85)

	F	VF
Bust/Rose on cross groat	£750	£2000
— halfgroat		Unique
— penny		Unique
Bust/Cross and pellets penny	£500	£1500
Shield/Three-crowns groat	£425	£850

Richard III bust/rose on cross groat.

HENRY VII (1485–1509)

	F	VF
Early issues (1483–90)		
Shield/Three crowns groat	£75	£175
— halfgroat	£150	£350
— penny	£400	£750
— halfpenny		Extremely rare
Later issues (1488–90)		
Shield/Three crowns groat	£70	£175
— halfgroat	£150	£350
— penny	£375	£750
Facing bust groat (1496–1505)	£90	£200
— halfgroat	£750	—
— penny	£650	—

LAMBERT SIMNEL (as EDWARD VI, Pretender, 1487)

	F	VF
Shield/Three crowns groat	£750	£2000

Henry VII "three crowns" half groat.

HENRY VIII (1509–47)

	F	VF
"Harp" groat	£50	£100
— halfgroat	£275	£650

The "Harp" coins have crowned initials either side of the reverse harp, e.g. HR (Henricus Rex), HA (Henry and Anne Boleyn), HI (Henry and Jane Seymour), HK (Henry and Katherine Howard).

	F	VF
Posthumous (Portrait) issues		
Sixpence	£75	£175
Threepence	£90	£200
Threehalfpence	£325	£850
Threefarthings	£400	£1000

Henry VIII "harp" halfgroat.

EDWARD VI (1547–53)

	F	VF
Shilling (base silver) 1552 (MDLII)	£600	£1250
Brass contemporary copy	£55	£175

MARY (1553–54)

	F	VF
Shilling 1553 (MDLIII)	£475	£1100
Shilling 1554 (MDLIIII)		Extremely rare
Groat		Extremely rare
Halfgroat		Extremely rare
Penny		Extremely rare

Mary Tudor shilling.

PHILIP & MARY (1554–58)

	F	VF
Shilling	£200	£650
Groat	£75	£200
Penny		Extremely rare

ELIZABETH I (1558–1603)

	F	VF
Base silver portrait coinage		
Shilling	£200	£650
Groat	£125	£325
Fine silver, portrait coinage (1561)		
Shilling	£145	£500
Groat	£225	£525
Third (base silver) shield coinage		
Shilling	£100	£375
Sixpence	£85	£200
Copper		
Threepence	£125	£350
Penny	£25	£80
Halfpenny	£50	£150

Reverse of a "fine" Elizabeth I shilling.

JAMES I (1603–25)

	F	VF
Shilling	£60	£150
Sixpence	£45	£125

Coins struck under Royal Licence from1613

	F	VF
"Harrington" farthing (small size)	£25	£75
"Harrington" farthing (large size)	£15	£50
"Lennox" farthing	£15	£50

James I sixpence.

CHARLES I (1625–49)

During the reign of Charles I and the Great Rebellion many coins were struck under unusual circumstances, making the series a difficult but fascinating area for study. Many of the "coins" were simply made from odd-shaped pieces of plate struck with the weight or value.

Charles I "Maltravers" farthing.

Coins struck under Royal Licence from1625

	F	VF
"Richmond" farthing	£15	£50
"Maltravers" farthing	£20	£65
"Rose" farthing	£15	£50

Siege money of the Irish Rebellion, 1642–49

"Inchiquin" Money (1642)

	F	VF
Crown	£1000	£2500
Halfcrown	£1000	£2500
Shilling		Extremely rare
Ninepence		Extremely rare
Sixpence		Extremely rare
Groat		Extremely rare

"Dublin" Money (1643)

	F	VF
Crown	£500	£1500
Halfcrown	£350	£1000

Coinage of the Great Rebellion—a "Dublin Money" crown.

"Ormonde" Money (1643–44)

	F	VF
Crown	£350	£750
Halfcrown	£250	£650
Shilling	£100	£250
Sixpence	£100	£250
Groat	£85	£200
Threepence	£75	£175
Twopence	£300	£650

"Ormonde" money threepence.

"Ormonde" gold coinage (1646)

	F	VF
Double pistole. 2 known (both in museums)		Extremely rare
Pistole 10 jbiwb (only 1 in private ownership		Extremely rare

"Ormonde" Money (1649)

	F	VF
Crown		Extremely rare
Halfcrown	£750	£2000

Dublin Money 1649

	F	VF
Crown	£1750	£4500
Halfcrown	£1250	£2750

Issues of the Confederated Catholics

Kilkenny issues (1642–43)

	F	VF
Halfpenny	£150	£400
Farthing	£300	£650

Rebel Money (1643–44)

	F	VF
Crown	£1250	£2500
Halfcrown	£1500	£3000

Kilkenny halfpenny.

	F	VF
"Blacksmith's" Money (16??)		
Imitation of English Tower halfcrown ...	£400	£1250

Local Town issues of "Cities of Refuge"

	F	VF
Bandon		
Farthing (copper)	Extremely rare	
Cork		
Shilling	Extremely rare	
Sixpence	£500	£1000
Halfpenny (copper)	Extremely rare	
Farthing (copper)	£300	—
Kinsale		
Farthing (copper)	£275	—
Youghal		
Farthing (copper)	£300	£800

"Cork" countermarked on a copper coin.

CHARLES II (1660–85)

	Fair	F	VF	EF
"Armstrong" coinage				
Farthing (1660–61)	£50	£150	—	—
"St Patrick's" coinage				
Halfpenny	£150	£300	—	—
Farthing	£50	£110	£350	£600
Legg's Regal coinage				
Halfpennies				
1680 large lettering	£20	£60	£140	—
1681 large lettering	—	£125	£400	—
1681 small lettering	Extremely rare			
1682 small lettering	—	£125	£400	—
1683 small lettering	£10	£25	£200	
1684 small lettering	£25	£75	£300	—

"St Patrick" farthing of Charles II.

JAMES II (1685–88)

Regal coinage

	Fair	F	VF	EF
Halfpennies				
1685	£5	£50	£200	£350
1686	£5	£35	£125	£250
1687	Extremely rare			
1688	£12	£35	£180	—

	Fair	F	VF	EF
Emergency coinage				
Gun Money				
Most of these coins were struck in gun metal but a few rare specimens are also known struck in gold and in silver				
Crowns				
1690 (many varieties) ....from	£15	£35	£95	—
Large halfcrowns				
Dated July 1689–May 1690				
Prices from	£10	£25	£75	—
Small halfcrowns				
Dated April–October1690				
Prices from	£10	£25	£75	—
Large shillings				
Dated from July 1689–April 1690				
Prices from	£5	£12	£45	£100
Small shillings				
Dated from April–September 1690				
Prices from	£5	£12	£45	£100
Sixpences				
Dated from June 1689–October 1690				
Prices from	£15	£35	£100	—
Pewter Money (1689–90)				
Crown	£400	£700	£1,400	—
Groat			Extremely rare	
Penny large bust	£150	£400	—	—
— small bust	£100	£300	£600	—
Halfpenny large bust	£100	£205	£450	—
— small bust	£80	£160	£400	—
Limerick Money (1690–91)				
Halfpenny reversed N in HIBERNIA	£10	£45	£100	—
Farthing reversed N in HIBERNIA	£12	£50	£100	—
— normal N	£15	£75	£150	—

A "Gunmoney" crown.

A "Gunmoney" shilling (large size).

WILLIAM & MARY (1688–94)

	Fair	F	VF	EF
Halfpennies				
1692	£5	£20	£75	£300
1693	£5	£20	£70	£300
1694	£5	£25	£80	£400

Reverse of a "Pewter Money" penny.

WILLIAM III (1694–1702)

	Fair	F	VF	EF
1696 Halfpenny draped bust	£20	£50	£100	—
1696 — crude undraped bust	£30	£200	—	—

No Irish coins were struck during the reign of Queen Anne (1706–11).

GEORGE I (1714–27)

DATE	F	VF	EF	UNC
Farthings				
1722 D.G. REX Harp to left (Pattern)	£500	£1000	£1750	—
1723 D.G. REX Harp to right	£85	£150	£300	—
1723 DEI GRATIA REX Harp to right	£20	£50	£145	£275
1723 — Silver Proof	—	—	—	£1000
1724 DEI GRATIA REX Harp to right	£45	£85	£220	£460
Halfpennies				
1722 Holding Harp left	£35	£95	£225	£500
1722 Holding Harp right	£30	£85	£225	£450
1723/2 Harp right	£30	£85	£225	£500
1723 Harp right	£15	£50	£145	£275
1723 Silver Proof	—	—	—	£2000
1723 Obv. Rs altered from Bs	£20	£75	£175	—
1723 No stop after date	£15	£60	£150	£275
1724 Rev. legend divided	£25	£75	£185	—
1724 Rev. legend continuous	£25	£75	£185	—

Farthing of George I.

GEORGE II (1727–60)

DATE	F	VF	EF	UNC
Farthings				
1737	£20	£45	£100	£200
1737 Proof	—	—	—	£250
1737 Silver Proof	—	—	—	£500
1738	£20	£45	£100	£200
1744	£20	£45	£100	£200
1760	£15	£30	£75	£150
Halfpennies				
1736	£15	£45	£125	£250
1736 Proof	—	—	—	£350
1736 Silver Proof	—	—	—	£700
1737	£15	£35	£115	—
1738	£20	£45	£125	—
1741	£20	£45	£125	—
1742	£20	£45	£125	—
1743	£20	£45	£125	—
1744/3	£20	£40	£115	—
1744	£20	£45	£150	—
1746	£20	£45	£125	—
1747	£20	£45	£125	—
1748	£20	£45	£125	—
1749	£20	£45	£125	—
1750	£20	£45	£125	—
1751	£20	£45	£125	—
1752	£20	£45	£125	—
1753	£20	£45	£125	—
1755	£22	£75	£200	—
*1760	£15	£40	£120	—

Halfpenny of George II.

GEORGE III (1760–1820)

All copper unless otherwise stated

DATE	F	VF	EF	UNC
Pennies				
1805	£10	£25	£100	£200
1805 Proof	—	—	—	£250
1805 in Bronze Proof	—	—	—	£275
1805 in Copper Gilt Proof	—	—	—	£275
1805 in Silver Proof (restrike)	—	—	—	£1500
1822	£10	£18	£100	£225

DATE	F	VF	EF	UNC
1822 Proof	—	—	—	£350
1823	£8	£15	£95	£225
1823 Proof	—	—	—	£350
Halfpennies				
*1766	£15	£38	£100	—
1769	£15	£38	£100	—
1769 Longer bust	£25	£55	£125	—
1774 Pattern only Proof	—	—	—	£1000
1775	£18	£35	£115	—
1775 Proof	—	—	—	£350
1776	£35	£100	£200	—
1781	£25	£40	£85	£200
1782	£25	£40	£85	£200
1805	£5	£10	£35	£100
1805 Copper Proof	—	—	—	£150
1805 in Bronze	—	—	—	£100
1805 in Gilt Copper	—	—	—	£200
1805 in Silver (restrike)	—	—	—	£750
1822	£10	£20	£55	£175
1822 Proof	—	—	—	£350
1823	£10	£20	£55	£175
1823	—	—	—	£300

1806 farthing.

NB Prooflike Unirculated Pennies and Halfpennies of 1822/23 are often misdescribed as Proofs. The true Proofs are rare. Some are on heavier, thicker flans.

DATE	F	VF	EF	UNC
Farthings				
*1806	£10	£20	£50	£100
1806 Copper Proof	—	—	—	£150
1806 Bronzed Copper Proof	—	—	—	£120
1806 Copper Gilt Proof	—	—	—	£150
1806 Silver Proof (restrike)	—	—	—	£550
1822 George IV (Pattern) Proof	—	—	—	£850

TOKEN ISSUES BY THE BANK OF IRELAND

DATE	F	VF	EF	UNC
Five Pence in Silver				
1805	£15	£30	£50	£150
1806	£20	£50	£100	£200
1806/5	£35	£100	£275	£750
Ten Pence in Silver				
1805	£12	£25	£75	£150
1806	£15	£45	£100	£175
*1813	£12	£25	£65	£135
1813 Proof	—	—	—	£300
Thirty Pence in Silver				
1808	£25	£75	£155	£300
Six Shillings				
*1804 in Silver	£75	£150	£300	£1000
1804 Proof	—	—	—	£1000
1804 in Copper (restrike)	—	—	—	£500
1804 Copper Gilt	—	—	—	£1000
1804 in Gilt Silver	—	—	—	£1750

In this series fully struck specimens, with sharp hair curls, etc., are worth appreciably more than the prices quoted.

IRISH FREE STATE/EIRE

DATE	F	VF	EF	UNC
TEN SHILLINGS				
*1966 Easter Rising	—	£5	£10	£15
1966 Cased Proof	—	—	—	£20
1966 special double case	—	—	—	£45
HALF CROWNS				
1928	£5	£10	£30	£50
1928 Proof	—	—	—	£55
1930	£5	£20	£100	£275
1931	£5	£25	£125	£300
1933	£5	£15	£120	£255
1934	£5	£10	£40	£125
1937	£40	£100	£375	£875
1938				Unique
*1939	£3	£8	£20	£50
1939 Proof	—	—	—	£475
1940	£3	£8	£20	£45
1941	£5	£12	£25	£55
1942	£5	£8	£20	£45
1943	£65	£125	£550	£1250
1951	£1	£2	£12	£30
1951 Proof	—	—	—	£350
1954	£1	£2	£8	£25
1954 Proof	—	—	—	£350
1955	£1	£2	£8	£20
1955	—	—	—	£450
1959	£1	£2	£8	£20
1961	£1	£2	£15	£35
1961 Obv as 1928, rev. as 1951	£15	£25	£150	—
1962	£1	£2	£5	£15
1963	£1	£2	£5	£12
1964	£1	£2	£5	£10
1966	£1	£2	£5	£10
1967	£1	£2	£5	£10
FLORINS				
1928	£2	£4	£15	£35
1928 Proof	—	—	—	£45
1930	£3	£10	£100	£275
1930 Proof				*Unique*
1931	£4	£17	£125	£300
1933	£3	£15	£100	£300
1934	£5	£85	£175	£475
1934 Proof	—	—	—	£2000
1935	£2	£9	£50	£125
1937	£5	£15	£100	£275
1939	£1	£3	£20	£40
1939 Proof	—	—	—	£475
1940	£2	£4	£20	£45
1941	£2	£4	£25	£50
1941 Proof	—	—	—	£550
1942	£3	£6	£20	£45
1943	£1000	£2000	£4000	£8000
1951	50p	£1	£8	£20
1951 Proof	—	—	—	£325
1954	50p	£1	£8	£20
1954 Proof	—	—	—	£250

DATE	F	VF	EF	UNC
1955	—	£1	£4	£20
1955 Proof	—	—	—	£275
1959	35p	£1	£5	£15
1961	50p	£2	£10	£30
1962	35p	£1	£5	£15
1963	25p	£1	£4	£10
1964	25p	£1	£4	£8
1965	25p	£1	£4	£8
1966	25p	£1	£4	£6
1968	25p	£1	£4	£6

SHILLINGS

DATE	F	VF	EF	UNC
1928	£1	£3	£10	£20
1928 Proof	—	—	—	£25
1930	£2	£15	£75	£250
1930 Proof	—	—	—	£650
1931	£2	£12	£75	£125
1933	£2	£12	£75	£175
1935	£2	£8	£35	£100
1937	£5	£45	£165	£750
1939	£1	£3	£15	£35
1939 Proof	—	—	—	£475
1940	£1	£3	£12	£25
1941	£2	£5	£16	£35
1942	£2	£3	£8	£25
1951	50p	£1	£5	£14
1951 Proof	—	—	—	£300
1954	50p	£1	£4	£12
1954 Proof	—	—	—	£350
1955	50p	£1	£5	£14
1959	50p	£1	£5	£18
1962	25p	£1	£2	£7
1963	25p	£1	£2	£5
1964	25p	£1	£2	£3
1966	25p	£1	£2	£3
1968	25p	£1	£2	£3

SIXPENCES

DATE	F	VF	EF	UNC
1928	50p	£1	£5	£18
1928 Proof	—	—	—	£20
1934	50p	£2	£15	£70
1935	75p	£2	£18	£85
1939	50p	£1	£5	£35
1939 Proof	—	—	—	£450
1940	50p	£1	£5	£35
1942	50p	£1	£8	£40
1945	£1	£5	£25	£75
1946	£2	£5	£50	£250
1947	£1	£2	£20	£55
1948	50p	£2	£12	£40
1949	50p	£1	£7	£30
1950	£1	£2	£20	£70
1952	50p	£1	£3	£15
1953	50p	£1	£3	£15
1953 Proof	—	—	—	£85
1955	50p	£1	£3	£15
1956	50p	£1	£2	£12
1956 Proof	—	—	—	£100
1958	£1	£2	£10	£45
1958 Proof	—	—	—	£250
1959	25p	50p	£2	£10
1960	25p	50p	£1	£10

DATE	F	VF	EF	UNC
1961	25p	50p	£1	£10
1962	£1	£5	£25	£50
1963	50p	£2	£5	£10
1964	50p	50p	£3	£6
1966	50p	50p	£3	£6
1967	50p	50p	£1	£4
1968	50p	50p	£1	£4
1969	£1	£2	£5	£10

THREEPENCES

1928	£1	£2	£6	£15
1928 Proof	—	—	—	£20
1933	£2	£8	£50	£250
1934	50p	£1	£8	£45
1935	£1	£3	£20	£125
1939	£2	£6	£50	£250
1939 Proof	—	—	—	£775
1940	£1	£2	£10	£45
1942	25p	£1	£5	£35
1943	£1	£2	£10	£55
1946	25p	75p	£5	£30
1946 Proof	—	—	—	£175
1948	£1	£2	£20	£55
1949	25p	£1	£5	£25
1949 Proof	—	—	—	£165
1950	25p	£1	£3	£8
1950 Proof	—	—	—	£155
1953	25p	£1	£3	£8
1956	25p	£1	£2	£5
1961	25p	50p	£1	£3
1962	25p	50p	£1	£5
1963	25p	50p	£1	£5
1964	20p	50p	£1	£3
1965	20p	50p	£1	£2
1966	20p	50p	£1	£2
1967	20p	50p	£1	£2
1968	20p	40p	£1	£2

PENNIES

1928	£1	£2	£8	£20
1928 Proof	—	—	—	£35
1931	£1	£3	£25	£75
1931 Proof	—	—	—	£750
1933	£1	£4	£40	£125
1935	50p	£1	£20	£45
1937	75p	£1	£25	£75
1937 Proof	—	—	—	£750
1938 2 known				*Unique*
1940	£5	£25	£100	—
1941	50p	£1	£8	£20
1942	25p	50p	£3	£12
1943	25p	£1	£4	£18
1946	25p	£1	£3	£12
1948	25p	£1	£3	£12
1949	25p	£1	£3	£12
1949 Proof	—	—	—	£275
1950	25p	75p	£5	£18
1952	25p	50p	£3	£6
1962	30p	75p	£3	£8
1962 Proof	—	—	—	£100
1963	10p	25p	£1	£4
1963 Proof	—	—	—	£75

DATE	F	VF	EF	UNC
1964	—	25p	£1	£4
1965	—	25p	50p	£3
1966	—	25p	50p	£3
1967	—	15p	25p	£2
1968	—	15p	25p	£2
1968 Proof	—	—	—	£155

HALFPENNIES

DATE	F	VF	EF	UNC
1928	£1	£2	£8	£20
1928 Proof	—	—	—	£20
1933	£3	£12	£50	£350
1935	£2	£5	£25	£115
1937	£1	£3	£10	£45
1939	£2	£5	£25	£125
1939 Proof	—	—	—	£575
1940	£1	£2	£35	£125
1941	50p	£1	£5	£20
1942	50p	£1	£5	£20
1943	50p	£1	£6	£22
1946	£1	£2	£15	£55
1949	50p	£1	£5	£20
1953	25p	£1	£2	£8
1953 Proof	—	—	—	£350
1964	—	25p	50p	£2
1965	—	30p	75p	£3
1966	—	25p	50p	£2
1967	—	25p	50p	£2

FARTHINGS

DATE	F	VF	EF	UNC
1928	£2	£3	£6	£10
1928 Proof	—	—	—	£20
1930	£2	£3	£8	£18
1931	£3	£5	£12	£25
1931 Proof	—	—	—	£575
1932	£3	£5	£15	£30
1933	£2	£3	£8	£18
1935	£3	£5	£12	£25
1936	£3	£5	£12	£25
1937	£2	£3	£8	£18
1939	£2	£3	£5	£9
1939 Proof	—	—	—	£400
1940	£3	£4	£7	£14
1941	£2	£3	£5	£9
1943	£2	£3	£5	£9
1944	£2	£3	£5	£9
1946	£2	£3	£5	£9
1949	£3	£5	£7	£14
1949 Proof	—	—	—	£300
1953	£2	£3	£4	£5
1953 Proof	—	—	—	£200
1959	£2	£3	£4	£5
1966	£2	£3	£4	£5

For the 1928–50 coppper issues it is worth noting that UNC means UNC with some lustre. BU examples with full lustre are extremely elusive and are worth much more than the quoted prices.

Decimal issues are not included in this publication but it should be noted that many dates are virtually impossible to find in uncirculated grade. An example is the 1986 set which was sold exclusively through souvenir shops and included the only specimens of the ½p for that year.

Official and semi-official commemorative Medals

It is probably a strong love of history, rather than the strict disciplines of coin collecting that make collectors turn to commemorative medals. The link between the two is intertwined, and it is to be hoped that collectors will be encouraged to venture into the wider world of medallions, encouraged by this brief guide, supplied by courtesy of Daniel Fearon, acknowledged expert and author of the *Catalogue of British Commemorative Medals*.

James I Coronation, 1603

DATE	VF	EF
JAMES I		
1603 Coronation *(possibly by C. Anthony)*, 29mm, Silver	£350	£750
QUEEN ANNE		
1603 Coronation,29mm, AR	£375	£750
CHARLES I		
1626 Coronation *(by N. Briot)*, 30mm, Silver	£250	£650
1633 Scottish Coronation *(by N. Briot)*, 28mm, Silver	£175	£350
1649 Memorial *(by J. Roettier)*. Struck after the Restoration, 50mm, Bronze	£100	£250
CHARLES II		
1651 Scottish Coronation, in exile *(from design by Sir J. Balfour)*, 32mm, Silver	£365	£850
CROMWELL		
1651 Lord Protector *(by T. Simon)*, 38mm, Silver	£350	£800
— Cast examples	£85	£175
CHARLES II		
1661 Coronation *(by T. Simon)*, 29mm		
— Gold	£800	£1500
— Silver	£100	£250
1685 Death *(by N. Roettier)*, 39mm, Bronze	£75	£175

Charles II Coronation, 1661

DATE	VF	EF
JAMES II		
1685 Coronation *(by J. Roettier)*, 34mm		
— Gold	£850	£1650
— Silver	£185	£350
MARY		
1685 Coronation *(by J. Roettier)*, 34mm		
— Gold	£850	£1700
— Silver	£150	£350
WILLIAM & MARY		
1689 Coronation *(by J. Roettier)*, 32mm		
— Gold	£750	£1600
— Silver	£125	£225
1689 Coronation,"Perseus" *(by G. Bower)*, 38mm, Gold	£675	£1500
MARY		
1694 Death *(by N. Roettier)*, 39mm,Bronze	£85	£200
WILLIAM III		
1697 "The State of Britain" *(by J. Croker)*, 69mm, Silver	£350	£850
ANNE		
1702 Accession, "Entirely English" *(by J. Croker)*, 34mm		
— Gold	£650	£1500
— Silver	£85	£175
1702 Coronation *(by J. Croker)*, 36mm		
— Gold	£550	£1500
— Silver	£85	£175
1707 Union with Scotland *(by J. Croker, rev. by S. Bull)*, 34mm		
— Gold	£500	£850
— Silver	£75	£150
1713 Peace of Utrecht *(by J. Croker—issued in gold to Members of Parliament)*, 34mm		
— Gold	£450	£950
— Silver	£75	£150
GEORGE I		
1714 Coronation*(by J. Croker)*, 34mm		
— Gold	£650	£1650
— Silver	£85	£175
1727 Death *(by J. Dassier)*, 31mm, Silver	£75	£150
GEORGE II		
1727Coronation *(by J. Croker)*, 34mm		
— Gold	£600	£1600
— Silver	£85	£175
QUEEN CAROLINE		
1727 Coronation *(by J. Croker)*, 34mm		
— Gold	£600	£1650
— Silver	£85	£175
1732 The Royal Family *(by J. Croker)*, 70mm		
— Silver	£155	£375
— Bronze	£85	£175

Charles II Coronation, 1661

George III, Coronation, 1761

DATE	VF	EF
GEORGE III		
1761 Coronation *(by L. Natter)*, 34mm		
— Gold	£650	£1800
— Silver	£125	£275
— Bronze	£55	£150
QUEEN CHARLOTTE		
1761 Coronation *(by L. Natter)*, 34mm		
— Gold	£650	£1850
— Silver	£125	£275
— Bronze	£55	£125
1810 Golden Jubilee, "Frogmore", 48mm, Silver	£80	£175
— Bronze	£55	£125
GEORGE IV		
1821 Coronation *(by B. Pistrucci)*, 35mm		
— Gold	£400	£750
— Silver	£55	£125
— Bronze	£40	£75
WILLIAM IV		
1831 Coronation *(by W. Wyon; rev.shows Queen Adelaide)*, 33mm		
— Gold	£375	£750
— Silver	£55	£120
— Bronze	£45	£85
QUEEN VICTORIA		
1838 Coronation *(by B. Pistrucci)*, 37mm		
— Gold	£385	£850
— Silver	£65	£150
— Bronze	£35	£85

George IV Coronation, 1841

Queen Victoria Coronation, 1838

Queen Victoria Diamond Jubilee 1897

DATE	VF	EF
1887 Golden Jubilee *(by J. E. Boehm, rev. by Lord Leighton)*		
— Gold, 58mm	£850	£1250
— Silver, 78mm	£85	£200
— Bronze, 78mm	£45	£120
1897 Diamond Jubilee *(by T. Brock),*		
— Gold, 56mm	£750	£1000
— Silver, 56mm	£45	£85
— Bronze, 56mm	£20	£35
— Gold, 21mm	£125	£165
— Silver, 21mm	£20	£35

George V Silver Jubilee, 1937

EDWARD VII

1902 Coronation (August 9) *(by G. W. de Saulles)*		
— Gold, 56mm	£750	£1000
— Silver, 56mm	£35	£75
— Bronze, 56mm	£20	£35
— Gold, 31mm	£135	£185
— Silver, 31mm	£20	£35

**Some rare examples of the official medal show the date as June 26, the original date set for the Coronation which was postponed because the King developed appendicitis.*

GEORGE V

1911 Coronation *(by B. Mackennal)*		
— Gold, 51mm	£750	£1000
— Silver, 51mm	£30	£75
— Bronze, 51mm	£15	£30
— Gold, 31mm	£145	£185
— Silver, 31mm	£15	£30
1935 Silver Jubilee *(by P. Metcalfe)*		
— Gold, 58mm	£750	£1000
— Silver, 58mm	£25	£65
— Gold, 32mm	£125	£175
— Silver, 32mm	£20	£35

PRINCE EDWARD

1911 Investiture as Prince of Wales *(by W. Goscombe John)*		
— Gold, 31mm	£275	£500
— Silver, 31mm	£35	£55

EDWARD VIII

1936 Abdication *(by L. E. Pinches)*, 35mm		
— Gold	£375	£750
— Silver	£35	£65
— Bronze	£15	£35

GEORGE VI

1937 Coronation *(by P. Metcalfe)*		
— Gold, 58mm	£850	£1250
— Silver, 58mm	£35	£75
— Gold, 32mm	£145	£185
— Silver, 32mm	£15	£25
— Bronze, 32mm	£5	£12

Edward, Prince of Wales, 1911

DATE	VF	EF
ELIZABETH II		
1953 Coronation *(by Spink & Son)*		
— Gold, 57mm	£750	£950
— Silver, 57mm	£25	£60
— Bronze, 57mm	£15	£25
— Gold, 32mm	£175	£250
— Silver, 32mm	£15	£25
— Bronze, 32mm	£10	£15
1977 Silver Jubilee *(by A. Machin)*		
— Silver, 57mm	—	£55
— Silver, 44mm	—	£35

**The gold medals are priced for 18ct—they can also be found as 22ct and 9ct, and prices should be adjusted accordingly.*

DATE	VF	EF
PRINCE CHARLES		
1969 Investiture as Prince of Wales *(by M. Rizello)*		
— Silver, 57mm	—	£50
— Bronze gilt, 57mm	—	£35
— Silver, 45mm	—	£35
— Gold, 32mm	—	£175
— Silver, 32mm	—	£35
— Bronze, 32mm	—	£15
QUEEN ELIZABETH THE QUEEN MOTHER		
1980 80th Birthday *(by L. Durbin)*		
— Silver, 57mm	—	£50
— Silver, 38mm	—	£35
— Bronze, 38mm	—	£20

N.B.—Official Medals usually command a premium when still in their original cases of issue.

Edward VIII Abdication, 1936

COIN grading

CONDITION is the secret to the value of virtually anything, whether it be antiques, jewellery, horses or second-hand cars—and coins are *certainly* no exception. When collecting coins it is vital to understand the recognised standard British system of grading, i.e. accurately assessing a coin's condition or state of wear. Grading is an art which can only be learned by experience and so often it remains one person's opinion against another's, therefore it is important for the beginner or inexperienced collector to seek assistance from a reputable dealer or knowledgeable numismatist when making major purchases.

The standard grades as used in the Price Guide are as follows:

UNC — **Uncirculated**
A coin that has never been in circulation, although it may show signs of contact with other coins during the minting process.

EF — **Extremely Fine**
A coin in this grade may appear uncirculated to the naked eye but on closer examination will show signs of minor friction on the highest surface.

VF — **Very Fine**
A coin that has had very little use, but shows signs of wear on the high surfaces.

F — **Fine**
A coin that has been in circulation and shows general signs of wear, but with all legends and date clearly visible.

Other grades used in the normal grading system are:

BU — **Brilliant Uncirculated**
As the name implies, a coin retaining its mint lustre.

Fair — A coin extensively worn but still quite recognisable and legends readable.

Poor — A coin very worn and only just recognisable.

Other abbreviations used in the Price Guide are:

Obv — **Obverse**

Rev — **Reverse**

Other abbreviations, mintmarks, etc. can be identified under the appropriate section of this Yearbook.

English Banknote price guide

This price guide, supplied by courtesy of Pam West of British Notes, is by no means definitive. It is possible to buy notes for less than listed here, just as some may cost more. The prices quoted are for VF to EF up to the end of Peppiatt and EF and Uncirculated from O'Brien, which is usually considered to be the start of the modern period. Obviously notes in current circulation can be obtained at face value and it is always a good idea to put an uncirculated note away occasionally. Sometimes they may have "half moon" machine cutting marks, though they have never been circulated. More detailed information, as well as prices for the bank notes of Scotland, Channel Islands, Isle of Man, Northern Ireland and the Republic of Ireland, is available in the BANKNOTE YEARBOOK.

TREASURY NOTES

ISSUE	VF	EF
1st ISSUE		
T1 Bradbury £1	£1000	£1850
T2 Bradbury £1	£1000	£1750
T3 Bradbury £1 5/6 digit	£350	£650
T4 Bradbury £1	£600	£1250
T5 Bradbury £1	£650	£1350
T6 Bradbury £1	£450	£1000
T7 Bradbury £1	—	—
T8 Bradbury 10/-	£450	£1000
T9 Bradbury 10/-	£250	£500
T10 Bradbury 10/-	£650	£1250
2nd ISSUE		
T11 Bradbury £1	£175	£500
T12 Bradbury 10/-	£150	£250
T13 Bradbury 10/-	£150	£275
T14 Bradbury £1 Dardenelles	£2500	£4500
T15 Bradbury 10/- Dardenelles	£450	£1000
3rd ISSUE		
T16 Bradbury £1	£100	£200

ISSUE	VF	EF
T16 with Anchor on rev. A1/B1 prefix	£175	£500
T17 Bradbury 10/-	£200	£350
T18 Bradbury 10/-	£150	£300
T19 Bradbury 10/-	£950	£1500
T20 Bradbury 10/-	£100	£250
1st ISSUE		
T24 Fisher £1	£30	£65
T25 Fisher 10/-	£65	£175
T26 Fisher 10/-	£55	£150
2nd ISSUE		
T30 Fisher 10/-	£60	£150
T31 Fisher £1	£45	£100
T32 Fisher £1	£65	£165
3rd ISSUE (NORTHERN IRELAND)		
T33 Fisher 10/-	£65	£145
T34 Fisher £1	£45	£125
T35 Fisher £1	£70	£175

BANK OF ENGLAND WHITE £5 NOTES

ISSUE	EF
B208b Nairne	£375
B209a Harvey	£275
B215 Mahon	£380
B228 Catterns	£370
B241 Peppiatt	£150

ISSUE	EF
B255 Peppiatt	£125
B264 Peppiatt	£125
B270 Beale	£135
B275 O'Brien	£135
B276 O'Brien	£135

White notes in better grades are becoming difficult to obtain thus earlier rarer dates and notes in exceptional condition should command a premium.

BANK OF ENGLAND ISSUES

	VF	EF
SERIES A—BRITANNIA		
B210 Mahon 10/-	£55	£120
B212 Mahon £1	£45	£95
B223 Catterns 10/-	£40	£75
B223 Catterns 10/- V prefix	£50	£125
B225 Catterns £1 LNN	£20	£40
B226 Catterns £1 NNL	£55	£125
1st PERIOD, GREEN		
B235 Peppiatt 10/- LNN	£20	£45
B235 Peppiatt 10/- LNN J Prefix	£35	£75
B236 Peppiatt 10/- NNL	£20	£50
B238 Peppiatt £1 NNL	£15	£30
B239 Peppiatt £1 LNNL	£15	£35
2nd PERIOD, BLUE (THREADED)		
B248 Peppiatt £1 Blue	£15	£35
B249 Peppiatt £1 Blue	£5	£15
B251 Peppiatt 10/- Mauve	£15	£35
3rd PERIOD, GREEN (UNTHREADED)		
B258 Peppiatt £1	£15	£30
B258 Peppiatt £1 S--A	£20	£35
B256 Peppiatt 10/- Red-brown	£45	£100
4th PERIOD, GREEN (THREADED)		
B260 Peppiatt £1	£15	£35
B261 Peppiatt £1 ®	£80	£175
B262 Peppiatt 10/-	£15	£30
B263 Peppiatt 10/- ® 01A	£350	£500
B265 Beale 10/- NNL	£20	£45
B266 Beale 10/- LNNL	£15	£25
B267 Beale 10/- ® 05A	£125	£250
B268 Beale £1	£4	£10
B269 Beale £1 ®	£20	£35
B271 O'Brien 10/-	£15	£30
B272 O'Brien 10/- ®	£50	£100
B273 O'Brien £1	£4	£8
B274 O'Brien £1 ®	£20	£40
B274 O'Brien £1 ® S--T	£20	£45

SERIES B—HELMETED BRITANNIA

	EF	UNC
B277 O'Brien £5 Shaded Symbol	£30	£65
— A01 (first)	£100	£200
B280 O'Brien £5 White Symbol	£30	£65
SERIES C—PORTRAIT		
B281 O'Brien £1 LNN	£3	£5
B282 O'Brien £1 LNNL	£3	£6
B283 O'Brien £1 "R" EXP LNNL	£250	£350
B284 O'Brien £1 LNNL	£10	£25
B285 O'Brien £1 ®	£15	£30
B286 O'Brien 10/-	£3	£6
B287 O'Brien 10/- ®	£12	£35
B288 Hollom £1 LNNL	£2	£5
B289 Hollom £1 ® LNN	£15	£35
B290 Hollom £1 ® NNL	£12	£25
B291 Hollom £1 ® LNNL	£20	£100
B292 Hollom £1 G	£4	£10
B293 Hollom £1 G ®	£15	£45
B294 Hollom 10/- LNN	£3	£6
B295 Hollom 10/- NNL	£2	£5
B296 Hollom 10/- ®	£20	£35
B297 Hollom £5	£12	£22
B298 Hollom £5 ®	£65	£175
B299 Hollom £10	£15	£30
B301 Fforde £1	£3	£8
B302 Fforde £1 R	£20	£45
B303 Fforde £1 G	£5	£12
B304 Fforde £1 G ®	£20	£45
B305 Fforde £1	£4	£8
B306 Fforde £1 ®	£14	£25 (types)
— R01M (first)	£75	£250
— Mid	£8	£15
— S01M (first)	£65	£200
B307 Fforde £1 G	£4	£12
B308 Fforde £1 G ®	£15	£45
B308 — T--M G	£75	£200
B309 Fforde 10/- LNN	£3	£10
B310 Fforde 10/- LNNL	£3	£8
B311 Fforde 10/- ®	£10	£22
B312 Fforde £5 LNN	£14	£25
B313 Fforde £5 ®	£60	£120
B314 Fforde £5 NNL	£14	£30
B315 Fforde £5 ®	£70	£150
B316 Fforde £10	£18	£35
B318 Fforde £20	£90	£185
B319 Fforde £20 ®	£100	£275
B320 Page £1 LNNL	£3	£8
B321 Page £1 ®	£10	£20
B322 Page £1 LLNN	£3	£8
B323 Page ® (Some types rarer)	£8	£20
B324 Page £5	£20	£35
B325 Page £5 ®	£85	£155
B326 Page £10	£20	£40
B327 Page £10 ®	£30	£45
SERIES D—PICTORIAL		
B328 Page £20	£30	£60
B329 Page £20 ®	£55	£100
B330 Page £10	£20	£32
B331 Page £10 ®	£55	£100
B332 Page £5 LNN no "L" on reverse	£15	£22
B333 Page £5 ®	£85	£150
B334 Page £5 NNL	£15	£22
B335 Page £5 ®	£70	£130
B336 Page £5 LLNN	£10	£15
B337 Page £1 LNN	£3	£6
B338 Page £1 ®	£175	£300
B339 Page £1 NNL	£3	£6
B339a Page £1 8l .. various	£125	£250
B340 Page £1 LNNL	£4	£8
B341 Somerset £1 W	£3	£6
B342 Somerset £1 EXP	£350	£675
B343 Somerset £5	£10	£20

The B343 series starts DN01 and runs through a variety of prefixes to end at LZ90, although a sub-series exists of NA01 to NC90.

	EF	UNC
— DN01	£60	£125
— NA01	£100	£250
— NC90	£12	£35
— Mid on NB	£15	£24
B344 Somerset £5 OCR EXP	£450	£850

	EF	UNC
B345 Somerset £5 Wide Thread	£10	£18
B346 Somerset £10 LNN	£25	£40
B347 Somerset £10 NNL	£18	£35
B348 Somerset £10 LLNN with "L"	£18	£32
B349 Somerset £10 Window Thread	£15	£32
B350 Somerset £20 LNN	£35	£55
B351 Somerset £20 NNL Window Thread	£40	£65
B352 Somerset £50	£75	£120
B353 Gill £5	£10	£20
—SE90 (last)	£42	£85
B354 Gill £10	£15	£22
B355 Gill £20	£25	£45
— 01L (first)	£40	£110
— 20X (last)	£90	£155
B356 Gill £50 Window Thread	£60	£110
B360— E01	£65	£120
SERIES E—HISTORICAL		
B357 Gill £5	—	£10
B358 Gill £20	—	£35
SERIES D		
B359 Kentfield £10	—	£30
B360 Kentfield £50	—	£95

	EF	UNC
SERIES E		
B361 Kentfield £5 MKI LNN	—	£10
— W18 (last)	£20	£50
B362 Kentfield £5 MKII LNN	—	£12
— AA01 (first)	£10	£18
B363 Kentfield £5 MKIII LLNN	—	£12
B364 Kentfield £10 MKI LNN	—	£20
B365 Kentfield "B" Ream £10 M/Y/Z LNN	—	£40
B366 Kentfield £10 MKII LLNN	—	£15
B367 Kentfield £20 LNN	—	£35
B368 Kentfield "B" Ream £20 A/B LNN	—	£85
& M/Z LNN	—	£85
B369 Kentfield £20 MKII LNN	—	£32
B370 Kentfield £20 MKII LLNN	—	£28
B371 Kentfield £50 LNN	—	£55
— A01	—	£100
Lowther £5 EA01	—	£20
Lowther £10 KL01	—	£50
Lowther £10 KL low nos	—	£18
Lowther "Darwin" £10	—	£15
Lowther £20 DA01	—	£75
Lowther "Elgar" £20 AA	—	£25
Lowther £50 J01	—	£120
Lowther "Fry" £5 HA01	—	£15

Only some prices for true firsts and lasts, i.e. A01s–Z99s, have been quoted as often the price is dictated by availability of the notes which on earlier and some modern material, are often in short supply. Some low numbers on firsts command higher prices.

There is a series of unissued fractional notes, printed during the two wars, which are very scarce and not generally found for anything less than £2,000 in EF. These include Bradbury T21 5/–, T22 2/6, T23 1/–, Fisher T27 5/–, T28 2/6, T29 1/–, Peppiatt B253 5/–, B254 2/6.

Abbreviations

®	Replacement	OCR	Optical Character Recognition
"R"	Research	L	Letter (of serial number)
EXP	Experimental	N	Number (of serial number)
G	Goebel		i.e. LNNL = letter, number, number, letter
W	Webb Off-set	"B"	B Ream

Why not Bank notes?

Millions of pounds worth of banknotes exchange hands every day, and yet most of us pay little attention to the coloured pieces of paper we are about to part with. To a collector however, they are to be studied and enjoyed. Sometimes they can be worth many times their face value. A historian, with careful study, can discover much about a county's history from prosperity through war, siege and its inflationary periods. Banknotes have also been used for spreading propaganda. The Gulf war is a recent example. Many banknotes still survive long after the country of issue has disappeared.

So how do you start and where can you get advice on forming a collection? The answers, together with a few interesting facts about paper money can be found here. But remember, this feature can only scratch the surface of this fascinating subject; its aim is to inspire and surprise you.

Paper money is not a modern phenomenon. Its origins can be found in China during the second century BC. Emperor Wu (140–86BC), frustrated with the time taken for heavily laden wagons of copper coins to complete their journey, used deerhide as a kind of tax money. Skins from white stags were cut into pieces each a foot square. The borders were decorated with designs of water plants and each skin was given a value of 40,000 copper coins. Around 105 AD paper, made from broken down plant fibres and old cotton textiles was invented by a Chinese minister of Agriculture. However, true paper money didn't appear in China until the Tang Dynasty somewhere between 650–800 AD. The earliest Chinese notes collectors are likely to come across are from the Ming Dynasty. Made from mulberry bark paper, these notes measure 230mm x 330mm. Although over six hundred years old, these notes can be bought for around £500. An interesting factor is that Asia was using paper money while Britain and Europe were still in the dark ages.

The first European bank to be established was in Stockholm, Sweden in July 1661. Unfortunately its banknotes were not government backed and the enterprise was forced to close within a few years.

On July 27, 1694 the Bank of England was founded by Royal Charter; the first European bank to survive to the present day. From its temporary offices at the Mercers' Hall, Cheapside, London, the Bank set to work producing its first

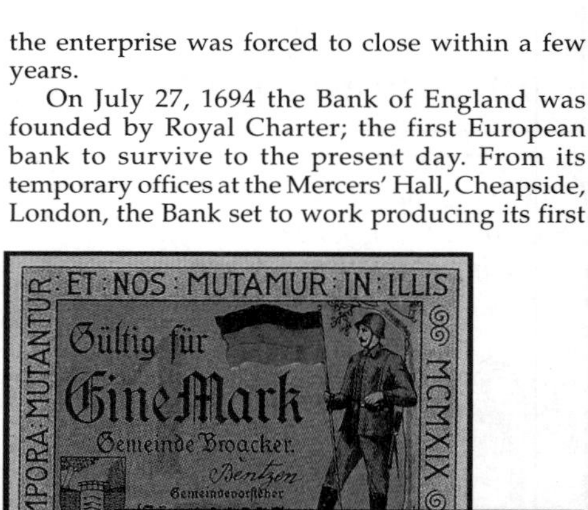

Notgeld, issued in Germany during the period of high inflation after World War I. The appearance of these highly colourful notes greatly stimulated the hobby of banknote collecting.

A Confederate States of America $100 note from the Montgomery issue, 1861. At the end of the American Civil War these notes had no face value but nevertheless remain interesting to collectors today.

issues. These have become known as running cash notes. At first they were written out entirely by hand on paper bought by the Bank's staff from local stationers. Forgery however, soon put a stop to this practice. Each note was made out to the bearer for the amount they had on deposit. Although there was no guarantee of conversion into gold, the notes could be cashed in for part of their original value. This led to endorsements appearing on the notes stating the date and amount paid off. The notes would change hands for payment of goods or services just as our modern banknotes do today.

During the last century many private banks were set up in towns and cities throughout Britain. The notes they issued were usually well printed and many carry a motif or vignette identifying with the place of issue. For example coats of arms often appear, so too do famous buildings. Others simply have embellished initials. It is these simple features that help to make these provincial notes popular with collectors today, coupled with the interest of owning a banknote actually issued in your town! Unfortunately most of these banks went into liquidation and many investors lost their money—it is quite common to find provincial notes with the bankruptcy court stamp or other marks on the reverse. Notes are also encountered which have been rejoined with paper strips as it was often the practice to cut notes in half—sending half by one means and the second portion at a later date, to be joined with its counterpart before it could be redeemed. This lessened the risk of the note being stolen or lost in transit.

The expression "Safe as the Bank of England" is held in high regard today. In reality the Bank has almost collapsed on at least two occasions, and in 1696 it had its first major crisis. An act passed by parliament ordered the recoinage of all metallic currency. As the notes circulated by the Bank had status of legal tender and therefore not legally convertible into gold, people naturally had more confidence in metal currency. Accounts submitted by the Bank to parliament in December of that year showed £764,000 worth of notes in circulation. These were backed by just under £36,000 worth of gold.

The second emergency for the Bank came in 1720 after the "bursting" of the South Sea Bubble. Holding the monopoly of trade with South America, the South Sea Company offered to take on the national debt in return for further concessions. Company shares soared but when the collapse came it was found that government ministers were deeply involved and a political crisis followed. Bankruptcy was rife and people naturally wished to obtain their money. The queue of those wanting to withdraw gold from the Bank of England stretched down Ludgate Hill into Fleet Street.

A Mafeking siege note emergency issue from the Boer War. Highly rare and very collectable.

The Bank managed to save the situation by employing it own staff to join the queue posing as customers. Each would withdraw large quantities of money and then take it round to the back of the Bank where is was redeposited. This meant the tills were kept opened until the public alarm subsided.

One modern day crisis for the Bank came during World War II when Hitler's Germany decided to forge the large white Bank of England notes in current circulation at the time, in huge quantities. This operation called for around 150 prisoners, each hand picked for their skills in engraving, printing and paper making. The original idea was to drop the undetectable forgeries on the British Isles and neutral nations in an effort to destroy Britain's economy but the plan never came to fruition, although millions of pounds in face value were produced. Most of the notes were dumped into Lake Toplitz by the fleeing German forces fearing Allied retribution. However, many have since been recovered and often appear on the market today. When encountering forgeries, collectors are in a difficult position. If they hold a note, knowing it to be a forgery, they are breaking the law. If they have the note checked, they run the risk of having it confiscated!

World War II notes. From top: Japanese Invasion Money (JIM money) intended for use by the Japanese in their occupied territories; Occupation notes issued in Guernsey during the German occupation.

A banknote need not be old to be worth collecting. Many interesting notes have been issued throughout the world each with their own story to tell. In 1954 the Canadian Central Bank issued notes in which the portrait of the Queen had what appeared to be the hidden face of the Devil in the folds of her hair. The public refused to handle them and the notes were withdrawn. To this day it is not known whether the engraving was done intentionally or not.

Most countries suffer from inflation but in 1923, Germany saw one of the biggest inflationary

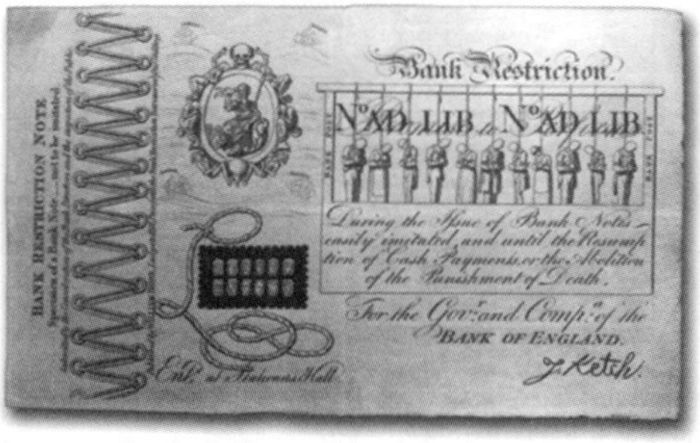

An example of a "skit note" (a piece of paper masquerading as a banknote). George Cruikshank's famous "Bank Restriction Note" produced as a protest against counterfeiting laws.

periods of modern times. On November 1 of that year the average wage packet was 28 million marks, equivalent to 1.3 million pounds at the 1913 exchange rate. This huge sum would not have been enough to buy a newspaper, which would have cost around 3,000 million marks. This period left a legacy of hundreds of different notes for the collector today.

Unlike coins, collecting of paper money is still in its infancy. It is still possible to obtain notes from many different countries for a modest outlay. Some dealers sell starter packs that include 50 uncirculated notes from 50 different counties, all for under £30. One reason why some notes are so cheap is that many countries devalue their currency. When a new set of notes are issued, the old set after a period, become worthless. Dealers can acquire large quantities of these notes for less than the original face value.

New collectors will find many books on the subject of paper money. A good introduction to the hobby of notaphily is *The Banknote Yearbook*. Published yearly by Token Publishing Ltd *The Banknote Yearbook* includes up to date values for notes of England, Scotland, Ireland, the Channel Islands and the Isle of Man. The useful volume also features hints and tips for the collector, a review of the current market trends, a world note identifier and much more. In short it is the essential guide to the hobby of banknote collecting. *(Call 01404 44166 for more details.)*

COIN NEWS is also a useful way of keeping in touch with the every day events of the banknote world. There is a dedicated banknote section in the magazine every month often giving vital pieces of information, for example the latest auction prices realised, forthcoming events and fairs and there are also informative articles designed to be of appeal to experienced collectors as well as newcomers.

Directory section

ON the following pages will be found the most useful names and addresses needed by the coin collector.

At the time of going to press with this edition of the YEARBOOK the information is correct, as far as we have been able to ascertain. However, people move and establishments change, so it is always advisable to make contact with the person or organisation listed before travelling any distance, to ensure that the journey is not wasted.

Should any of the information in this section not be correct we would very much appreciate being advised in good time for the preparation of the next edition of the COIN YEARBOOK.

Dealers who display this symbol are Members of the

BRITISH NUMISMATIC TRADE ASSOCIATION

The primary purpose of the Association is to promote and safeguard the highest standards of professionalism in dealings between its Members and the public. In official consultations it is the recognised representative of commercial numismatics in Britain.

For free a Membership Directory please send a stamped addressed envelope to:

General Secretary, BNTA
PO Box 2, Rye, East Sussex TN31 7WE
Tel/Fax: 01797 229988

The BNTA will be organising the following events:

COINEX LONDON - 10/11 October 2003
08/09 October 2004
Marriott Hotel, Grosvenor Square W1

The BNTA is a member of the International Numismatic Commisson.

BNTA MEMBERSHIPS IN COUNTY ORDER

(Those members with a retail premises are indicated with an*)

LONDON AREA
*A. H. Baldwin & Son Ltd.
Arsantiqva Ltd.
ATS Bullion Ltd.
Beaver Coin Room
*Philip Cohen Numismatics
Andre de Clermont
Michael Dickinson
*Dix Noonan Webb
Christopher Eimer
Glendining's
Harrow Coin & Stamp Centre
*Knightsbridge Coins
Lubbock & Son Ltd.
C. J. Martin (Coins) Ltd.
Morton & Eden Ltd.
*Colin Narbeth & Son Ltd.
*Seaby Coins/C.N.G. Inc
Simmons Gallery
*Spink & Son Ltd.
Surena Ancient Art & Numismatic

BERKSHIRE
Frank Milward

BUCKINGHAMSHIRE
Europa Numismatics

CAMBRIDGESHIRE
*Lockdale Coins Ltd

DORSET
*Dorset Coin Co. Ltd

HAMPSHIRE
*SPM Jewellers
Studio Coins
West Essex Coin Investments

HERTFORDSHIRE
KB Coins
David Miller

KENT
C. J. Denton (Coins of Ireland)
London Coins
*Peter Morris

LANCASHIRE
*B. J. Dawson (Coins)
*Colin de Rouffignac
*Peter Ireland Ltd
*R & L Coins

LINCONSHIRE
Grantham Coins

NORFOLK
*Roderick Richardson
Chris Rudd

NORTHUMBERLAND
*Corbitt Stamps Ltd.

OXFORDSHIRE
Simon R. Porter

SHROPSHIRE
*Collectors Gallery

SUFFOLK
*Lockdale Coins Ltd.
Schwer Coins

SURREY
British Notes
The Duncannon Partnership
KMCC Ltd.
Graeme & Linda Monk
Mark Rasmussen Numismatist
Nigel Tooley Ltd.

SUSSEX
*Brighton Coin Co.

WEST MIDLANDS
*Format of Birmingham Ltd.
Mint Coins Ltd

WARWICKSHIRE
*Warwick & Warwick Ltd.

WORCESTERSHIRE
Whitmore

YORKSHIRE
Airedale Coins
Paul Clayton
Paul Davis Ltd
*J. Smith

WALES
Lloyd Bennett
*North Wales Coins Ltd.
Colin Rumney

Museums and Libraries

Listed below are the Museums and Libraries in the UK which have coins or items of numismatic interest on display or available to the general public.

A

Anthropological Museum, University of Aberdeen, Broad Street, **Aberdeen,** AB9 1AS (01224 272014).

Curtis Museum (1855), High Street, **Alton,** Hants (01420 2802). *General collection of British coins.*

Ashburton Museum, 1 West Street, **Ashburton,** Devon. *Ancient British and Roman antiquities including local coin finds.*

Ashwell Village Museum (1930), Swan Street, **Ashwell,** Baldock, Herts. *Roman coins from local finds, local trade tokens, Anglo-Gallic coins and jetons.*

Buckinghamshire County Museum (1862), Church Street, **Aylesbury,** Bucks (01296 88849). *Roman and medieval English coins found locally, 17th/18th century Buckinghamshire tokens, commemorative medals.*

B

Public Library and Museum (1948), Marlborough Road, **Banbury,** Oxon (01295 259855). *Wrexlin Hoard of Roman coins.*

Museum of North Devon (1931), The Square, **Barnstaple,** EX32 8LN (01271 46747). *General coin and medal collection, including local finds. Medals of the Royal Devonshire Yeomanry.*

Roman Baths Museum, Pump Room, **Bath,** Avon (01225 461111 ext 2785). *Comprehensive collection of Roman coins from local finds.*

Bagshaw Museum and Art Gallery (1911), Wilton Park, **Batley,** West Yorkshire (01924 472514). *Roman, Scottish, Irish, English hammered, British and foreign coins, local traders' tokens, political medalets, campaign medals and decorations.*

Bedford Museum (1961), Castle Lane, **Bedford** (01234 353323). *Collections of the Bedford Library and Scientific Institute, the Beds Archaeological Society and Bedford Modern School (Pritchard Memorial) Museum.*

Ulster Museum (1928), Botanic Gardens, **Belfast** BT9 5AB (01232 381251). *Irish, English and British coins and commemorative medals.*

Berwick Borough Museum (1867), The Clock Block, Berwick Barracks, Ravensdowne, **Berwick**. TD15 1DQ (01289 330044). *Roman, Scottish and medievial coins.*

Public Library, Art Gallery and Museum (1910), Champney Road, **Beverley,** Humberside (01482 882255). *Beverley trade tokens, Roman, English, British and foreign coins.*

Bignor Roman Villa (1811), **Bignor,** nr Pulborough, West Sussex (017987 202). *Roman coins found locally.*

City Museum and Art Gallery (1861), Chamberlain Square, **Birmingham** B3 3DH (0121 235 2834). *Coins, medals and tokens, with special emphasis on the products of the Soho, Heaton, Birmingham and Watt mints.*

Blackburn Museum, Museum Street, **Blackburn,** Lancs (01254 667130). *Incorporates the Hart (5,000 Greek, Roman and early English) and Hornby (500 English coins) collections, as well as the museum's own collection of British and Commonwealth coins.*

Museum Collection, Town Hall, **Bognor Regis,** West Sussex. *Roman, English and British coins and trade tokens.*

Museum and Art Gallery,(1893), Civic Centre, **Bolton,** Lancashire (01204 22311 ext 2191). *General collection of about 3000 British and foreign coins, and over 500 British medals. Numismatic library.*

Art Gallery and Museum, Central Library, Oriel Road, **Bootle,** Lancs. *Greek, Roman, English, British and some foreign coins, local trade tokens.*

Roman Town and Museum (1949) Main Street, **Boroughbridge,** N. Yorks. YO2 3PH (01423 322768). *Roman coins.*

The Museum (1929), The Guildhall, **Boston,** Lincs (01205 365954). *Small collection of English coins.*

Natural Science Society Museum (1903), 39 Christchurch Road, **Bournemouth,** Dorset (01202 553525). *Greek, Roman and English hammered coins (including the Hengistbury Hoard), local trade tokens.*

Bolling Hall Museum (1915), Bolling Hall Road, **Bradford,** West Yorkshire BD4 7LP (01274 723057). *Some 2,000 coins and tokens, mostly 18th–20th centuries.*

Cartwright Hall Museum and Art Gallery (1904), Lister Park, **Bradford,** West Yorkshire BD9 4NS (01274 493313). *Roman coins found locally.*

Museum and Art Gallery (1932), South Street, **Bridport,** Dorset (01308 22116). *Roman coins, mainly from excavations at Claudian Fort.*

The City Museum (1820), Queen's Road, **Bristol** BS8 1RL (0117 9 27256). *Ancient British, Roman (mainly from local hoards), English hammered coins, especially from the Bristol mint, and several hundred local trade tokens.*

District Library and Museum (1891), Terrace Road, **Buxton,** Derbyshire SK17 6DU (01298 24658). *English and British coins, tokens and commemorative medals. Numismatic library.*

C

Segontium Museum (1928), Beddgelert Road, **Caernarfon,** Gwynedd (01286 675625) *Roman coins and artifacts excavated from the fort.*

Fitzwilliam Museum (1816), Department of Coins and Medals, Trumpington Street, **Cambridge** (01223 332900). *Ancient, English, medieval European, oriental coins, medals, plaques, seals and cameos.*

National Museum & Galleries of Wales, Cathays Park, **Cardiff** (029 20397951). *Greek, Celtic, Roman and British coins and tokens with the emphasis on Welsh interest. Also military, civilian and commemorative medals.*

Guildhall Museum (1979), Greenmarket, **Carlisle,** Cumbria (01228 819925). *General collection of coins and medals.*

Tullie House (1877), Castle Street, **Carlisle,** Cumbria (01228 34781). *Roman, medieval and later coins from local finds, including medieval counterfeiter's coin-moulds.*

Gough's Caves Museum (1934), The Cliffs, **Cheddar,** Somerset (01934 343). *Roman coins.*

Chelmsford and Essex Museum (1835), Oaklands Park, Moulsham Street, **Chelmsford,** Essex CM2 9AQ (01245 615100). *Ancient British, Roman, medieval and later coins mainly from local finds, local medals.*

Town Gate Museum (1949), **Chepstow,** Gwent. *Local coins and trade tokens.*

Grosvenor Museum (1886), Grosvenor Street, **Chester** (01244 21616). *Roman coins from the fortress site, Anglo-Saxon, English medieval and post-medieval coins of the Chester and Rhuddlan mints, trade tokens of Chester and Cheshire, English and British milled coins.*

Public Library (1879), Corporation Street, **Chesterfield,** Derbyshire (01246 2047). *Roman coins from local finds, Derbyshire trade tokens, medals, seals and railway passes. Numismatic library. Numismatic library and publications.*

Red House Museum (1919), Quay Road, **Christchurch,** Dorset (01202 482860). *Coins of archaeological significance from Hampshire and Dorset, notably the South Hants Hoard, ancient British, Armorican, Gallo-Belgic, Celtic and Roman coins, local trade tokens and medals.*

Corinium Museum (1856), Park Street, **Cirencester,** Glos (01285 655611). *Roman coins from archaeological excavations.*

Colchester and Essex Museum (1860), The Castle, **Colchester,** Essex (01206 712931/2). *Ancient British and Roman coins from local finds, medieval coins (especially the Colchester Hoard), later English coins and Essex trade tokens, commemorative medals.*

D

Public Library, Museum and Art Gallery (1921), Crown Street, **Darlington,** Co Durham (01325 463795). *General collection of coins, medals and tokens.*

Borough Museum (1908), Central Park, **Dartford,** Kent (01322 343555). *Roman, medieval and later English hammered coins, trade tokens and commemorative medals.*

Dartmouth Museum (1953), The Butterknowle, **Dartmouth,** Devon (01803 832923). *Coins and medals of a historical and maritime nature.*

Museum and Art Gallery (1878), The Strand, **Derby** (01332 255586). *Roman coins, English silver and copper regal coins, Derbyshire tradesmen's tokens, British campaign medals and decorations of the Derbyshire Yeomanry and the 9/12 Royal Lancers.*

Museum and Art Gallery (1909), Chequer Road, **Doncaster,** South Yorkshire (01302 734293). *General collection of English and foreign silver and bronze coins. Representative collection of Roman imperial silver and bronze coins, including a number from local hoards. English trade tokens, principally of local issues, medals.*

Dorset County Museum(1846), **Dorchester,** Dorset (01305 262735). *British, Roman, medieval and later coins of local interest.*

Central Museum (1884), Central Library, St James's Road, **Dudley,** West Midlands (01384 453576). *Small general collection of coins, medals and tokens.*

Burgh Museum (1835), The Observatory, Corberry Hill, **Dumfries** (01387 53374). *Greek, Roman, Anglo-Saxon, medieval English and Scottish coins, especially from local hoards. Numismatic library.*

Dundee Art Galleries and Museums (1873). Albert Square, **Dundee** DD1 1DA (01382 23141). *Coins and medals of local interest.*

The Cathedral Treasury (995 AD), The College, **Durham** (0191-384 4854). *Greek and Roman coins bequeathed by Canon Sir George Wheeler (1724), general collection of medals from the Renaissance to modern times, medieval English coins, especially those struck at the Durham ecclesiastical mint.*

Durham Heritage Centre, St Mary le Bow, North Bailey, **Durham** (0191-384 2214). *Roman, medieval and later coins, mainly from local finds.*

E

Royal Museum of Scotland (1781), Queen Street, **Edinburgh** EH1 (0131 225 7534). *Roman, Anglo-Saxon, Englsh and Scottish coins, trade tokens, commemorative medals and communion tokens. Numismatic library. Publications.*

Royal Albert Memorial Museum (1868), Queen St, **Exeter** EX4 3RX (01392 265858). *Roman and medieval. Coins of the Exeter Mint.*

G

Hunterian Museum (1807), Glasgow University, University Avenue, **Glasgow** G12 8QQ (041 339 8855). *Greek, Roman, Byzantine, Scottish, English and Irish coins, Papal and other European medals, Indian and Oriental coins, trade and communion tokens.*

Art Gallery and Museum (1888), Kelvingrove, **Glasgow** G3 (0141 357 3929). *General collection of coins, trade tokens, communion tokens, commemorative and military medals.*

Museum of Transport (1974), Kelvin Hall, Bunhouse Road, **Glasgow** G3 (0141 357 3929). *Transport tokens and passes, commemorative medals, badges and insignia of railway companies and shipping lines.*

City Museum and Art Gallery (1859), Brunswick Road, **Gloucester** (01452 524131). *Ancient British, Roman, Anglo-Saxon (from local finds), early medieval (from local mints), Gloucestershire trade tokens.*

Guernsey Museum and Art Gallery, St Peter Port, **Guernsey** (01481 726518). *Armorican, Roman, medieval and later coins, including the coins, medals, tokens and paper money of Guernsey.*

Guildford Museum (1898), Castle Arch, **Guildford,** Surrey GU1 3SX (01483 444750). *Roman and medieval coins and later medals.*

H

Gray Museum and Art Gallery, Clarence Road, **Hartlepool,** Cleveland (01429 268916). *General collection, including coins from local finds.*

Public Museum and Art Gallery (1890), John's Place, Cambridge Road, **Hastings,** East Sussex (01424 721952). *General collection of English and British coins, collection of Anglo-Saxon coins from Sussex mints.*

City Museum (1874), Broad Street, **Hereford** (01432 268121 ext 207). *Coins from the Hereford mint and local finds, Herefordshire trade tokens, general collection of later coins and medals.*

Hertford Museum (1902), 18 Bull Plain, **Hertford** (01992 582686). *British, Roman, medieval and later English coins and medals.*

Honiton and Allhallows Public Museum (1946), High Street, **Honiton,** Devon (01404 44966). *Small general collection, including coins from local finds.*

Museum and Art Gallery (1891), 19 New Church Road, **Hove,** East Sussex (01273 779410). *English coins, Sussex trade tokens and hop tallies, campaign medals, orders and decorations, commemorative medals.*

Tolson Memorial Museum (1920), Ravensknowle Park, **Huddersfield,** West Yorkshire (01484 541455). *Representative collection of British coins and tokens, Roman and medieval coins, mainly from local finds.*

Hull and East Riding Museum (1928), 36 High Street, **Hull** (01482 593902). *Celtic, Roman and medieval coins and artifacts from local finds. Some later coins including tradesmen's tokens.*

I

The Manx Museum, Douglas, **Isle of Man** (01624 675522). *Roman, Celtic, Hiberno-Norse, Viking, medieval English and Scottish coins, mainly from local finds, Manx traders' tokens from the 17th to 19th centuries, Manx coins from 1709 to the present day.*

J

Jersey Museum, Weighbridge, St Helier, **Jersey** (01534 30511). *Armorican, Gallo-Belgic, Roman, medieval English and French coins, coins, paper money and tokens of Jersey.*

K

Dick Institute Museum and Art Gallery (1893), Elmbank Avenue, **Kilmarnock,** Ayrshire (01563 26401). *General collection of coins and medals, and the Hunter-Selkirk collection of communion tokens.*

L

City Museum (1923), Old Town Hall, Market Square, **Lancaster** (01524 64637). *Roman, Anglo-Saxon, medieval English coins, provincial trade tokens, medals of the King's Own Royal Lancashire Regiment.*

City Museum (1820), Municipal Buildings, The Headrow, **Leeds,** West Yorkshire (01532 478279). *Greek, Roman, Anglo-Saxon, English medieval, Scottish, Irish, British, Commonwealth and foreign coins. Several Roman and Saxon hoards. The Backhouse collection of Yorkshire banknotes, the Thornton collection of Yorkshire tokens, British and foreign commemorative medals.*

Leicester Museum and Art Gallery (1849), New Walk, **Leicester** (01533 554100). *Roman, medieval and later coins, mainly from local finds, tokens, commemorative medals, campaign medals and decorations.*

Pennington Hall Museum and Art Gallery, **Leigh,** Lancashire. *General collection of Roman, English and British coins and medals.*

Museum and Art Gallery (1914), Broadway, **Letchworth,** Herts (01462 65647). *Ancient British coins minted at Camulodunum, Roman, medieval and English coins, Hertfordshire trade tokens, commemorative and campaign medals.*

City Library, Art Gallery and Museum (1859), Bird Street, **Lichfield,** Staffs (01543 2177). *Roman, medieval and later English coins, Staffordshire trade tokens and commemorative medals.*

Liverpool Museum(1851), William Brown Street, **Liverpool** L3 8EN (0151 207 0001). *General collection of Roman, medievaland later British coins, tokens.*

Bank of England Museum, Threadneedle Street, **London** EC2 (020-7601 5545). *Exhibits relating to gold bullion, coins, tokens and medals, the design and manufacture of banknotes, and a comprehensive collection of bank notes dating from the 17th century to the present day.*

British Museum(1752), HSBC Coin Gallery, Great Russell Street, **London** WC1 (020-7636 1555). *Almost a million coins, medals, tokens and badges of all period from Lydia, 7th century BC to the present time. Extensive library of books and periodicals.*

British Numismatic Society (1903), Warburg Institute, Woburn Square, **London** WC1. *Library containing over 5,000 volumes, including sale catalogues, periodicals and pamphlets. Open to members only.*

Cuming Museum (1906), Walworth Road, **London** SE17 (020-7703 3324/5529). *Some 8,000 items, including Greek, Roman, medieval English and modern British coins, English tokens and commemorative medals.*

Gunnersbury Park Museum (1927), Acton, **London** W3. *Ancient British, Greek, Roman, medieval English, British and some foreign coins, tradesmen's tokens and commemorative medals, including local finds. Small numismatic library.*

Horniman Museum and Library (1890), London Road, Forest Hill, **London** SE23 (020-7699 2339). *General collection, primitive currency, some tokens.*

Imperial War Museum, Lambeth Road, **London** SE1 6HZ (020-7416 5000). *Emergency coinage of two world wars, occupation and invasion money, extensive collection of German Notgeld, commemorative, propaganda and military medals, badges and insignia.*

Sir John Soane's Museum (1833), 13 Lincoln's Inn Fields, **London** WC2 (020-7405 2107). *Napoleonic medals and medallic series of the late 18th and early 19th centuries.*

National Maritime Museum, Romney Road, Greenwich, **London** SE10 (020-8858 4422). *Commemorative medals with a nautical or maritime theme, naval medals and decorations.*

Victoria and Albert Museum (1852), South Kensington, **London** SW7 (020-7938 8441). *Byzantine gold and medieval Hispano-Mauresque coins (Department of Metalwork), large collection of Renaissance and later medals (Department of Architecture and Sculpture). Library of numismatic books.*

Ludlow Museum (1833). The Assembly Rooms. Castle Square, **Ludlow** (01584 873857). *Roman and medieval coins from local finds.*

Luton Museum and Art Gallery (1927), Wardown Park, **Luton**, Beds (01582 36941). *Coins, tokens and medals.*

M

Museum and Art Gallery (1858), **Maidstone**, Kent (01622 754497). *Ancient British, Roman, Anglo-Saxon and medieval coins found in Kent, modern British coins, Kent trade tokens, banknotes, hop tallies and tokens, primitive currency, collections of Kent Numismatic Society.*

The Manchester Museum (1868), The University, **Manchester** M13 (0161-275 2634). *Very fine collections of Greek and Roman coins, comprehensive collections of English, European and Oriental coins, over 30,000 in all.*

Margate Museum (1923), The Old Town Hall, Market Place, **Margate**, Kent (01843 225511 ext 2520). *Small collection of coins, including Roman from local finds.*

Montrose Museum and Art Gallery (1836). Panmure Place, **Montrose**, Angus DD10 8HE (01674 73232). *Scottish and British coins.*

N

Newark-on-Trent Museum (1912), Appleton Gate, **Newark**, Notts (01636 702358). *Siege pieces, trade tokens and coins from local finds and hoards.*

Newbury District Museum, The Wharf, **Newbury**, Berkshire (01635 30511). *Ancient British, Roman and medieval coins and artifacts, later coins and tokens.*

The Greek Museum, Percy Building, **Newcastle-upon-Tyne** (0191 2226000 ext 7966). *Ancient coins.*

O

Heberden Coin Room, Ashmolean Museum (1683), **Oxford** (01865 278000). *Extensive collections of all periods, notably Greek, Roman, English and Oriental coins, Renaissance portrait and later medals, tokens and paper money. Large library. Numerous publications.*

P

Peterborough Museum (1881), Priestgate, **Peterborough**, Cambs (01733 340 3329). *Roman (mainly from local hoards and finds), Anglo-Saxon, medieval English, British and modern European coins, English and British commemorative medals and tokens.*

City Museum and Art Gallery (1897), Drake Circus, **Plymouth**, Devon (01752 264878). *General collections of British and Commonwealth coins and tokens, Devon trade tokens and Plymouth tradesmen's checks, Ancient British and Roman coins from local sites.*

Waterfront Museum, 4 High Street, **Poole**, Dorset (01202 683138). *General collection of British and foreign coins, medals and tokens (view by appointment).*

City Museum (1972), Museum Road, Old **Portsmouth** PO1 (023 80827261). *Roman, medieval and later coins mainly from local finds and archaeological excavation, British coins, trade tokens of Hampshire, commemorative medals.*

Harris Museum and Art Gallery (1893), Market Square, **Preston**, Lancashire (01772 58248). *English and British coins, tokens and medals.*

R

The Museum of Reading (1883), Blagrave Street, **Reading**, Berks (0118 939 9800). *British, Roman and medieval English coins, many from local finds, tradesmen's tokens and commemorative medals.*

Rochdale Museum (1905), Sparrow Hill, **Rochdale**, Lancs (01706 41085). *Roman and medieval coins from local finds, Rochdale trade tokens, miscellaneous British and foreign coins and medals.*

Municipal Museum and Art Gallery (1893), Clifton Park, **Rotherham** (01709 382121). *Roman coins from Templeborough Forts, medieval English coins from local hoards and a general collection of British coins.*

S

Saffron Walden Museum (1832) (1939), Museum Street, **Saffron** Walden, Essex (01799 522494). *Ancient British, Roman, medieval and later coins, mainly from local finds and archaeological excavation, trade tokens and commemorative medals.*

Verulamium Museum, St Michael's, **St Albans**, Herts (01727 819339). *Coins and artifacts excavated from the Roman town.*

Salisbury and South Wiltshire Museum (1861), The Cathedral Close, **Salisbury,** Wilts (01722 332151). *Collection of coins minted or found locally, including finds of Iron Age, Roman, Saxon and medieval coins, as well as 18th and 19th century tradesmen's tokens.*

Richborough Castle Museum (1930), **Sandwich,** Kent (0304 612013). *Roman coins of 1st–5th centuries from excavations of the Richborough site.*

Scarborough Museum (1829), The Rotunda, Vernon Road, **Scarborough**, North Yorkshire (01723 374839). *Over 4,000 Roman coins, 1,500 English and 600 coins from local finds, siege pieces and trade tokens.*

Shaftesbury and Dorset Local History Museum (1946), 1 Gold Hill, **Shaftesbury**, Dorset (01747 52157). *Hoard of Saxon coins.*

City Museum (1875), Weston Park, **Sheffield** (0114 2 768588). *Over 5,000 coins of all periods, but mainly English and modern British. European coins, imperial Roman (including three hoards of about 500 coins each), Yorkshire trade tokens, British historical medals, campaign medals. Library.*

Rowley's House Museum, Barker Street, **Shrewsbury**, Salop (01743 361196). *Coins minted at Shrewsbury 925-1180, Civil War coinage of 1642, Shropshire tradesmen's tokens, English coins and medals.*

Museum of Archaeology (1951), God's House Tower, Town Quay, **Southampton**, Hants (023 8022 0007). *Main emphasis lies in Ancient British, Roman and medieval English coins from local archaeological excavations. General collection of later coins and medals.*

Atkinson Art Gallery (1878), Lord Street, **Southport,** Lancs (01704 533133). *Roman coins.*

Botanic Gardens Museum, Churchtown, **Southport,** Lancs (01704 87547). *English and British coins and medals, military medals and decorations.*

Southwold Museum (1933), St Bartholomew's Green, **Southwold,** Suffolk (01502 722375). *General collection of coins, specialised Suffolk trade tokens.*

Stamford Museum (1961), Broad Street, **Stamford**, Lincs (01780 66317). *General collection of coins, medals and tokens, including a selection from the Stamford mint.*

Municipal Museum (1860), Vernon Park, Turncroft Lane, **Stockport**, Cheshire (0161 474 4460) *Miscellaneous general collection of coins, tokens and medals.*

Stroud Museum (1899), Lansdown, **Stroud**, Glos (01453 376394). *Ancient British, Roman, Saxon, Norman, later medieval English, British coins and Gloucestershire trade tokens.*

Museum and Art Gallery (1846), Borough Road, **Sunderland,** Tyne & Wear (0191 514 1235). *Roman imperial, medieval and later English, including examples of the pennies minted at Durham, modern British and foreign coins, 17th-19th century tradesmen's tokens, local medallions and campaign medals.*

Swansea Museum (1835), Victoria Road, **Swansea**, W. Glamorgan, SA1 1SN (0792 653765). *Coins and medals of local interest.*

T

Tamworth Castle and Museum (1899), The Holloway, **Tamworth**, Staffs (01827 63563). *Anglo-Saxon coins, medieval English including coins of the Tamworth mint, later English and British coins, tokens, commemorative medallions and medals.*

Somerset County Museum, Taunton Castle, **Taunton**, Somerset (01823 255510/320200). *Celtic, Roman, Anglo-Saxon, early Medieval, tokens, medallions and banknotes. Strong emphasis on locally-found items.*

Thurrock Local History Museum (1956), Civic Square, **Tilbury**, Essex (01375 390000 ext 2414). *Roman coins.*

Royal Cornwall Museum (1818), River Street, **Truro,** Cornwall (01872 72205). *Coins, tokens and medals pertaining principally to the county of Cornwall.*

W

Wakefield Museum (1919), Wood Street, **Wakefield,** West Yorkshire (01924 295351). *Roman and medieval English silver and copper coins.*

Epping Forest District Museum, 39/41 Sun Street, **Waltham Abbey**, Essex EN 9. *Ancient British, Roman and medieval coins, Essex tradesmen's tokensof local interest.*

Warrington Museum and Art Gallery (1848). Bold Street, **Warrington**, Cheshire, WA1 1JG (01925 30550). *Coins, medals and tokens.*

Worcester City Museum (1833), Foregate Street, **Worcester** (01905 25371). *Roman, medieval and later coins and tokens. Coins of the Worcester mint.*

Wells Museum (18903), 8 Cathedral Green, **Wells,** Somerset (01749 3477). *Ancient and modern British and world coins, local trade tokens and medals.*

Municipal Museum and Art Gallery (1878), Station Road, **Wigan**, Lancashire. *British, Commonwealth and foreign coins from about 1660 to the present. Roman coins from local sites, commemorative medals.*

City Museum (1851), The Square, **Winchester**, Hants (01962 848269). *Roman and medieval coins chiefly from local hoards and finds. Hampshire tradesmen's tokens and commemorative medals. Small reference library.*

Wisbech and Fenland Museum (1835), Museum Square, **Wisbech,** Cambridgeshire (01945 583817), *British Roman, medieval and later coins, medals and tokens.*

Y

The Museum of South Somerset (1928), Hendford, **Yeovil,** Somerset (01935 24774). *Roman coins from local sites, medieval English, modern British coins and medals and a fine collection of tokens (particularly 17th century Somerset).*

Castle Museum (1938), **York** (01904 653611). *English and British coins, campaign medals, orders and decorations, comemorative medals.*

Jorvik Viking Centre (1984), Coppergate, **York** (01904 643211). *Coins and artefacts pertaining to the Viking occupation of York.*

The Yorkshire Museum (1823), **York** (01904 629745). *Roman imperial, medieval English and later coins, about 12,000 in all.*

Club directory

Details given here are the names of Numismatic Clubs and Societies, their date of foundation, and their usual venues, days and times of meetings. Meetings are monthly unless otherwise stated. Finally, the telephone number of the club secretary is given; the names and addresses of club secretaries are withheld for security reasons, but full details may be obtained by writing to the Secretary of the British Association of Numismatic Societies, Philip Mernick, c/o General Services, 42 Campbell Road, London E3 4DT. Telephone 020 8980 5672. E-mail: phil@mernicks.com.

Banbury & District Numismatic Society (1967). Banbury British Rail Working Mens Club. 2nd Mon (exc Jul & Aug), 19.45. (01295 254451).

Bath & Bristol Numismatic Society (1950). Ship Inn, Temple Street, Keynsham, Bristol. 2nd Thu, 19.30. (01275 472385).

Bedford Numismatic Society (1966). RAF Association Club, 93 Ashburnham Road, Bedford MK40 1EA. 3rd Mon, 19.30. (01234 228833/ 358369).

Bexley Coin Club (1968). St Martin's Church Hall, Erith Road, Barnehurst, Bexleyheath, Kent. 1st Mon (exc Jan & Aug), 20.00. (020 8303 0510).

Birmingham Numismatic Society (1964). Friend's Meeting House, Linden Road, Bournville, Birmingham 30. 2nd Wed, 19.45. (0121 308 1616).

Matthew Boulton Society (1994). PO Box 395, Birmingham B31 2TB (0121 781 6558 fax 0121 781 6574).

Bradford & District Numismatic Society (1967). East Bowling Unity Club, Leicester Street, Bradford, West Yorkshire. 3rd Mon, 19.00. (01532 677151).

Brighton & Hove Coin Club (1971). Methodist Church Hall, St Patrick's Road, Hove, East Sussex. Last Wed (exc Dec), 20.00. (01273 419303).

British Cheque Collectors' Society (1980). John Purser, 71 Mile Lane, Cheylesmore, Coventry, West Midlands CV3 5GB.

British Numismatic Society (1903). Warburg Institute, Woburn Square, London WC1H 0AB. Monthly (exc Aug & Dec), 18.00.

Cambridgeshire Numismatic Society (1946). Friends' Meeting House, 12 Jesus Lane (entrance in Park Street), Cambridge, CB5 8BA. 3rd Mon, Sept–June, 19.30. (01767 312112).

Chester & North Wales Coin & Banknote Society (1996). Liver Hotel, 110 Brook Street, Chester. 4th Tue, 20.00. (0151 478 4293)

Cheltenham Numismatic Society, The Reddings & District Community Association, North Road, The Reddings, Cheltenham. 3rd Mon, 19.45 (01242 673263)

Coin Correspondence Club (1988). Postal only. A.H. Chubb, 49 White Hart Lane, Barnes, London SW13 0PP. (0181-878 0472).

Cornwall Collectors' Club (1990). The Swan Inn, 40 Bosvigo Road, Truro. 1st Wed, 20.00. (01872 73376).

Crawley Coin Club (1969). Furnace Green Community Centre, Ashburnham Road, Furnace Green, Crawley, West Sussex. 1st Tue, 20.00. (01293 548671).

Crewe & District Coin & Medal Club (1968). Memorial Hall, Church Lane, Wistaston, Crewe, 2nd Tue (exc Jan & July), 19.30. (01270 69836).

Darlington & District Numismatic Society (1968). Darlington Arts Centre, Vane Terrace, Darlington, Co Durhm. 3rd Wed, 19.30. (01609 772976).

Derbyshire Numismatic Society (1964). The Friends' Meeting House, St Helens Street, Derby. 3rd Mon (exc August), 19.45. (01283 211623).

Devon & Exeter Numismatic Society (1965). Red Cross Centre, Butts Road, Heavitree, Exeter, Devon. 3rd Tue, 19.30. (01392 461013).

Edinburgh Numismatic Society (1996). Department of History and Applied Arts, Royal Museum of Scotland, Chambers Street, Edinburgh EH1 1JF. 3rd Mon, 19.30. (0131 225 7534).

Enfield & District Numismatic Society (1969). Millfield House Arts Centre, Silver Street, Edmonton, London N18 1PJ. 3rd Mon, 20.00. (0181-340 0767).

Essex Numismatic Society (1966). Chelmsford & Essex Museum, Moulsham Street, Chelmsford, Essex. 4th Fri (exc Dec), 20.00. (01376 21846).

Glasgow & West of Scotland Numismatic Society (1947). The College Club, University of Glasgow, University Avenue, Glasgow G12. 2nd Thu, Oct-May, 19.30. (0141 633 5422).

Harrow & North West Middlesex Numismatic Society (1968). Harrow Arts Centre, Hatch End, Harrow, Middlesex. 2nd and 4th Mon, 19.30. (020 8952 8765).

Havering Numismatic Society (1967). Fairkytes Arts Centre, Billet Lane, Hornchurch, Essex. 1st Tue, 19.30. (01708 704201).

Horncastle & District Coin Club (1963). Bull Hotel, Bull Ring, Horncastle, Lincs. 2nd Thu (exc Aug), 19.30. (01754 2706).

Huddersfield Numismatic Society (1947). Tolson Memorial Museum, Ravensknowle Park, Huddersfield, West Yorkshire. 1st Mon (exc Jul & Aug), 19.30. (01484 226300).

Hull & District Numismatic Society (1967). The Young People's Institute, George Street, Hull. Monthly (exc Aug & Dec), 19.30. (01482 441933).

International Bank Note Society (1961). Victory Services Club, 63–79 Seymour Street, London W1. Last Thu (exc Dec), 18.00. (020-8969 9493).

International Bank Note Society, Scottish Chapter (1995). West End Hotel, Palmerston Place, Edinburgh. Last Sat (exc Dec), 14.30.

Ireland, Numismatic Society of (Northern Branch). Denman International, Clandeboye Road, Bangor or Maysfield Leisure Centre, Belfast. 1st Fri (exc Jan) 19.30. (028 9146 6743)

Ireland, Numismatic Society of. (Southern Branch). Ely House, 8 Ely Place, Dublin. Last Fri, 20.00. (0035 3 283 2027).

Ipswich Numismatic Society (1966). Ipswich Citizens Advice Bureau, 19 Tower Street, Ipswich, Suffolk. Monthly meetings, 19.30. (01473 711158).

Kent Towns Numismatic Society (1913). Adult Education Centre, 9 Sittingbourne Road (Maidstone) and King's School Preparatory School, King Edward Road (Rochester). 1st Fri of month, 19.30 alternately at Maidstone and Rochester. (01622 843881).

Kingston Numismatic Society (1966). King Athelstan's School, Villiers Road, Kingston-upon-Thames, Surrey. 3rd Thu (exc Dec & Jan), 19.30. (020-8397 6944).

Lancashire & Cheshire Numismatic Society (1933). Manchester Central Library, St Peter's Square, Manchester M2 5PD. Monthly, Sep-June, Wed (18.30) or Sat (14.30). (0161 445 2042).

Lincolnshire Numismatic Society (1932). Grimsby Bridge Club, Bargate, Grimsby, South Humberside. 4th Wed (exc Aug), 19.30.

London Numismatic Club (1947). Institute of Archaeology, 31–34 Gordon Square, London WC1H 0PY. Monthly, 18.30.

Loughborough Coin & Search Society (1964). Wallace Humphry Room, Shelthorpe Community Centre, Loughborough, Leics. 1st Thu, 19.30. (01509 261352).

Merseyside Numismatic Society (1947). The Lecture Theatre, Liverpool Museum, William Brown Street, Liverpool L3 8EN. Monthly (exc July & Aug), 19.00. (0151-929 2143).

Mid Lanark Coin Circle (1969). Hospitality Room, The Civic Centre, Motherwell, Lanarkshire. 4th Thu, Sep–Apr (exc Dec), 19.30. (0141-552 2083).

Morecambe & Lancaster Numismatic Society. Monthly, 19.30. (01524 411036).

Newbury Coin & Medal Club (1971). Monthly, 20.00. (01635 41233).

Northampton Numismatic Society (1969). Old Scouts RFC, Rushmere Road, Northampton. 1st Thurs, 20.00.

Norwich Numismatic Society (1967). Assembly House, Theatre Street, Norwich, Norfolk. 3rd Mon, 19.30. (01493 651577).

Nottinghamshire Numismatic Society (1948). The Cecil Roberts Room, County Library, Angel Row, Nottingham NG1 6HP. 2nd Tue (Sep-Apr), 18.45. (0115 9257674).

Nuneaton & District Coin Club (1968). United Reformed Church Room, Coton Road, opposite Council House, Nuneaton, Warwickshire. 2nd Tue, 19.30. (01203 371556).

Orders & Medals Research Society (1942). National Army Museum, Royal Hospital Road, Chelsea, London SW3. Monthly, 14.30 (020-8680 2701).

Ormskirk & West Lancashire Numismatic Society (1970).The Eagle & Child, Maltkiln Lane, Bispham Green L40 1SN. 1st Thu, 20.15. (01704 531266).

Peterborough Coin & Medal Club (1967). The Club Room, APV-Baker Social Club, Alma Road, Peter-borough, Cambs. Last Tue (exc July & Aug), 19.30.

Plymouth Coin & Medal Club (1970). RAFA Club, 5 Ermington Terrace, Mutley Plain, Plymouth, Devon. 2nd Wed (exc Dec), 19.30. (01752 663803).

Preston & District Numismatic Society (1965). Eldon Hotel, Eldon Street, Preston, Lancs. 1st and 3rd Tue, 20.00. (012572 66869).

Reading Coin Club (1964). Abbey Baptist Church, Abbey Square, Reading. 1st Mon, 19.00. (0118 9332843).

Rochford Hundred Numismatic Society. Civic Suite, Rayleigh Town Hall, Rayleigh, Essex. 2nd Thu, 20.00. (01702 230950).

Romsey Numismatic Society (1969). Romsey WM Conservative Club, Market Place, Romsey, Hants SO5 8NA. 4th Fri (exc Dec), 19.30. (01703 253921).

Rotherham & District Coin Club (1982). Rotherham Art Centre, Rotherham, South Yorkshire. 1st Wed, 19.00. (01709 528179).

Royal Mint Coin Club, PO Box 500, Cardiff CF1 1HA (01443 222111).

Royal Numismatic Society (1836). Society of Antiquaries, Piccadilly, London W1. Monthly (Oct-June), 17.30. Joe Cribb, Coins and Medals, British Museum, London WC1B 3DG (020-7323 8585).

Rye Coin Club (1955). Rye Further Education Centre, Lion Street, Rye, East Sussex. 2nd Thu (Oct-Dec, Feb-May), 19.30. (01424 422974).

St Albans & Hertfordshire Numismatic Society (1948). St Michael's Parish Centre, Museum Entrance, Verulamium Park, St Albans, Herts AL3 4SL. 2nd Tue (exc Aug), 19.30. (01727 824434).

Sheffield Numismatic Society. Telephone for venue. 2nd Wed, 19.00. (0114 2817129)

South East Hants Numismatic Society. Different locations. 1st Fri. Contact: Tony Matthews, 8 King George Road, Totton, Southampton SO4 3FE.

South Manchester Numismatic Society (1967). Nursery Inn, Green Lane, Heaton Mersey, Stockport. 1st & 3rd Mondays of each month (excl. Public hols), 20.00. (0161-485 7017).

South Wales & Monmouthshire Numismatic Society (1958). The W. R. Lysaght Institute, Corporation Road, Newport. 2nd Tues, 19.30. (029 20561564).

Thurrock Numismatic Society (1970). Stanley Lazell Hall, Dell Road, Grays, Essex. 3rd Wed, 19.00.

Tyneside Numismatic Society (1954). RAFA Club, Eric Nelson House, 16 Berwick Road, Gateshead, Tyne & Wear. 2nd Wed, 19.30. (0191 372 2266).

Wessex NS (1948). Hotel Bristowe, Grange Road, Southbourne, Bournemouth, Dorset. 2nd Thurs (exc Aug), 20.00. (020 7731 1702).

Wiltshire Numismatic Society (1965). Raven Inn, Poulshot, Nr Devizes, Wiltshire. 3rd Mon, Mar-Dec, 20.00. (01225 703143).

Worthing & District Numismatic Society (1967). Kingsway Hotel, Marine Parade, Worthing, West Sussex BN11 3QQ. 3rd Thu, 20.00. (01903 241503).

Yorkshire Numismatic Society (1909). Leeds Museum, The Headrow , Leeds. 1st Sat (exc Jan, Aug & Dec) (0113 286 4914).

IMPORTANT NOTICE

Club Secretaries:

If your details as listed are incorrect please let us know in time for the next edition of the COIN YEARBOOK

IMPORTANT ORGANISATIONS

ADA
The Antiquities Dealers Association

Secretary: Susan Hadida, Duke's Court, 32 Duke Street, London SW1Y 6DU

BNTA
The British Numismatic Trade Association

Secretary: Mrs R. Cooke, General Secretary, BNTA, PO Box 2, Rye, East Sussex TN31 7WE

ANA
The American Numismatic Association

818 North Cascade Avenue, Colorado Springs, CO 80903-3279, USA

IAPN
International Association of Professional Numismatists

Secretary: Jean-Luc Van der Schueren, 14 Rue de la Bourse, B–1000, Brussels.

IBNS
International Bank Note Society

Membership Secretary:
Franco Spinelli, PO Box 4WX, London W1A 4WX

RNS
Royal Numismatic Society
Ms V. Hewitt, Dept of Coins & Medals, British Museum, London WC1B 3DG. Tel: 020 7323 8228.

BAMS
British Art Medal Society
Philip Attwood, Dept of Coins & Medals, British Museum, London WC1B 3DG.

Directory of Auctioneers

Listed here are the major UK auction houses which handle coins, medals, banknotes and other items of numismatic interest. Many of them hold regular public auctions, whilst others handle numismatic material infrequently. A number of coin companies also hold regular Postal Auctions—these are marked with a P.

Arsantiqva
Auctions held at Westbury, New Bond Street, London. (788 4434967 fax: 0039 0332 232130, website: www.arsantiqva.com

Baldwin's Auctions Ltd
11 Adelphi Terrace, London WC2N 6BJ (020 7930 9808 fax 020 7930 9450, e-mail auctions@baldwin.sh, website: www.baldwin.sh)

Banking Memorabilia
PO Box 14, Carlisle CA3 8DZ (016974 76465).

A. F. Brock & Company
269 London Road, Hazel Grove, Stockport, Cheshire SK7 4PL (0161 456 5050 fax 0161 456 5112, website www.afbrock.co.uk, email info@afbrock.co.uk).

Christie, Manson & Wood Ltd
8 King Street, St James's, London SW1Y 6QT (020 7839 9060).

Christie's Scotland Ltd
164–166 Bath Street, Glasgow G2 4TG (0141 332 8134 fax 0141 332 5759).

Classical Numismatic Group Inc (Seaby Coins)
14 Old Bond Street, London W1X 4JL (020 7495 1888 fax 020-7499 5916, email cng@historicalcoins.com, website: www.historicalcoins.com). **P**

Corbitts
5 Moseley Sreet, Newcastle upon Tyne NE1 1YE (0191-232 7268 fax 0191-261 4130).

Croydon Coin Auctions
272 Melfort Road, Thornton Heath, Surrey CR7 7RR (020 8240 7924 or 020 8656 4583, website www.croydoncoinauctions.co.uk, email: croydoncoinauctions.co.uk).

Dix Noonan Webb
16 Bolton Street, Piccadilly, London. Website: www.dnw.co.uk, email: auctions@dnw.co.uk)

Edinburgh Coin Shop
11 West Crosscauseway, Edinburgh EH8 9JW (0131 668 2928 fax 0131 668 2926). **P**

Fellows & Sons
Augusta House, 19 Augusta Street, Hockley, Birmingham B18 6JA (0121-212 2131).

B. Frank & Son
3 South Avenue, Ryton, Tyne & Wear NE40 3LD (0191 413 8749 fax 0191 413 2957, email bfrankandson@aol.com).

T. Gillingham
42 Highbury Park, Warminster, Wilts BA12 9JF (01985 216486).

Gillio Coins International
1013 State Street, Santa Barbara, CA 93101, USA (805 9631345—London contact Eric Green 020-7586 3964).

Glendining & Co
101 New Bond Street, London W1Y 9LG (020 7 493 2445 fax 020 7491 9181, website: phillips-auctions.com)).

Graves, Son & Pilcher Fine Arts
71 Church Road, Hove, East Sussex BN3 2GL (01273 735266 fax 01273 723813).

Hoods Postal Coin Auctions
23 High Street, Kilbirnie, Ayrshire KA25 7EX (fax/tel 01505 682157). **P**

Kleeford Coin Auctions
19 Craythorns Crescent, Dishforth, Thirsk YO7 3LY. (tel/fax 01845 577977). *P*

W. H. Lane & Son
65 Morrab Road, Penzance, Cornwall TR18 2QT (01736 61447 fax 01736 50097) also: Trafalgar House, Malpas Road, Truro, Cornwall TR1 1QH (01872 223379).

Lawrence Fine Art Auctioneers
South Street, Crewkerne, Somerset TA18 8AB (01460 73041).

Lockdale Coins
Shops at: 37 Upper Orwell Street, Ipswich IP4 1BR.(01473 218588), 168 London Road South, Lowestoft NR33 0BB (01473 218588) & 23 Magdalene Street, Cambridge, CB3 OAF (01223 361163) website: www.lockdales.co.uk

London Coin Auctions
12, Redhill Wood, New Ash Green, Kent DA3 8QH (01474 871464 , email: Slockcoin@aol.com www.londoncoins.co.uk)

Moreton & Eden Ltd
45 Maddox Street, London W1S 2PE (020 7493 5344 fax 020 7495 6325, email info@mortonand eden.com, www.mortonandeden.com)

Neales
192–194 Mansfield Road, Nottingham NG1 3HU (0115 9624141 fax 0115 9856890).

R & W Coin Auctions
307 Bretch Hill, Banbury, Oxon OX16 0JD (01295 275128).

Serendip Collectibles
10, Briar Road, Kingswood, Herts WD25 0HN (01923 672909). **P**

Sheffield Coin Auctions
7 Beacon Close, Sheffield S9 1AA (0114 249 0442).

Simmons Gallery
PO Box 104, Leytonstone, London. Tel: 0207 898 8097. www.simmonsgallery.co.uk email: info@simmonsgallery.co.uk

Spink & Son Ltd
69 Southampton Row, Bloomsbury, London. WC1B 4ET (020 7563 4055, fax 020 7563 4068, website www.spink-online.com, email info@spinkandson.com).

Sussex Auction Galleries
59 Perrymount Road, Haywards Heath, West Sussex RH16 3DS (01444 414935 fax 01444 450402).

Warwick & Warwick
Chalon House, Scarbank, Millers Road, Warwick CV34 5DB (01926 499031 fax 01926 491906, email info@warwickandwarwick.com, website: www.warwickandwarwick.com)

directory of *Fairs*

Listed below are the names of the fair organisers, their venue details where known along with contact telephone numbers. Please call the organisers direct for information on dates etc.

Aberdeen
Jarvis Amatola Hotel, Great Western Road, also venues in **Glenrothes** and **Glasgow.** *Cornucopia Collectors Fairs. (01382 224946)*

Birmingham
National Motor Cycle Museum, Bickenhill, Birmingham. *Midland Stamp & Coin Fair. (024 7671 6587)*

Bristol
Jury's Hotel, Prince Street. *AMP Fairs. (01952 597 587).*

Cardiff
City Hall. *AMP Fairs. (01952 597 587)*

Cheltenham
Town Hall or White House Hotel. *AMP Fairs. (01952 597 587)*

Exeter
St Georges Hall, George Street. *Gold Star Fairs. (01823 251563)*

Leeds-Morley
Cedar Court Hotel, Denby Dale Road, Calder Grove, Wakefield WF4 3QZ. *N. C. S. Promotions. (01552 684681).*

Lichfield
Civic Hall, Castle Dyke, City Centre. *C. S. Fairs. (01562 710424)*

London
Holiday Inn, Coram St., Bloomsbury, London WC1. *London Coin Fair. (020 7831 2080)*

London
The Bonnington Hotel, 92 Southampton Row, London WC1. *West Promotions. (020 8641 3224).*

London
The Commonwealth Institute, Kensington High Street, London W8. *Davidson Monk Fairs. (020 8656 4583 or 020 8651 3890)*

Malvern
Lyttleton Rooms. *AMP Fairs. (01952 597 587)*

Sutton Coldfield
Fellowship Hall, South Parade. *C. S. Fairs. (01562 710424)*

Newcastle upon Tyne
The Royal Station Hotel. B. Frank & Son. (0191 413 8749

West Bromwich
Town Hall, High Street. *C. S. Fairs. (01562 710424)*

York
The Grandstand, York Racecourse. *York Coin Fair (01793 513431 or 020 8946 4489)*

Annual events
The B.N.T.A. (Coinex)
Tel: 01797 229 988 for details
The I.B.N.S. (World Paper Money Fair)
Tel: 020 8428 4002 for details

Directory of Dealers

The dealers listed below have comprehensive stocks of coins and medals, unless otherwise stated. Specialities, where known, are noted. Many of those listed are postal dealers only, so to avoid disappointment always make contact by telephone or mail in the first instance, particularly before travelling any distance.

Abbreviations:
ADA—Antiquities Dealers Association
ANA—American Numismatic Association
BADA—British Antique Dealers Association
BNTA—British Numismatic Trade Association
IAPN—International Association of Professional Numismatists
IBNS—International Bank Note Society
P—Postal only
L—Publishes regular lists

A. Ackroyd (IBNS)
62 Albert Road, Parkstone, Poole, Dorset BH12 2DB (tel/fax 01202 739039, website www.AAnotes.com). *P. L. Banknotes, cheques and related collectables.*

Afribilia Ltd
16 Bury Place, London WC1A 2JL (020 7404 7134, fax: 020 7404 7138, email: info@afribilia.com, www.afribilia.com). *Medals, coins, banknotes etc*

Airedale Coins (ANA, BNTA)
PO Box 7, Bingley, West Yorkshire, BD16 1XU (01535 272754 fax 01535 275727, website www.airedalecoins.com, email info@airedalecoins.com).
P. L. British and modern coins of the world.

All Gold of Sevenoaks
Email: goldsovereigns@aol.com. (01732 462255) *Quality Sovereigns*

David Allen Coins and Collectables
PO Box 125, Pinner, Middlesex HA5 2TX (020 866 6796). *P. L. British and world coins, tokens, banknotes.*

Joan Allen Electronics Ltd
190 Main Road, Biggin Hill, Kent TN16 3BB (01959 71255). Mon-Sat 09.00–17.00. *Metal detectors.*

Ancient & Gothic (ADA)
PO Box 5390, Bournemouth, BH7 6XR (01202 431721). *P. L. Greek, Roman and medieval antiquities with occasional groups of coins.*

Ancient World
16 High Petergate, York, YO1 2EH (01904 624062) 10.30–17.00 weekdays. *Greek, Roman, Celtic and medieval coins, also antiquities.*

Antiquestall.com
On line numismatic market place. *Coins, medals, banknotes etc*

Keith Austin (IBNS)
PO Box 89, Carlise, Cumbria CA3 0GH (01228 819149, fax 01228 521176, email kaustin@kabc.freeserve.co.uk). L. *Banknotes.*

N. J. Aves
PO Box 811, Yeovil, Somerset (01935 72368). P. *Coins, tokens and medals.*

Mark Bailey
120 Sterte Court, Sterte Close, Poole, Dorset BH15 2AY (01202 674936). *P. L. Ancient, modern, world coins and antiquities.*

A. H. Baldwin & Sons Ltd (ANA, BADA, BNTA, IAPN)
11 Adelphi Terrace, London WC2N 6BJ. 09.00–17.00 weekdays. (email coins@baldwin.sh) *Coins, tokens, commemorative medals, war medals and decorations, numismatic books.*

Banking Memorabilia (IBNS)
PO Box 14, Carlisle, Cumbria (016974 76465). 09.00– 18.00 (not Sun). *Cheques, banknotes, related ephemera.*

Banknotes 4 U
Roger and Liz Outing, PO Box 123, Huddersfield HD8 9WY www.banknotes4u.co.uk e mail rogerouting@aol.com (01484 860415). *World banknotes*

Banknotes of Auld Scotland
Sconser, Isle of Skye IV48 8TD. (01478 650459, website www.scottish-banknotes.com, email johnaunc@aol.com).

D. G. Barney
Greenfield, Colyton Hill, Colyton, Devon EX24 6HY (01297 552702, email:doug.barney@onmail.com). *British and world coins, tokens and banknotes.*

G. Barrington Smith
Cross Street, Oadby, Leicestershire LE2 4DD (01533 712114). 08.30–17.15 weekdays. *Albums, catalogues and accessories.*

Bath Stamp and Coin Shop
Pulteney Bridge, Bath, Avon BA2 4AY (01225 463073). Mon-Sat 09.30–17.30. *British*

Michael Beaumont
PO Box 8, Carlton, Notts NG4 4QZ (0115 9878361). *P. Coins, medals and tokens of the world.*

Beaver Coin Room (BNTA)
57 Philbeach Gardens, LondonSW5 9ED (020 7373 4553). *P. European coins and medals.*

R. P. & P. J. Beckett
Maesyderw, Capel Dewi, Llandyssul, Dyfed SA44 4PJ. (Fax only 01559 395631, email rppjbeckett@btinternet.com) *P. World crowns, coin sets and banknotes.*

Lloyd Bennett (BNTA)
PO Box 2, Monmouth, Gwent NP5 3YE (01600 890634). Abergavenny Market (Tue), Monmouth Market (Fri–Sat) 09.00–16.00. *English hammered, milled and coins of the world.*

Berkshire Coin Centre
35 Castle Street, Reading, Berkshire RG1 7SB (01734 575593). 10.00–16.00 weekdays, half-day Sat. *British and world coins.*

Beron Coins
64 Rosewood Close, Glascote, Tamworth, Staffs B77 3PD (01827 54541). *P. L. British & world coins.*

Stephen J. Betts
4 Victoria Street, Narborough, Leics LE9 5DP (0116 2864434). *P. L. Medieval and modern coins, counters, jetons and tokens, countermarks and medals.*

Bigbury Mint
River Park, Ermington Mill, Ivybridge, Devon PL21 9NT (01548 830717. *Specialists in reproduction hammered coins*

Birchin Lane Gold Coin Company
6 Castle Court, St Michael's Alley (off Cornhill), London EC3V 9DS (020 7621 0370 and 020 7263 3981). Mon-Fri 10.00–16.30. *Gold and bullion coins.*

Barry Boswell
24 Townsend Lane, Upper Boddington, Daventry, Northants NN11 6DR (01327 261877, fax 01327 261391, email Barry.Boswell@btinternet.com). *P. L. British and world banknotes.*

James & C. Brett
17 Dale Road, Lewes, East Sussex BN7 1LH. *P. L. British and world coins.*

J. Bridgeman Coins
129a Blackburn Road, Accrington, Lancs (01254 384757). 09.30–17.00. *British & World coins.*

Brighton Coin Company (ANA, BNTA)
The Hove Coin Shop, Church Road, Hove, (01278 737537) Mon-Fri 9.45–17.30, Sat 9.45–15.30 (closed alternate Wednesdays and Saturdays). *World coins.*

Britannia Jewellery Co
234 Yorkshire Street, Rochdale, Lancs OL16 2DP (01706 341046/55507. Mon-Sat 10.00–17.00.

BRM Coins
3 Minshull Street, Knutsford, Cheshire WA16 6HG (01565) 651480 and 0606 74522). Mon-Sat 10,00–17.00. *British coins.*

Peter F. Broadbelt
10 Dragon Road, Harrogate, North Yorkshire HG1 5DF (01423 562037). Mon-Sat 11–18.00. *Specialist in Foreign coins.*

A. F. Brock & Company
269 London Road, Hazel Grove, Stockport, Cheshire SK7 4PL (0161 456 5050/5112, email info@afbrock.co.uk, www.afbrock.co.uk). Mon-Sat 09.30–17.30. *Auctioneers and valuers.*

E. J. & C. A. Brooks (BNTA, IBNS)
44 Kiln Road, Thundersley, Essex SS7 1TB (01268 753835). Any time up to 23.00. *L. British*

Iain Burn
2 Compton Gardens, 53 Park Road, Camberley, Surrey GU15 2SP (01276 23304). *Bank of England & Treasury notes*

Butler & Co
111 Promenade, Cheltenham, Glos GL50 1NN (01242 522272). Sat only. *World coins.*

BBM Coins
8–9 Lion Street, Kidderminster, Hereford & Worcester, DY10 1PT (01562 744118). Mon, Wed-Sat 10.00–17.00. *World coins.*

Cambridge Stamp Centre Ltd
9 Sussex Street, Cambridge CB4 4HU (01223 63980). Mon-Sat 09.00–17.30. *British coins.*

Castle Curios
165 Wellgate, Rotherham, South Yorkshire S60 4DT. Wed-Sat 11.00–17.00. *English coins.*

Castle Galleries
81 Castle Street, Salisbury, Wiltshire SP1 3SP (01722 333734). Tue, Thu Fri 09.00–17.00, Sat 09.30–16.00. *British coins, medals and tokens.*

Cathedral Coins
23 Kirkgate, Ripon, North Yorkshire HG4 1PB (01765 701400). Mon-Sat 10.00–17.00.

David L. Cavanagh
49 Cockburn Street, Edinburgh EH1 1PB (0131 226 3391). Mon-Sat 10.30–17.00. *British coins.*

Cavendish Coins
14 Longfields, Ongar, Essex CM5 9BZ. *P. Modern crown-sized coins.*

Central Bank of Ireland
Currency Centre, Sandyford Road, Dublin 16, Ireland. *New coin and banknote issues of Ireland.*

Lance Chaplin
17 Wanstead Lane, Ilford, Essex IG1 3SB (020 8554 7154). *P. L. Roman, Greek, Celtic, hammered coins and antiquities.*

Chard (BNTA)
521 Lytham Road, Blackpool, Lancs FY4 1RJ (01253 343081). Mon-Sat 09.00–17.00. www.chards.co.uk. *British, Commonwealth and European coins.*

Chelsea Coins Ltd (BNTA)
PO Box 2, Fulham Road, London SW10 9PQ. (020 8870 5501 Fax 020 8875 1459). *P. World coins.*

Nigel A. Clark
28 Ulundi Road, Blackheath, London SE3 7UG (020 8858 4020). *P. L. Mainly 17th century tokens.*

Classical Numismatic Group
14 Old Bond Street, London W1X 4JL. (020 7495 1888 Fax 020 7499 5916, Email cng@historicalcoins.com). *P. Ancient and world coins. Publishers of the Classical Numismatic Review.*

Paul Clayton (BNTA)
PO Box 21, Wetherby, West Yorkshire LS22 5JY. (01937 72441). *Modern gold coins.*

André de Clermont (BNTA)
PO Box 3615, London, SW10 0YD. (020 7351 5727, Fax 020 7352 8127). *World coins, especially Islamic & Oriental coins, Latin America.*

M. Coeshaw
PO Box 115, Leicester LE3 8JJ (0116 287 3808). *P. Coins, banknotes, coin albums and cases*

Philip Cohen Numismatics (ANA, BNTA)
20 Cecil Court, Charing Cross Road, London WC2N 4HE (020 7379 0615). Mon-Sat 10.30–17.30 (half-days Mon and Sat).

Coin & Collectors Centre
PO Box 22, Pontefract, West Yorkshire WF8 1YT (01977 704112, website www.coincentre.co.uk, email sales@coincentre.co.uk). *P. British coins.*

Coincraft (ANA, IBNS)
44/45 Great Russell Street, London WC1B 3LU (020 7636 1188 and 020 7637 8785 fax 020 7323 2860, Website www.coincraft.com Email info@coincraft.com). Mon-Fri 09.30–17.00, Sat 10.00–14.30. *L (newspaper format). Coins and banknotes.*

Coinote Services Ltd
PO Box 53, Sorting Office, Clarke Street, Hartlepool TS26 NYL (01429 890894). Shop at 74 Elwick Road, Hartlepool, TS26 9AP *P. L. Coins and banknotes 1615 todate. Accessories and books.*

Coins of Beeston
PO Box 19, Beeston, Notts BG9 2NE. *P. L. Tokens, medals and paranumismatics.*

Coins of Canterbury
PO Box 47, Faversham, Kent ME13 7HX (01795 531980). *P. English coins.*

Coliseum Coins
30 Staunton Avenue, Hayling Island, Hants PO11 0EN (01705 464332). *P. Greek, Roman, Oriental coins.*

Collecta Coins Limited
PO Box 101, Northampton NN1 3LT (01604 766607/27076). Mon-Sat 09.00–21.00. *World coins.*

The Collector
242 High Street, Orpington, Kent BR6 0LZ (01689 890045). Mon-Sat 09.45–17.30 (closed Tue). *Coins, medals, banknotes, badges, militaria, cigarette cards etc*

Collectors' Corner
East Street, Crescent Road, Faversham, Kent ME13 8AD (01795 539721). Mon-Fri 10.00–15.00 (closed Wednesdays). *Coins and medals.*

Collectors' Corner
Watford Market (off High Street), Watford, Herts (020 8904 0552). Tue, Fri, Sat 09.00-17.00. *World coins.*

Collectors Gallery (BNTA, IBNS)
24 The Parade, St Mary's Place, Shrewsbury SY1 1DL (01743 272140 fax 01743 366041). Mon-Fri 09.00–18.00, half-day Sat. www.collectors-gallery.co.uk. *Coins and banknotes, accessories and related books. Agents for the Abafil range of coin cases.*

Collectors' World
188 Wollaton Road, Wollaton, Nottingham NG8 1HJ. (01159 280347). *Coins, Tokens, Banknotes, Accessories.*

Constantia CB
15 Church Road, Northwood, Middlesex HA6 1AR. *P. Roman and medieval hammered coins.*

Colin Cooke
257 Brooklands Road, Manchester M23 9HF (0161 973 2395 fax 0161 962 2864, email coins@colincooke.com). *L. British coins.*

Corbitts (BNTA)
5 Mosley Street, Newcastle Upon Tyne NE1 1YE (0191 232 7268 fax: 0191 261 4130). *Dealers and auctioneers of all coins and medals.*

G. D. Courtenay
58 New Peachey Lane, Uxbridge, Middlesex UB8 3SX. *P. L. Coins, medals, tokens and banknotes.*

David Craddock
PO Box 3785, Camp Hill, Birmingham B11 2NF. (0121 733 2259) *L. Crown to farthings. Copper and bronze specialist. Some foreign.*

John Cummings Ltd
Parthenon Gallery, 25 Bury Place, WC1A 2JH (020 7242 5656). *P. Greek, Roman, Byzantine, Celtic, Saxon, and English hammered coins. Catalogue.*

Mark Davidson
PO Box 197, South Croydon, Surrey CR3 0ZD (020 8651 3890). *Ancient, hammered coinage.*

Davidson Monk Fairs
PO Box 201, Croydon, Surrey CR9 7AQ (020 8656 4583). *Organiser of monthly fairs at the Common wealth Institute, Kensington High Street, London W8.*

Paul Davies Ltd (ANA, BNTA, IAPN)
PO Box 17, Ilkley, West Yorkshire LS29 8TZ (01943 603116 fax 01943 816326). *P. World coins.*

Paul Davis
PO Box 418, Birmingham B17 0RZ (0121 427 7179). *P. Hammered gold and silver coins.*

Ian Davison
PO Box 256, Durham DH1 2GW (0191 3750808. L. *English hammered and milled coins 1066–1910.*

DD Coins of Windsor
24–28 St Leonards Road, Suite 100, Windsor, Berks SL4 3BB. (01753 739487). *L. GB milled list.*

B. J. Dawson (Coins) (BNTA)
52 St Helens Road, Lancs BL3 3NH (01204 63732). Mon Tue Sat 09.30–16.00, Thu Fri 09.30–17.30, Wed 09.30–13.00. *L. Ancient, hammered and milled coins, tokens and banknotes.*

Decus Coins
The Haven, Brockweir, Chepstow, Gwent NP6 7NN (01291 689216). *P.*

Dei Gratia
PO Box 3568, Buckingham MK18 4ZS (01280 848000). *P. L. Pre-Roman to modern coins, antiquities, banknotes.*

Clive Dennett (BNTA)
66 St Benedicts Street, Norwich, Norfolk NR2 4AR (01603 624315). Mon-Fri 09.00–17.30, Sat 09.00–16.00 (closed Thu). *L. World paper money.*

C. J. Denton (ANA, BNTA, FRNS)
PO Box 25, Orpington, Kent BR6 8PU (01689 873690). *P. Irish coins.*

Detecnicks
3 Orchard Crescent, Arundel Road, Fontwell. West Sussex BN18 0SA (01243 545060 fax 01243 545922 *Retail shop. Wide range of detectors and accessories.*

Michael Dickinson (ANA, BNTA)
Ramsay House, 825 High Road Finchley, London N12 8UB (0181 441 7175). *P. British and world coins.*

Dolphin Coins (ANA)
22 High Street, Leighton Buzzard, Beds. LU7 7EB. (01525 383822 fax 01525 383872)
Mon-Fri 09.30– 17.00. Sat appt only. *L. British and world coins.*

Dorset Coin Co Ltd (BNTA)
193 Ashley Road, Parkstone, Poole, Dorset BH14 9DL (01202 739606, fax 01202 739230). *P. L. Separate coin and banknote lists.*

Drizen Coins
1 Hawthorns, Leigh-on-Sea, Essex SS9 4JT (01702 521094). *P. L. British and world coins.*

Dyas Coins & Medals
30 Shaftmoor Lane, Acocks Green, Birmingham B27 7RS (0121 707 2808). Fri 10.30–18.30, Sun 10.30–13.00. *World coins and medals.*

Eagle Coins
Winterhaven, Mourneabbey, Mallow, Co. Cork, Ireland (010 35322 29385). *P. L. Irish and English coins.*

Eden Coins
PO Box 77, Brierley Hill, West Midlands DY5 2GS (01384 834648). *P. English coins, tokens and medals.*

Edinburgh Coin Shop (ANA)
11 West Crosscauseway, Edinburgh EH8 9JW (0131 668 2928 fax 0131 668 2926). Mon-Sat 10.00–17.30. *L. World coins and medals. Postal auctions.*

Christopher Eimer (ANA, BNTA)
PO Box 352 London NW11 7RF (020 8458 9933 fax 020 8455 3535, email art@christophereimer.co.uk). *P. Commemorative medals.*

Elm Hill Stamps & Coins
27 Elm Hill, Norwich, Norfolk NR3 1HN (01603 627413). Mon-Fri 09.00–16.45, half-day Sat. *Mainly stamps, occasionally coins*

Ely Stamp & Coin Shop
27 Fore Hill, Ely, Cambs CB7 1AA (01353 663919). Tues-Sat 09.30–17.30. *World coins and medals.*

Europa Numismatics (ANA, BNTA)
PO Box 119, High Wycombe, Bucks HP11 1QL (01494 437307). *P. European coins.*

Evesham Stamp & Coin Centre
Magpie Antiques, Paris House, 61 High Street, Evesham, Worcs WR11 4DA (01386 41631). Mon-Sat 09.00–17.30. *British coins.*

Michael E. Ewins
Meyrick Heights, 20 Meyrick Park Crescent, Bournemouth, Dorset BH3 7AQ (01202 290674). *P. World coins.*

I. Fine & Son Ltd
Victoria House, 93 Manor Farm Road, Wembley, Middlesex HA10 1XB (020 8997 5055). *P. British & World coins.*

Patrick Finn
PO Box 26, kendal, Cumbria LA9 7AB (01539 730008 fax 01539 721800 P.L. *Early British, Irish, Scottish and Anglo-Gallic Cions*

Robin Finnegan Stamp Shop
83 Skinnergate, Darlington, Co Durham DL3 7LX (01325 489820/357674). Mon-Sat 10.00–17.30 (closed Wed). *World coins.*

Richard N. Flashman
54 Ebbsfleet Walk, Gravesend, Kent, DA11 9EW. *L. P. British banknotes.*

David Fletcher (Mint Coins) (ANA, BNTA)
PO Box 64, Coventry, Warwickshire CV5 6SN (024 7671 5425, Fax 024 7667 7985). *P. World new issues*

Folley Island Coins
PO Box 361, Dunstable, Bedfordshire LU5 4YU. (01582 667734). *World and English coins.*

Format of Birmingham Ltd (ANA, BNTA, IAPN, IBNS)
18 Bennetts Hill, Birmingham B2 5QJ (0121 643 2058 fax 0121 643 2210). Mon-Fri 09.30-7.00. *L. Coins, tokens and medals.*

B. Frank & Son (ANA, IBNS)
3 South Avenue, Ryton, Tyne & Wear NE40 3LD (0191 413 8749). *P. L. Banknotes and cheques, coins of the world. Organiser of the North of England fair.*

Frank Milward (BNTA)
2 Ravensworth Road, Mortimer, Berks, RG7 3UU (01734 332843). Mon-Sat 09.00-18.00. *British and World coins.*

Dennis Fudge Coins
127 Hadrian Road, Jarrow, Tyne & Wear NE32 3TS (0191 421 6221). *P. L. Ancient coins.*

Galata Coins Ltd (ANA)
The Old White Lion, Market Street, Llanfylin, Powys SY22 5BX (01691 648 765). *P. British and world coins.*

G. Gant
Glazenwood, 37 Augustus Way, Witham, Essex CM8 1HH. *P. British and Commonwealth coins.*

James Garriock
38 Hazel Close Bemerton Heath, Salisbury, Wiltshire SP2 977 (01722 500590). *P. L. Mainly hammered coins.*

John Gaunt
21 Harvey Road, Bedford MK41 9LF (01234 217685). By appointment. *Numismatic books.*

Alistair Gibb (IBNS)
5 West Albert Road, Kirkcaldy, Fife KY1 1DL (01592 269045). *P. L. Banknotes and books on banking.*

A. & S. Gillis
59 Roykilner Way, Wombwell, Barnsley, South Yorkshire S73 8DY. (01226 750371, website www.gilliscoins.com, email: catalogues@gilliscoins.com) *P. L. Ancient and medieval coins.*

Richard Gladdle
9 Cork Street, London W1X 1P9. (01327 858511). *Tokens. P. L.*

Glance Back Books
17 Upper Street, Chepstow, Gwent NP6 5EX (01291 626562). 10.30–17.30. *World coins, medals, banknotes.*

Glendining's (Bonhams) (ANA, BNTA)
101 New Bond Street, London W1Y 9LG (020 7493 2445). Mon-Fri 08.30-17.00, Sat 08.30–13.00. *Auctioneers.*

GM Coins
www.onlinecoins.co.uk/gmcoins, email: gmcoins@cleeve95.freeserve.co.uk, (01242 701144) *Hammered and milled coins*

Phil Goodwin (ANA)
PO Box 69, Portsmouth, Hants PO1 5SH (02392 423267 or 02392 752006 incl. fax). *P or by appoint ment.L. Ancient coins and antiquities.*

Ian Gradon
PO Box 359, Durham DH7 6WZ (0191 3719 700, email: ian@worldnotes.co.uk, www.worldnotes.co.uk). *L. World banknotes.*

Granta Stamp & Coin Shop
23 Magdalene Street, Cambridge CB3 0AF (01223 361662) Mon-Sat 10.30-17.00. *English coins and medals.*

Grantham Coins (BNTA)
PO Box 60, Grantham, Lincs (01476 870565). *P. L. English coins and banknotes.*

Eric Green—Agent in UK for Ronald J. Gillio Inc,
1013 State Street, Santa Barbara, California, USA 93101 (020 8907 0015, Mobile 0468 454948). *Gold coins, medals and paper money of the world.*

Barry Greenaway
PO Box 2151, Swindon, Wilts SN5 3GT. (01793 771079, fax 01793 772556, email bdgreenaway@beeb.net). *Tokens, Checks. P.L.*

R. I. Groves
82 Burntscarth Green, Locharbriggs, Dumfries DG1 1UL (01387 710636). *P. World, esp. Scandinavian coins.*

Ian Haines
PO Box 45, Hereford, HR2 7YP (01432 268178). *P. L. British and foreign coins and banknotes.*
Anthony Halse
The Headlands, Chepstow Road, Langstone, Newport, Gwent NP6 2JN (01633 413238). *P. L. English and foreign coins and tokens.*
A. D. Hamilton & Co (ANA)
7 St Vincent Place, Glasgow G1 5JA (0141 221 5423, fax 0141 248 6019, website www.antiquesglasgow, email jeffrey@hamiltons.junglelink.co.uk). Mon-Sat 10.00-17.00. *British and World coins.*
Peter Hancock
40 West Street, Chichester, West Sussex PO19 1RP (01243 786173). Mon-Sat. *World coins.*
P. Hanson
160 Princess Road, Buckhurst Hill, Essex IG9 5DJ. *P. L. Inexpensive world coins.*
Munthandel G. Henzen
PO Box 42, NL - 3958ZT, Amerogngen, Nether lands. (0031 343 430564 fax 0031 343 430542, email henzen.coins@tiscali.nl *Ancients, Dutch & foreign coins. L*
History In Coins.com
www.historyincoins.com (01949 836988) *World Coins*
Craig Holmes
6 Marlborough Drive, Bangor, Co Down BT19 1HB. *P. L. Low cost banknotes of the world.*
R. G. Holmes
11 Cross Park, Ilfracombe, Devon EX34 8BJ (01271 864474). *P. L. Coins, world crowns and banknotes.*
John L. Homan
Oxford Grange, Marsh Lane, Barrow Haven, Barrow-on-Humber, South Humberside DN19 7ER (01469 32109). *P. Greek, Roman and Byzantine coins.*
Homeland Holding Ltd (IBNS)
Homeland, St John, Jersey, Channel Islands JE3 4AB (01534 65339). Mon-Fri 09.00-2.00. *World coins.*
HTSM Coins
26 Dosk Avenue, Glasgow G13 4LQ. *P. L. British and foreign coins and banknotes.*
T. A. Hull
15 Tangmere Crescent, Hornchurch, Essex RM12 5PL. *P. L. British coins, farthings to crowns, tokens.*
Humber Coins (BNTA)
PO Box 16, Scunthorpe Humberside DN15 7AA (01724 763990) *P. British Coins*
J. Hume
107 Halsbury Road East, Northolt, Middlesex UB5 4PY (020 8864 1731). *P. L. Chinese coins.*
D. A. Hunter
www.dahunter.co.uk/coins, email coins@dahunter.co.uk. *P., L. UKand world coins.*
D. D. & A. Ingle
380 Carlton Hill, Nottingham (0115 9873325). Mon-Sat 09.30–17.00. *World coins.*
R. Ingram Coins
206 Honeysuckle Road, Bassett, Southampton, Hants SO16 3BU. (023 8032 4258, website: www.ringramcoins.com, email: ybu36@dial.pipex.com. *P. L. Dealers in UK coins*
Intercol London (ANA, IBNS)
43 Templars Cresent, London N3 3QR (020 7349 2207) *P Paper money of the world*
Peter Ireland Ltd (BNTA, IBNS)
31 Clifton Street, Blackpool, Lancs FY1 1JQ (01253 621588 fax 01253 621589). Mon-Sat 09.00-17.30. *British and world coins, medals and tokens.*
JAK (IBNS)
31 Vapron Road, Mannamead, Plymouth, Devon PL3 5NJ (01752 665405). *P. L. GB and Commonwealth banknotes.*
F. J. Jeffery & Son Ltd
23 Catalina Court, Melksham, Wiltshire SN12 6FA. (01225 703143). *P. British, Commonwealth and foreign coins.*
Richard W. Jeffery
Trebehor, Porthcurno, Penzance, Cornwall TR19 6LS (01736 871263). *P. British and world coins.*
Jersey Coin Co Ltd
26 Halkett Street, St Helier, Jersey, Channel Islands (01534 25743). Mon-Sat 09.00–17.00. *World coins.*
J. G. Coins
PO Box 206, Southshore, Blackpool FY1 6GZ. (01253 349138). *P. L British Coins.*
Ian Johnson
PO Box 28, Swinton, Manchester M27 3FR (01204 393944). *P. L. Ancient European and Oriental coins.*
I. L. Johnson
63, Sedley Close, Parkwood, Kent ME8 9QZ. (01634 261037) *P. L. English coins 1672–1967*
Robert Johnson Coin Co
PO Box 194, 15 Bury Place, London WC1A 2JN (020 7831 0305). Mon-Fri 10.30-18.00, Sat 10.30-15.00. *British and world coins.*
Jumbo Coins
22 Woodend Lane, Stalybridge, Cheshire SK15 2SR (0161 338 5741). Fri-Sat 14.00-19.00. *World coins, medals and tokens.*
Kates Paper Money
Kate Gibson, Dept C, 79 Grayswood Drive, Mychett, Camberley , Surrey, GU16 6AS. www.katespapermoney.co.uk (01276 24954) *Banknotes*
KB Coins (BNTA)
50 Lingfield Road, Martins Wood, Stevenage, Herts SG1 5SL (01438 312661, fax 01438 311990). 09.00–18.00 by appointment only. *L. Mainly British coins.*
Knightsbridge Coins (ANA, BNTA, IAPN, PNG)
43 Duke Street, St James's, London SW1Y 6DD (020 7930 8215/7597 Fax 020 7930 8214). Mon-Fri 10.00–17.30. *Quality coins of the world.*
Lancashire Coin & Medal Co
31 Adelaide Street, Fleetwood, Lancs FY7 6AD (01253 779308). *P. British coins and medals.*
Lennox Gallery Ltd
K12/13, 4 Davies Mews, London, W1Y 1AR. (020 7629 9119 fax 020 7629 9119). *Ancient coins.*
Peter Licence
31 Reigate Way, Wallington, Surrey SM6 8NU (020 8688 5297). *P. British and World coins.*
Lighthouse Publications (UK BNTA)
4 Beaufort Road, Reigate, Surrey RH2 9DJ (01737 244222 Fax 0737 24743). *L. Manufacturers and stockists of coin albums, cabinets and numismatic accessories.*
Lindner Publications Ltd
13 Fore Street, Hayle, Cornwall TR27 4DX (01736 751914 fax: 01736 751911, email lindneruk@cs.com). Mon–Fri 09.00–13.00. *L. Manufacturers of coin albums, cabinets and accessories.*
Jan Lis (BNTA)
Beaver Coin Room, 57 Philbeach Gardens, London SW5 9ED (020 7373 4553 fax 020 7373 4555). *By appointment only. European coins.*

Keith Lloyd
45 Bramblewood, The Beeches, Ipswich, Suffolk IP8 3RS (01473 603067). *P. L. Greek, Roman coins.*

Lockdale Coins (BNTA)
37 Upper Orwell Street, Ipswich. (01473 218588). Also at 168 London Road South, Lowestoft NR33 0BB. (01502 568468. L. (Shops open 9.30–4.30 Mon–Sat). *World coins, medals, banknotes and accessories.*

Stephen Lockett (BNTA)
12, Redhill Wood, New Ash Green, Kent DA3 8QH (01474 871464). *British and world coins.*

Mike Longfield Detectors
83 Station Road, Balsall Common, nr Coventry, Warwickshire CV7 7FN (01676 533274). Mon-Sat 09.30-17.00. *Metal detectors.*

Richard M. Lubbock (ANA, BNTA, IAPN, IBNS)
PO Box 352, London E14 7WB (020 7790 5115 fax 020 7790 5445). *World coins and medals.*

Don MacRae Coins
PO Box 233, Uxbridge, Middlesex UB9 4HY (01895 832625). *P. British and world coins.*

David Magnay
11 Lake Hill Drive, Cowbridge, Vale of Glamorgan, Wales UK CF71 7HR. (01446 774335) *Toy and Model Coins, Imitation Spade Guineas.*

Mannin Collections Ltd
5 Castle Street, Peel, Isle of Man (01624 843897). Mon-Sat 10.00-17.00. Half-day Thu. *British coins.*

Manston Coins of Bath
Bartletts St. Antique Centre, Bath (01761 416133. *Coins, tokens, medals.*

I. Markovits
1-3 Cobbold Mews, London W12 9LB (020 8749 3000). *Enamelled coins.*

Marron Coins
7 Beacon Close, Sheffield, South Yorkshire S9 1AA (0114 2433500, website www.marroncoins.free-online.co.uk, email marronsca@aol.com). *P. English coins.*

C. J. Martin (Coins) Ltd (BNTA)
85 The Vale, Southgate, London N14 6AT (020 8882 1509, www.ancientart.co.uk). P. L. Bi-monthly catalogue. *Greek, Roman & English hammered coins.*

M. G. Coins & Antiquities
12 Mansfield, High Wych, Herts cm21 0JT. (01279 721719). *L. Ancient and hammered coins, antiquities.*

Giuseppe Micelli
204 Bants Lane, Duston, Northampton NN5 6AH (01604 581533). *P.L. British coins and medals.*

Michael Coins
6 Hillgate Street, London W8 7SR (020 7727 1518). Mon-Fri 10.00-17.00. *World coins and banknotes.*

David Miller Coins & Antiquities (ANA, BNTA)
PO Box 711, Hemel Hempstead, HP2 4UH (tel/fax 01442 251492). *Ancient and hammered English coins.*

Timothy Millett
PO Box 20851, London SE22 0YN (tel: 020 8693 1111, fax: 020 8299 3733). *L. Historical medals.*

Frank Milward (ANA, BNTA)
2 Ravensworth Road, Mortimer, Berkshire RG7 3UU (01734 322843). *P. European coins.*

Graeme & Linda Monk (ANA, BNTA)
PO Box 201, Croydon, Surrey, CR9 7AQ (020 8656 4583 fax 020 8656 4583). *P. Fair organisers.*

Mike Morey
9 Elmtrees, Long Crendon, Bucks HP18 9DG. *P. L. British coins, halfcrowns to farthings.*

Peter Morris (BNTA, IBNS)
1 Station Concourse, Bromley North Station, Bromley, BR1 1NN or PO Box 223, Bromley, BR1 4EQ (020 8313 3410 fax 020 8466 8502, website www.petermorris.co.uk, email info@petermorris.co.uk). Mon-Fri 10.00–18.00, Sat 0900-14.00 or by appointment. *L. British and world coins, proof sets and numismatic books.*

James Murphy
PO Box 122, Chorley, Lancashire PR7 2GE. *(01257 274 381). P. L. Ancient coins and antiquities.*

Colin Narbeth & Son Ltd (ANA, IBNS)
20 Cecil Court, Leicester Square, London WC2N 4HE (020 7379 6975 fax 01727 811 244, website http://www.colin-narbeth.com). Mon-Sat 10.30-17.00. *World banknotes.*

New Forest Leaves
Bisterne Close, Burley, Ringwood, Hants BH24 4BA (014253 3315). *Publishers of numismatic books.*

Peter Nichols
2 Norman Road, St Leonards on Sea, East Sussex TN37 6NH. (01424 436682, website www.coincabinets.com, email coincabinets@freezone.co.uk).

Wayne Nicholls
PO Box 44, Bilston, West Midlands. (01543 45476) *L. Choice English coins*

North Wales Coins Ltd (BNTA)
1b Penrhyn Road, Colwyn Bay, Clwyd (01492 533023/532129). Mon-Sat (closed Wed) 09.30–17.30. *British coins.*

Notability (IBNS)
'Mallards', Chirton, Devizes, Wilts SN10 3QX (01380 723961, website www.notability.org.uk, email: banknotes@ukdealers.com. *P. L. Banknotes of the world.*

NP Collectables
9 Main Street, Gedney Dyke, Spalding, Lincs PE12 0AJ (01406 365211Ireland (010 35322 29385). *P. L. English Hammered and Milled coins.*

Glenn S. Ogden
Duncraig, Canada Hill, Ogwell, Newton Abbot, Devon TQ12 6AF. (01626 331663) *P. L. English milled.*

John Ogden Coins
Hodge Clough Cottage, Moorside, Oldham OL1 4JW (0161 678 0709) *P. L. Ancient and hammered coins.*

Michael O'Grady (IBNS)
PO Box 307, Pinner, Middlesex HA5 4XT (020 8428 4002). *P. British and world paper money.*

Colin James O'Keefe
5 Pettits Place, Dagenham, Essex RM10 8NL. *P. British and European coins.*

Don Oliver Gold Coins
The Coin Gallery, Stanford House, 23 Market Street, Stourbridge, West Midlands DY8 1AB (01384 373899). Mon-Fri 10.00–17.00, Sat 10.00-13.00 (closed Thu). *Gold coins of the world.*

Ongar Coins
14 Longfields, Marden Ash, Ongar, Essex IG7 6DS. *P.World coins.*

Tim Owen Coins
63 Allerton Grange Rise, Leeds 17, West Yorkshire (0113 2688015). *P. L. Quality hammered coins.*

Oxford Coins
25, Weldon Road, New Marston, Oxford OX3 0HP (01865 726939). *British coins.*

P&D Medallions
PO Box 269, Berkhampstead, Herts HP4 3FT. (01442 865127, email P&D@medallions.freeserve.co.uk). *Historical and Commemorative medals of the world. P.*

Pavlos S. Pavlou
Stand L17, Grays Antique Market, 1-7 Davies Mews, Mayfair, London W1Y 2LP (020 7629 9449) email: pspavlou@hotmail.com. *Ancient, Medieval & Modern Coins*

Penrith Coin & Stamp Centre
37 King Street, Penrith, Cumbria CA11 7AY (01768 64185). Mon-Sat 09.00–17.30. *World coins.*

Pentland Coins (IBNS)
Pentland House, 92 High Street, Wick, Caithness KW14 L5. *P. British and world coins and world banknotes.*

John Phillimore
The Old Post Office, Northwood, Shropshire SY4 5NN. *L. Foreign coins 1600–1950.*

Phil Phipps
PO Box 31, Emsworth, Hants PO10 7WE (tel/fax 01243 376086, email philip@worldcurrency.cc). *P. L. World and German banknotes.*

David C. Pinder
20 Princess Road West, Leicester LE1 6TP (0116 2702439). *P. Greek, Roman and Byzantine coins.*

Pobjoy Mint Ltd (ANA)
Millennium House, Kingswood Park, Bonsor Drive, Kingswood, Surrey KT20 6AY (01737 818181 fax 01737 818199). Mon-Fri 09.00–17.00. *Europe's largest private mint. New issues.*

S. R. Porter (BNTA)
18 Trinity Road, Headington Quarry, Oxford OX3 8LQ (01865 766851). *P. L. Ancient and British coins, some foreign, tokens, banknotes and accessories.*

David Pratchett
Trafalgar Square Collectors Centre, 7 Whitcombe Street, London WC2H 7HA. (020 7930 1979, fax 020 7930 1152, website www.coinsonline.co.uk, email info@coinsonline.co.uk). Mon-Fri 10.00–7.30. *Specialist in gold and silverworld coins.*

Predecimal.com
Hauptstr. 33, Burkhardsdorf, 09235, Germany. (+491741 477182) www.predecimal.com. *British coins*

George Rankin Coin Co Ltd (ANA)
325 Bethnal Green Road, London E2 6AH (020 7729 1280 fax 020 7729 5023). Mon-Sat 10.00-18.00 (half-day Thu). *World coins.*

Mark Rasmussen (BNTA)
PO Box 42, Betchworth RH3 7YR (01737 84100, email mark.rasmussen@btinternet.com). *Hammered and milled coins. L*

Mark T. Ray (formerly MTR Coins)
22a Kingsnorth Close, Newark, Notts NG24 1PS. (01636 703152). *P. British coins.* 2379). Mon-Sat

Rhyl Coin Shop
12 Sussex Street, Rhyl, Clwyd (01745 338112). Mon-Sat 10.00-17.30. *World coins and banknotes.*

Chris Rigby
PO Box 181, Worcester WR1 1YE (01905 28028). *P. L. Modern British coins.*

Roderick Richardson (BNTA)
The Old Granary Antiques Centre, King's Staithe Lane, King's Lynn, Norfolk. (01553 670833) *L. English, Hammered and early milled coins.*

F. J. Rist
PO Box 4, Ibstock, Leics LE67 6ZJ (01530 264278). *P. L. Ancient and medieval coins, British coins and antiquities.*

Ian Robinson
PO Box 929, Burgess Hill, West Sussex RH15 9FN (01444 242215, website www.iamcoins.co.uk, email ian@iamcoins.co.uk). *P. L. Quality English milled coins.*

S. J. Rood & Co Ltd
52–53 Burlington Arcade, London W1V 9AE (0171 493 0739). Mon-Sat 09.30-17.00. *World gold coins.*

Bill Rosedale
17 Priory Close, Abbots Park, Chester CH1 4BX (01244 382554, email bill@banknotes40freeserve.com) *P. L. World paper money*

Royal Gold Exchange
PO Box 123, Saxonwold, 2132, South Africa, e-mail royalg@iafrica.com (+27 11 442 4321) *Gold Coins*

Royal Mint Coin Club
PO Box 500, Cardiff CF1 1YY (01443 623456). *P. New issues struck by the Royal Mint.*

Colin de Rouffignac (BNTA)
57, Wigan Lane, Wigan, Lancs WN1 2LF (01942 237927) *P. English and Scottish hammered.*

Chris A. Rudd (IAPN, BNTA)
PO Box 222, Aylsham, Norfolk, NR11 6TY (01263 735007 fax 01263 731777, website www.celticcoins.com). *P. L. Celtic coins.*

Colin Rumney (BNTA)
26 Caer Felin, Llanrheadr, Denbigh, Clwyd LL16 4PR (074 578621). *All world including ancients.*

R & J Coins
21b Alexandra Street, Southend-on-Sea, Essex SS1 1DA (01702 345995). Mon-Sat 10.00–16.00 (closed Wed). *World coins.*

Safe Albums (UK) Ltd
16 Falcon Business Park, 38 Ivanhoe Road, Finchampstead, Berkshire RG40 4QQ. (0118 932 8976 fax 0118 932 8612).

Saltford Coins
Harcourt, Bath Road, Saltford, Bristol, Avon BS31 3DQ (01225 873512). *P. British, Commonwealth and world coins.*

Satin
PO Box 63, Stockport, Cheshire SK4 5BU. (07940 393583 answer machine)

Schwer Coins (ANA, BNTA)
6 South Hill, Felixstowe, Suffolk, IP11 8AA (01394 278580 fax 0394 271348). *P. World coins.*

David Seaman
PO Box 449, Waltham Cross EN9 3WZ. (020 7607 5607, email davidseamancoins@lineone.net). *P. L. Hammered, Milled, Maundy.*

Patrick Semmens
3 Hospital Road, Half Key, Malvern, Worcs WR14 1UZ (0886 33123). *P. European and British coins.*

Mark Senior
553 Falmer Road, Woodingdean, Brighton, Sussex (01273 309359). By appointment only. *P. L. Saxon, Norman and English hammered coins.*

S. E. Sewell
PO Box 104, Ipswich, Suffolk IP5 7QL (01473 626 950). *Mainly British milled coins.*

R. D. Shah (BNTA)
9 Lansdowne Grove, Neasden, London NW10 1LP (020 8452 5160). *Ancient India and Indian states.*

Robert Sharman Numismatist (ANA)
36 Dairsie Road, Eltham, London SE9 1XH (020 8850 6450). *P. British coins.*

Shepshed Coins & Jewellery
24 Charnwood Road, Shepshed, Leics LE12 9QF (01509 502511). Mon, Wed-Sat 09.15-16.30. *British coins.*

Simmons Gallery (ANA, BNTA, IBNS)
53 Lamb's Conduit Street, London WC1N 3NB (020 7831 2080 fax 020 7831 2090, website www.simmonsgallery.co.uk, email info@simmonsgallery.co.uk). *Organisers of the London Coin Fair, Holiday Inn, Bloomsbury, London W1. L. Coins, tokens and medals.*

Raymond J. Sleet
11 Seagull Close, Kempshott, Basingstoke, Hants RG22 5QR (01256 53256 fax 01256 63525) *General world coins and tokens.*

E. Smith (ANA, IBNS)
PO Box 348, Lincoln LN6 0TX (01522 684681 fax 01522 689528). *P. Organiser of the Morley, Leeds, monthly coin fair. World coins and paper money.*

J. Smith (BNTA)
47 The Shambles, York YO1 2LX (01904 654769). Mon-Sat 09.30–17.00. *World coins.*

Neil Smith
PO Box 348, Lincoln LN6 0TX (01522 684681 fax 01522 689528). *GB and World Gold coins 1816 to date, including modern proof issues.*

Jim Smythe
PO Box 6970, Birmingham B23 7WD (e-mail Jimdens@aol.com). *P. L. 19th/20th century British and world coins.*

S & B Coins
Suite 313, St Loyes House, 20 Loyes Street, Bedford MK40 1ZL (01234 270260). *P. L. British coins and medallions.*

Sovereign State Coins
PO Box 304, Oldham OL2 6HY. ((07759 521664 Mobile). *Quality ancient, hammered and milled coins.*

George Sowden
Coins Galore, The Lizard, nr Helston, Cornwall TR12 7NU (01326 290300). *P. World coins.*

Spink & Son Ltd (ANA, BNTA, IAPN, IBNS)
69 Southampton Row, Bloomsbury, London. WC1B 4ET (020 7563 2820, fax 020 7563 4066, website www.spink-online.com, email info@spinkandson.com). *Ancient to modern world coins, orders, medals and decorations, banknotes and numismatic books*

SPM Jewellers (BNTA)
112 East Street, Southampton, Hants SO14 3HD (023 80 223255/020 80 227923, fax 023 80 335634, wwbsite www.spmgoldcoins.co.uk, email user@spm.in2home.co.uk).
Tue-Sat 09.15–17.00, Sat 09.15–16.00. *World coins and medals.*

Stamp & Collectors Centre
404 York Town Road, College Town, Camberley, Surrey GU15 4PR (01276 32587 fax 01276 32505). Mon, Tue, Thu, Sat 09.00–17.00, Wed, Fri 09.00–1900. *World coins and medals.*

St Edmunds Coins & Banknotes
PO Box 118, Bury St Edmunds IP33 2NE. (01284 761894)

Sterling Coins & Medals
2 Somerset Road, Boscombe, Bournemouth, Dorset BH7 6JH (01202 423881). Mon-Sat 09.30–16.30 (closed Wed). *World coins and medals.*

Strawbridge
Tanglewood, Ivy Tree Hill, Stokeinteignhead, Newton Abbott, Devon TQ12 4QH (01626 873783, emailjim@strawbridge.co.uk).
P. L. Coins, tokens, medals, banknotes.

Studio Coins (ANA, BNTA)
16 Kilham Lane, Winchester, Hants SO22 5PT (01962 853156 fax 01962 624246). *P. English coins.*

Surena Numismatics (BNTA)
PO Box 2194, London NW8 6QQ (0831 220010). *P. Parthian, Sassanian, Islamic coins.*

The Collector
PO Box 335, Tiptree, Colchester, Essex CO5 9WP (01376 572755 fax 01376 573883, email the collector@btinternet.com). *Collectable items.*

The Coin Exchange
www.the-coin-exchange.com Email: info@the-coin-exchange.com. Phone 01340 881422. *British coins*

Time Line Originals
PO Box 193, Upminster, RM14 3WH Tel: (01708) 222384. Mobile 07775 651218, Email: sales@time-line.co.uk

Stuart J. Timmins
Smallwood Lodge Bookshop, Newport, Salop (01952 813232). Mon-Sat 09.30–17.00. *Numismatic literature.*

R. Tims
39 Villiers Road, Watford, Herts WD1 4AL. *P. L. Uncirculated world banknotes.*

Trafalgar Square Collectors' Centre (ANA, LM, OMRS)
7 Whitcomb Street, Trafalgar Square, London WC2H 7HA (020 7930 1979). Mon-Fri 10.00–17.30. *World coins and commemorative medals. War medals and decorations.*

D. A. Travis
8 Cookridge Drive, Leeds LS16 7LT. *P. L. US coins.*

Michael Trenerry Ltd
PO Box 55, Truro, Cornwall TR1 2YQ (01872 277977 fax 01872 225565). By appointment only. *L. Roman, Celtic and English hammered coins, tokens.*

Vera Trinder Ltd
38 Bedford Street, Strand, London WC2E 9EU (020 7836 2365/6). Mon-Fri 08.30-17.30. *L. Coin catalogues and books, albums, envelopes, cases etc*

Robert Tye
Poll Toran, Loch Eynort, South Uist PA81 5SJ. *P. European and Oriental hammered coins.*

Valda Coins
80 Aberfan Road, Aberfan, Mid Glamorgan CF48 4QJ. (01443 690452). *P. L.*

Vale (ADA BNTA)
21 Tranquil Vale, Blackheath, London SE3 0BU (020 8852 9817. Mon-Sat 10.00–17.30 (closed Thu). *British coins and medals.*

Valued History
9 Market Place, Ely, Cambs CB7 4NP. (01353 654080, www.historyforsale.co.uk). *Coins and antiquities.*

Tony Vaughan Collectables
PO Box 364, Wolverhampton, WV3 9PW (01902 27351). *P. L. World coins and medals.*

Victory Coins
184 Chichester Road, North End, Portsmouth, Hants PO2 0AX (01705 751908/663450). Mon-Sat 09.15–17.30. *British and world coins.*

Viking Metal Detectors
1 angela Street, Mill Hill, Blacburn, Lancashire BB2 4DJ (01254 55887 fax 01254 676901, email viking@metaldetectors.co.uk)). *Metal detectors and accessories*

Mark J. Vincenzi (BNTA)
Rylands, Earls Colne, Essex. CO6 2LE (01787 222555). *P. Greek, Roman, Hammered.*

Vista World Banknotes
5 Greenfields Way, Burley-in-Wharfedale, Ilkley, W. Yorks LS29 7RB. (Email vistabanknotes@barclays.net).

Mike Vosper
PO Box 32, Hockwold, Brandon IP26 4HX (01842 828292, website www.vosper4coins.co.uk, email mikevosper@vosper4coins.co.uk).

B. M. & S. A. Weeks
PO Box 1447, Salisbury, Wilts SP5 2YG (01725 510311). *L. British coins, world crowns and medals.*

John Welsh
PO Box 150, Burton-on-Trent, Staffs DE13 7LB (01543 73073 fax 0543 473234). *P. L. British coins.*

Pam West (IBNS, BNTA)
PO Box 257, Sutton, Surrey SM3 9WW (020 8641 3224, website west-banknotes.co.uk, email pamwestbritnotes@compuserve.com). *P. L. English banknotes.*

West Cornwall Stamp Centre
13 Fore Street, Hayle, Cornwall TR27 4DX (01736 751910 fax: 01736 751911. *L. Coin Accessories.*

West Essex Coin Investments (BNTA, IBNS)
Croft Cottage, Station Road, Alderholt, Fordingbridge, Hants SP6 3AZ (01425 656 459). *British and World coins and paper money.*

R & J White (IBNS)
29 Shortacre, Basildon, Essex SS14 2LR (01268 522923). *P. L. Banknotes and world ephemera.*

Whites Electronics (UK) Ltd
35 Harbour Road, Inverness IV1 1UA (01463 223456 , email sales@whelects.demon.co.uk) *Metal detectors*

Whitmore (BNTA)
Teynham Lodge, Chase Road, Upper Colwall, Malvern, Worcs WR13 6DT (01684 40651). *P. World coins, tokens and medals.*

World Coins
35–36 Broad Street, Canterbury, Kent CT1 2LR (01227 768887). Mon-Sat 09.30–17.30 (half-day Thu). *World coins.*

Worldwide Coins (IBNS)
PO Box 11, Wavertree, Liverpool L15 0FG. email: sales@worldwidecoins.co.uk, www.worldwidecoins.co.uk. *World coins and paper money.*

World Treasure Books
PO Box 5, Newport, Isle of Wight PO30 5QE (01983 740712). *L. Coins, books, metal detectors*

Barry Wright,
54 Dooley Drive, Bootle, Merseyside. L3O 8RT. *P. L. World banknotes.*

I. S. Wright (Australia Numismatic Co)
208 Sturt Street, Ballarat, Vic. Australia 3350 (0061 3 5332 3856 fax 0061 3 5331 6426, email ausnumis@netconnect.comau. *P. Coins, banknotes, medallions, tokens.*

B. N. Yarwood (ANA)
Yarwood Hall, Luttongate Road, Sutton St Edmund, Spalding, Lincs PE12 0LH. *P. British and US coins.*

York Coins
P.M.B #387 7211 Austin Street, Forest Street, New York. Tel/fax: (718) 544 0120 email: antony@yorkcoins.com

Banks, Mints and Numismatic Bureaux of the world

Many national banks and mints operate numismatic bureaux and sales agencies from which coins, medals and other numismatic products may be obtained direct. The conditions under which purchases may be made vary considerably. In many cases at the present time bureaux will accept orders from overseas customers quoting their credit card number and its expiry date; but in others payment can only be made by certified bank cheque, or international money order, or by girobank. Cash is seldom, if ever, acceptable. It is best to write in the first instance to enquire about methods of payment.

A

National Mint, Baghe Arg, Kabul, Afghanistan

Bank Mille Afghan, Kabul, Afghanistan

Banque d'Algerie, Sucursale d'Alger, 8 Boulevard Carnot, Alger, Algeria

Banco de Angola, Luanda, Daroal, Angola

Casa de Moneda de la Nacion, Avenida Antartica, Buenos Aires, BA, Argentina

Royal Australian Mint, Department of the Treasury, Canberra, ACT, Australia

GoldCorp Australia, Perth Mint Buildings, GPO Box M924, Perth, Western Australia 6001

Oesterreichsiches Hauptmunzamt, Am Heumarkt 1, A-1031 Wien, Postfach 225, Austria

Oesterreichische Nationalbank, A-1090 Wien, Otto Wagner-platz 3, Austria

B

Treasury Department, PO Box 557, Nassau, Bahamas (*coins*)

Ministry of Finance, PO Box 300, Nassau, Bahamas (*banknotes*)

Bank of Bahrain, PO Box 106, Manama, Bahrain

Eastern Bank, PO Box 29, Manama, Bahrain

Monnaie Royale de Belgique, Avenue de Pacheco 32, B-1000 Bruxelles, Belgium

Banque Nationale de Belgique SA, Caisse Centrale, Bruxelles, Belgium

Banque de Bruxelles SA, 2 Rue de la Regence, Bruxelles 1, Belgium

Casa de la Moneda, Potosi, Bolivia

Banco Central de Bolivia, La Paz, Bolivia

Casa da Moeda, Praca da Republica 173, Rio de Janeiro, Brazil

Hemus FTO, 7 Vasil Levski Street, Sofia C-1, Bulgaria

Banque de la Republique, Bujumbura, Burundi

C

Banque Centrale, Douala, Boite Postale 5.445, Cameroun

Royal Canadian Mint, 320 Sussex Drive, Ottawa 2, Ontario, Canada K1A 0G8

Casa de Moneda, Quinta Normal, Santiago, Chile

Casa de Moneda, Calle 11 no 4-93, Bogota, Colombia

Numismatic Section, The Treasury, Avarua, Rarotonga, Cook Islands

Banco Centrale de Costa Rica, Departamento de Contabilidad, San Jose, Costa Rica, CA

Central Bank of Cyprus, PO Box 1087, Nicosia, Cyprus

Artia, Ve Smekach 30, PO Box 790, Praha 1, Czech Republic

D

Den Kongelige Mønt, Amager Boulevard 115, København S, Denmark

Danmarks Nationalbank, Holmens Kanal 17, 1060 København K, Denmark

Banco Central de Santo Domingo, Santo Domingo, Dominican Republic

E

Banco Central, Quito, Ecuador

Mint House, Abbassia, Cairo, Egyptian Arab Republic

Exchange Control Department, National Bank of Egypt, Cairo, Egyptian Arab Republic

Banco Central de la Republica, Santa Isabel, Equatorial Guinea

Commercial Bank of Ethiopia, Foreign Branch, PO Box 255, Addis Ababa, Ethiopia

F

Currency Board, Victoria Parade, Suva, Fiji

Suomen Rahapaja, Katajanokanlaituri 3, Helsinki 16, Finland

Suomen Pankki, PO Box 10160, Helsinki 10, Finland

Hotel de Monnaie, 11 Quai de Conti, 75-Paris 6e, France

G

Banque Centrale Libreville, Boite Postale 112, Gabon

Verkaufstelle fur Sammlermunzen, D-638 Bad Homburg vdH, Bahnhofstrasse 16–18, Germany

Staatliche Munze Karlsruhe, Stephanienstrasse 28a, 75 Karlsruhe, Germany

Staatliche Munze Cannstatt, Taubenheimerstrasse 77, 7 Stuttgart-Bad, Germany

Bayerisches Hauptmunzamt, Hofgraben 4, 8 Munich, Germany

Hamburgische Munze, Norderstrasse 66, 2 Hamburg 1, Germany

Bank of Ghana, PO Box 2674, Accra, Ghana

Pobjoy Mint, Mint House, 92 Oldfields Road, Sutton, Surrey SM1 2NW

Royal Mint, Llantrisant, Mid Glamorgan, Wales, CF7 8YT

Royal Mint Coin Club, PO Box 500, Cardiff, CF1 1HA

Bank of Greece, Treasury Department, Cash, Delivery & Despatch Division, PO Box 105, Athens, Greece

Casa Nacional de Moneda, 6a Calle 4-28, Zona 1, Ciudad Guatemala, Republica de Guatemala CA

States Treasury, St Peter Port, Guernsey, Channel Islands

Bank of Guyana, PO Box 658, Georgetown, Guyana

H

Banque Nationale de la Republique d'Haiti, Rue Americaine et Rue Fereu, Port-au-Prince, Haiti

Banco Central de Honduras, Tegucigalpa DC, Honduras CA

State Mint, Ulloi utca 102, Budapest VIII, Hungary

Artex, PO Box 167, Budapest 62, Hungary

Magyar Nemzeti Bank, Board of Exchange, Budapest 54, Hungary

I

Sedlabanki Islands, Reykjavik, Iceland

Indian Government Mint, Bombay 1, India

Arthie Vasa, Keabajoran Baru, Djakarta, Indonesia

Perum Peruri, Djakarta, Indonesia

National Mint, Tehran, Iran

Bank Markazi Iran, Tehran, IranCentral Bank of Iraq, PO Box 64, Baghdad, Iraq

Central Bank of Ireland, Dublin 2, Republic of Ireland

The Treasury, Government Buildings, Prospect Hill, Douglas, Isle of Man

Israel Stamp and Coin Gallery, 4 Maze Street, Tel Aviv, Israel

Istituto Poligraphico e Zecca dello Stato, Via Principe Umberto, Roma, Italy

J

Decimal Currency Board, PO Box 8000, Kingston, Jamaica

Mint Bureau, 1 Shinkawasakicho, Kita-ku, Osaka 530, Japan

Numismatic Section, Treasury Department, St Helier, Jersey

Central Bank of Jordan, Amman, Jordan

Banque Nationale du Liban, Rue Masraf Loubnan, Beirut, Lebanon

K

Central Bank, PO Box 526, Kuwait

L

Bank of Lithuania, Cash Department, Gedimino av. 6, 2001 Vilius, Lithuania

Caisse Generale de l'Etat, 5 Rue Goethe, Luxembourg-Ville, Grande Duche de Luxembourg

M

Institut d'Emission Malgache, Boite Postale 205, Tananarive, Madagascar

Central Bank of Malta, Valletta 1, Malta

Casa de Moneda, Calle del Apartado no 13, Mexico 1, DF, Mexico

Le Tresorier General des Finances, Monte Carlo, Principaute de Monaco

Banque de l'Etat du Maroc, Rabat, Morocco

Banco Nacional Ultramarino, Maputo, Republica de Mocambique

British Bank of the Middle East, Muscat

N

Royal Mint, Dharahara, Katmandu, Nepal

Nepal Rastra Bank, Katmandu, Nepal

Rijks Munt, Leidseweg 90, Utrecht, Netherlands

Hollandsche Bank-Unie NV, Willemstad, Breedestraat 1, Curacao, Netherlands Antilles

Central Bank of Curacao, Willemstad, Curacao, Netherlands Antilles

The Treasury, Private Bag, Lambton Quay, Wellington, New Zealand

Banco de Nicaragua, Departamento de Emison, La Tresoria, Apartada 2252, Managua, Nicaragua

Nigerian Security Printing and Minting Corporation, Ahmadu Bello Road, Victoria Island, Lagos, Nigeria

Central Bank of Nigeria, Tinubu Square LB, Lagos, Nigeria

Norges Bank, Oslo, Norway

Den Kongelige Mynt, Hyttegaten, Konigsberg, Norway

P

Pakistan State Mint, Baghban Pura, Lahore 9, Pakistan

National Development Bank, Asuncion, Paraguay

Casa Nacional de Moneda, Calle Junin 791, Lima, Peru

Central Bank of the Philippines, Manila, Philippines

Bank Handlowy w Warszawie, Ul. Romuald Traugutta 7, Warsaw, Poland

Desa Foreign Trade Department, Al. Jerozolimskie 2, Warszawa, Poland

Casa da Moeda, Avenida Dr Antonio Jose de Almeida, Lisbon 1, Portugal

R

Cartimex, 14-18 Aristide Briand St, PO Box 134-135, Bucharest, Roumania

Bank of Foreign Trade, Commercial Department, Moscow K 16, Neglinnaja 12, Russian Federation

Banque Nationale du Rwanda, Boite Postale 351, Kigali, Republique Rwandaise

S

Numismatic Section, Box 194, GPO, Apia, Samoa

Azienda Autonoma di Stato Filatelica-Numismatica, Casalla Postale 1, 47031 Repubblica di San Marino

Banque Internationale pour le Commerce, 2 Avenue Roume, Dakar, Senegal

Bank of Yugoslavia, PO Box 1010, Belgrade, Serbia

The Treasury, PO Box 59, Victoria, Seychelles

Bank of Sierra Leone, PO Box 30, Freetown, Sierra Leone

The Singapore Mint, 249 Jalan Boon Lay, Jurong, Singapore

South African Mint, PO Box 464, Pretoria, South Africa

Government Printing Agency, 93 Bukchang Dong, Chungku, Seoul, Republic of South Korea

Fabrica Nacional de Moneda y Timbre, Jorge Juan 106, Madrid 9, Spain

Bank of Sri Lanka, PO Box 241, Colombo, Sri Lanka

Hong Kong and Shanghai Banking Corporation, PO Box 73, Colombo 1, Sri Lanka

Sudan Mint, PO Box 43, Khartoum, Sudan

Bank of Sudan, PO Box 313, Khartoum, Sudan

Bank of Paramaribo, Paramaribo, Suriname

Kungelige Mynt och Justeringsverket, Box 22055, Stockholm 22, Sweden

Eidgenossische Staatskasse, Bundesgasse 14, CH-3003, Berne, Switzerland

Central Bank of Syria, Damascus, Syrian Arab Republic

T

Central Mint of China, 44 Chiu Chuan Street, Taipei, Taiwan, ROC

Royal Thai Mint, 4 Chao Fah Road, Bangkok, Thailand

Numismatic Section, The Treasury, Nuku'alofa, Tonga

Central Bank of Trinidad and Tobago, PO Box 1250, Port of Spain, Trinidad

Banque Centrale de Tunisie, Tunis, Tunisia

State Mint, Maliye Bakanligi Darphane Mudurlugu, Istanbul, Turkey

U

Bank of Uganda, PO Box 7120, Kampala, Uganda

Numismatic Service, US Assay Office, 350 Duboce Avenue, San Francisco, CA, 94102, USA

Office of the Director of the Mint, Treasury Department, Washington, DC, 20220, USA

Philadelphia Mint, 16th and Spring Garden Streets, Philadelphia, PA, 19130, USA

Franklin Mint, Franklin Center, Pennsylvania, 19063, USA

Banco Central del Uruguay, Cerrito 351, Montevideo, RO del Uruguay

V

Ufficio Numismatico, Governatorato dello Stato della Citta de Vaticano, Italy

Banco Central de Venezuela, Caracas, Venezuela

Y

Yemen Bank, Sana'a, Yemen.

Z

Bank of Zambia, PO Box 80, Lusaka, Zambia

Chief Cashier, Reserve Bank, PO Box 1283, Harare, Zimbabwe

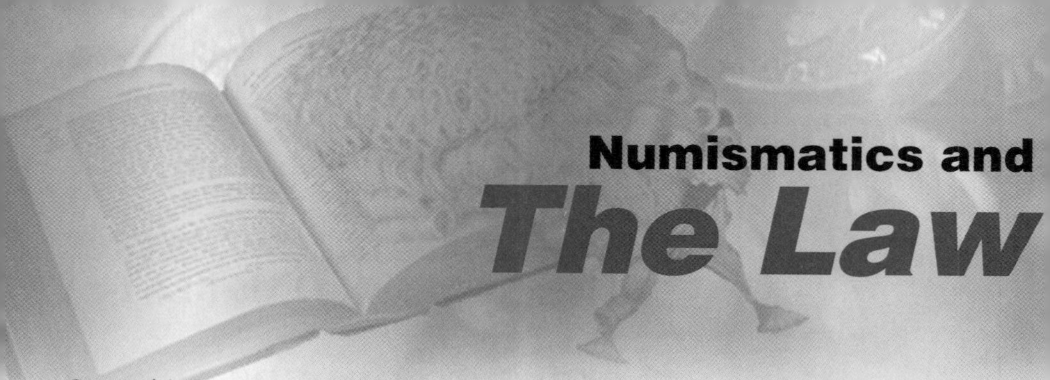

Numismatics and The Law

Counterfeit Currency

A counterfeit is a forgery or imitation of a coin or banknote produced with the intention of defrauding the revenue of the State or deceiving members of the public. By the Coinage Offences Act (1861) it was a felony to counterfeit gold or silver coins. Lesser offences included the gilding of farthings and sixpences to pass them off as half-sovereigns, the possession of moulds, machines or tools clandestinely removed from the Royal Mint, the impairment or diminution of gold or silver coins by filing or clipping (or even the possession of such filings and clippings).

The Coinage Act of 1870 made provision for the counterfeiting of base-metal coins, or the stamping of letters or words on coins of any kind, or the forging of colonial coinage. The most celebrated prosecution under this Act occurred in 1930 when Martin Coles Harman was convicted and fined £5 for issuing bronze coins resembling the British penny and halfpenny for the island of Lundy of which he was then the proprietor. Interestingly, no attempt was made to prosecute the Birmingham Mint which actually struck the coins (prudently omitting the H mintmark).

The making of medals or coins resembling current coin became a misdemeanour under the Counterfeit Medal Act of 1883.This Act is invoked from time to time against manufacturers or distributors of medallic pieces or coin jewellery. Such pieces, often struck in 9 carat gold, are deemed to infringe the Act if, for example, they have a figure even vaguely resembling St George and the Dragon on one side. The use of the royal effigy, however, without due authorisation, is regarded as a misdemeanour punishable by an unlimited fine and the confiscation of tools, dies and instruments. At the present time it is a serious offence to make a counterfeit of a currency note or coin with the intention of passing it off or tendering it as genuine. This offence carries a maximum penalty of ten years' imprisonment or an unlimited fine, or both. Making a counterfeit of a currency note or coin without lawful authority incurs a penalty up to two years' imprisonment or an unlimited fine, or both.

Passing or tendering as genuine anything which is known or believed to be a counterfeit of a currency note or coin renders the criminal on conviction to a term of ten years' imprisonment or an unlimited fine, or both. The mere possession of any forged note or coin is itself a criminal offence. Possessing countertfeits without authority or permission so to do, and doing so knowingly, renders the possessor liable to two years' imprisonment or an unlimited fine, or both. The Act also stipulates that the reproduction of a current banknote—of the Bank of England or of the Scottish and Northern Irish banks is a serious offence. This clause covers even such apparently innocent acts as making a photocopy (whether in black and white or full colour) of a current banknote, the photography of such a note or the illustration of such a note in any book, magazine or newspaper. Strict regulations are laid down concerning the legitimate illustration of notes, whether current or not, in books and periodicals; such illustrations must be either greatly reduced or enlarged *and* must bear a prominent defacement, such as SPECIMEN or CANCELLED. It is also a serious offence to utilise a reproduction of a current British banknote in any medium. Theoretically this includes such things as tea-towels, T-shirts, mugs, plates and other souvenirs in glass or ceramics, but in practice the law seems to turn a blind eye to such practices. Imitations and parodies of notes and coins are also regarded as infringements of the law, but in these instances prosecution of the offender seldom proceeds; a warning is generally regarded as sufficient, provided that the offending article or articles are withdrawn and suppressed.

The advent of high-definition colour photo-copying in recent years has brought the offence of reproduction into prominence once more. The regulations have been tightened considerably and there have been several cases of successful prosecution. In each case, however, the intent deliberately to deceive the public by uttering a colour photocopy as a genuine note was proved. Technically the offence takes places as soon as the photocopy is made, for whatever purpose, but as a rule only those cases in which an element of fraudulent deception subsequently arose are pursued with the full rigour of the law. The law is quite clear, however, and it is a criminal offence to make a photocopy or photograph of any current British note unless permission to do so has been obtained from the Treasury. The maximum penalty on conviction is an unlimited fine.

The note-issuing banks have, of course, taken steps in recent years to incorporate further security devices into their notes, notably the use of latent images and underprints in colours which are difficult, if not impossible to photocopy accurately. At the same time, the adoption of metal strips and more complex watermark devices has theoretically made the task of the forger much more difficult. If, by some unlucky chance, someone passes a dud note on to you, you must make no attempt to pass it in turn. To do so renders you liable to prosecution for uttering a forgery. Forged notes must be handed over to the police as soon as possible. If you receive a forged note in payment for goods or services you are entitled to claim its face value from the person who gave it to you. Even if the person giving you the note did not realise that it was counterfeit, it is assumed in law that he or she represented to you that the note was worth its face value at the time the note was passed. If the tenderer knew that the note was forged, he can be prosecuted; but at the end of the day he is still liable to you for the fraud and can be sued in the civil courts for the recovery of the sum involved. If, on the other hand, you received the money as a gift, you have no legal claim against the person who gave it to you. If you pay someone with a counterfeit note or coin unknowingly, you have committed no offence, but you must pay again. The degree of culpability is often difficult to prove or disprove, but it is unlikely that a prosecution would be initiated on the basis of a single note or coin.

It is also a serious offence to manufacture blanks, discs or washers which are intended to defraud the proprietors of vending machines, or to possess tools and equipment for the dishonest manufacture or alteration of such blanks for this purpose. Under the Gold and Silver Export Control Act (1920) melting down gold or silver coins to extract their precious metal content is an offence punishable by a fine of £100 or two years' imprisonment, or both.

Legal Tender

The dictionary defines this as currency which a creditor is bound by law to accept as payment of a money debt. Debts and purchases must be paid for in cash of legal tender unless the creditor or seller is willing to accept payment in another form, such as a postal order, money order, cheque or, nowadays, credit card. Bank of England notes of any denomination are legal tender in England and Wales. Formerly Bank of England pound notes (but no other) were legal tender in Scotland. Technically, since the demise of the pound note, no Bank of England notes are legal tender in Scotland, although in practice they circulate freely north of the Border. Even more surprisingly, Scottish banknotes are not legal tender anywhere, not even in Scotland! The subtle difference is reflected in the actual wording of the promise on English and Scottish banknotes. Thus English notes are inscribed *"I promise to pay the bearer on demand the sum of . . ."* without stipulating any specific place, the promise being made by the Chief Cashier. Scottish notes, on the other hand, have the promise in the third person. It is the bank itself which makes the promise *"to pay the bearer on demand . . . pounds sterling at their head office here in Edinburgh, by order of the Board"*. In practice, however, Scottish banknotes are accepted without question, not only throughout Scotland but also in parts of England, and are generally accepted in London, although there is no obligation on the part of a creditor so to do.

Apart from gold coins, the base-metal pound coin is legal tender for payment of any amounts. So, too, presumably, are the various two-pound and five-pound base-metal coins of recent years, even though they have been struck as commemoratives and not intended for general circulation in the ordinary sense. Smaller denominations are only legal tender up to a maximum value in each case. In the case of 50p coins, 25p crowns and 20p coins, they may be used alone, or in combination with each other, in payment of amounts up to £10. 10p and 5p coins, alone or in combination, may be used for sums up to £5. Bronze 1p and 2p coins, however, can only be used for payment of amounts up to 20p. In practice, of course, you can probably get away with making payment in larger quantities (within reason!) although strictly speaking there is no obligation on the part of your creditor to accept them.

An Offence to Possess Legal Tender Coins

From the foregoing it will be seen that gold coins are, and always have been, legal tender. Since 1817 the legal tender gold coin of the United Kingdom has been the sovereign (with its sub-division and multiples). Yet there have been times when actual possession of these legal tender coins has been, *per se*, an illegal act. The first attempt to regulate the movement and possession of gold coins arose in 1947 with the passage of the Exchange Control Act which made it illegal to buy, borrow, lend or sell any gold or foreign currency, unless authorised to deal in gold. Moreover it was stipulated that *"any person possessing gold should offer it for sale to an authorised dealer at a price not exceeding the authorised price, unless the Treasury consented to this retention of the gold"*.

The serious implications of this Act were mitigated in the case of numismatists by the Exchange Control (Collectors' Pieces Exemption) Order 1947, which allowed collectors to hold on to *"any gold coin which was minted in 1816 or earlier, and any gold coin which was minted after 1816 and which has a numismatic value greater than the value of the gold content which would have been received if the coin had been sold to an authorised (bullion) dealer"*. In effect this meant that numismatists and coin dealers were not hindered from buying and selling gold coins as long as the coins were in collectable condition and possessed numismatic interest. This loophole was brazenly breached in the 1960s and led to the Exchange Control (Gold Coins Exemption) Order of 1966 which aimed to prevent the loss of currency reserves caused by the import of gold coins from abroad, and to eliminate the hoarding of gold by speculators. By the terms of this Order no one was permitted to hold more than four gold coins minted after 1837 unless they had received express permission from the Treasury. The maximum was set at four coins so that people who had one or two sovereigns as mementoes could keep them without breaking the law. Numismatists who possessed more than four post-1837 gold coins on April 27, 1966 had to apply to the Treasury for permission to retain them. To do so they had to prove that they were *bona fide* collectors by completing form GC 1, providing a detailed list of the coins in their possession—not only in gold, but also in silver (pre-1816, 1816–1919 and post-1919) and base metals (before and after 1860). Several individuals were successfully prosecuted under this draconian legislation and their holdings of gold sovereigns confiscated, although no one was imprisoned or heavily fined as the legislation provided. The 1966 order was rescinded in 1970, re-imposed in a modified form in 1975, and finally revoked in 1979. Since that date numismatists and speculators alike have been free to collect (or hoard) gold to their hearts' content.

Value Added Tax

This is a matter which primarily concerns dealers, but it also applies to those who dabble in coins on a part-time basis, and has implications for collectors at all levels. Briefly, anyone conducting a business, or in self-employment, who has a turnover in excess of £43,000 per annum, must register with HM Customs and Excise for the collection and payment of Value Added Tax. Anyone whose turnover is less than £43,000 is exempt from the obligation to register, but is at liberty to register if he or she feels that this would be advantageous. It is nice to think that there is an element of choice in this, although one would be hard pressed to think why anyone would voluntarily register for VAT unless they absolutely had to! Incidentally, the government raised the VAT registration level by 40 per cent to £35,000 in March 1991 with the avowed intention of relieving a large number of businesses from this burden, at a time when the rate of tax was increased from 15 per cent to 17.5 per cent. Assuming that you are a dealer with a turnover above the magic limit, then you are committing a serious offence if you fail to register. Registration then lays you open to the full machinery of the system. You have to charge VAT on all goods and services, issuing VAT invoices and receipts and keeping detailed accounts which are liable to snap inspection at any time. You have to make quarterly returns to Customs and Excise of the amount of tax you have collected. From this you are allowed to deduct the VAT which you yourself have paid out in the course of your business, and you then have to remit the difference to the VAT collector. Of course, should the amount you have paid exceed the tax you have collected, you receive a repayment in due course. This arises in businesses which handle zero-rated goods and services, but coins and medals do not come within that category.

For dealers in gold bullion, coins or medals, there is a special VAT leaflet which covers regulations specific to such matters. Since January 2000 investment gold has been exempt from VAT. A coin is classified as investment gold if it satisfies the following conditions: 1. Minted after 1800; 2. At least .900 fine; 3. Is or has been legal tender of its country of origin; 4. Is of a description of coin that is normally sold at a price that does not exceed 180% of the open market value of the gold contained in the coin. This is a complicated issue and further advice can be obtained from Customs & Excise Public Notice 701/21/99. A list of coins qualifying as investment gold is published in Public Notice 701/21A/99. When VAT is applicable of course it needs to be accounted for on the profit margin. It is vital therefore to maintain accurate records of all buying and selling, and which coins and medals are subject to VAT and which are exempt. Furthermore, the onus is on you to ensure that the source of the gold you bring into the country is impeccable. There are extremely heavy penalties for smuggling gold, and ignorance of the law, or apparently innocent handling of smuggled gold subsequently, are no defence.

From January 1, 1995 the special margin scheme of accounting for VAT currently available for certain second-hand goods, such as cars, was extended to almost all second-hand goods. The scheme allows businesses buying and selling eligible goods to account for VAT only on the difference between the buying and selling prices of these items.

A special system of accounting exists which enables some dealers to account for VAT without the need to keep a detailed record of every transaction. Certain works of art, antiques and collector's items, including "secondhand" coins, defined in Notice 712 *Second-hand goods*, were exempt from VAT at import. From January 1, 1996 these items became subject to VAT at import at an effective rate of 2.5 per cent.

Export and Import

Some coins do require an export licence before they can be taken out of the country and unfortunately these controls have been extended during the past year. Following the lifting of the export regulations relating to gold coins in 1979, then prior to April 1, 1993 the only coins which required any export licence were those with a value in excess of £35,000. However the agreement by the UK to implement an EC directive on the removal of cultural goods has resulted in a fresh interpretation of previous UK legislation on these coins which are on the market as a result of an archaeological find. Therefore as from April 1, 1993, any coin *whatever its value* which has come from an archaeological source within the UK will require an export licence even to take it to another EC country. Certain other coins of EC provenance other than the UK will now require an EC export licence. The value limit for non-archaeological source coins has been increased to £39,600 (Ecu 50,000). Both types of licence are issued by the Department of National Heritage, 2–4 Cockspur Street, Trafalgar Square, London SW1Y 5DH who can also supply a handy flow-chart to enable you to tell at a glance whether a licence is needed and what type. These new regulations are imposing an enormous additional burden on the trade and the British Numismatic Trade Association has held numerous meetings with the authorities in an attempt to reduce to a minimum the number of licence applications needed. Hopefully, by next year's edition there will be better news.

The restrictions applied to the importation of gold coins were removed in 1979, as previously mentioned. Coins of any kind are now permitted under Open General Import licence from any country and a specific or individual licence is no longer required. Details of any duties which may be payable on imported coins can be obtained from HM Customs and Excise, King's Beam House, Southwark, London SE1 or any local Customs and Excise office. Until recently, the only gold coins under embargo were Krugerrands. This was a political decision, aimed at tightening sanctions against South Africa, and applied to the importation of new gold coins from that country, but not to Krugerrands which had been brought into the United Kingdom, or any of the countries of the European Community, prior to the imposition of sanctions. In practice, it was very difficult to regulate the movement, let alone the importation, of Krugerrands, and with the relaxation of Apartheid this regulation has been lifted.

Importing Coins by Mail

Elsewhere in this volume will be found the names and addresses of mints, banks and numismatic bureaux around the world from whom it may be possible to obtain currency direct. It is a wise precaution to write to these bodies in the first instance for details of their sales and distribution. In some cases they appoint a dealer in Britain as an agent and this is a method of purchase that removes a great deal of the hassle and red tape. Nowadays, however, many mints and banks are quite happy to use the credit card system to make it easy to part you from your money. The problem arises, however, when the coins are despatched. As a rule, banks and mints stipulate quite clearly that they will not accept orders prepaid in cash, and it is an offence to send coins or banknotes out of the country as payment, except through banks authorised for this purpose. Cheques drawn on British banks should not be used. Indeed, this may be actively discouraged by the imposition of heavy clearance and handling charges at the other end. The converse is also true, although Americans seem to think that dollar cheques drawn on some obscure mid-West bank will be eagerly accepted here, and are consequently aggrieved when it is tactfully pointed out to them that this creates enormous problems—to say nothing of the swingeing bank charges incurred in converting such cheques to sterling. Other than credit cards, the Girobank system is probably the best method of remitting currency from one country to another; full details may be obtained from any post office. Details on the preferred method of sending remittances, or transferring cash to another country, as well as the transmission of coins by post to different countries, will be found in the *Royal Mail International Service Guide*. This also lists, among the prohibitions pertaining to each country, which countries accept gold or silver, and which ban the transmission of precious metals by post.

The receipt of postal packets containing coins from abroad makes you liable for Value Added Tax on their importation. As a rule, the despatching mint or bank will have affixed a Customs declaration to the packet, listing the contents, their weight and value, and it is on that basis that VAT will be calculated. The position regarding the import and export of coins by post is more complicated, and applies also to goods sent on approval. In such cases you must consult your Customs and Excise office who will advise you on the correct procedure and what your liabilities will be to tax in either case. This also applies to dealers taking stock out of the country to a coin show and then re-importing the unsold stock afterwards, or importing material purchased at the show.

Buying and Selling

When goods are sold, the seller and the buyer enter into a contract which confers rights and imposes obligations on both parties. The contract need not be in writing. There is no law governing the quality of goods sold by a private individual. If you purchase a coin from a fellow-collector as a result of an informal meeting at the local numismatic society it is incumbent on you to ensure that what you buy is what you think you are buying. If you purchase something from a dealer or shopkeeper, however, you are entitled under the Sale of Goods Act to goods of "merchantable quality" which means that they must be reasonably fit for their purpose. Items sold under a specific description, on the other hand, must correspond exactly with that description. If they do not, the seller *even a private individual* can be sued under the Sale of Goods Act. This is an important distinction because there is an erroneous notion that the Act does not apply to transactions between private individuals.

If A sells a coin to B, purporting it to be a rare date, and B subsequently discovers that the date has been deliberately altered, then B can sue A. Even if A claims that he made the sale in good faith, believing the coin to be a genuine rare date, he will still be liable for restitution (giving B his money back) and may also face a claim for damages. The Sale of Goods Act thus overturns the traditional adage *caveat emptor* which, in its full formula, translates as "let the buyer beware for he ought not to be ignorant of the nature of the property which he is buying from another party". Traditionally this was the maxim applicable at auctions. Once the auctioneer's gavel had dropped, the successful bidder had, in effect, made a contract with the vendor and was bound to pay for the lot, even if he subsequently discovered that what he had purchased was not what he had imagined. The view was that it was up to the purchaser to ensure beforehand that what he purchased was genuine and answered the description in the sale catalogue.

Because of vexatious disputes arising from questions of authenticity, and with the Sale of Goods Act breathing down their necks, many auctioneers now have a safety net, in the form of extensions. These enable successful bidders to delay payment for two or three weeks while they seek expertisation of doubtful material. In other words, the law allows a cooling-off period, but only for he legitimate purpose of verifying the authenticity of items over which there may be some doubt. This is only operative in cases where a coin or medal is sold as genuine, and described and estimated in value accordingly. In many doubtful cases, however, an auctioneer will cover himself by adding the crucial words "as is" to the description of a lot. Then, indeed, it is a case of *caveat emptor*. The auctioneer has done everything humanly possible to draw attention to the controversial nature of the item, and it must then rest on the judgment of the purchaser.

On the subject of auctions there are legal aspects which are not always apparent, as well as subtle differences in law and practice between England and Scotland. These tend to arise in cases where coins and medals come up for sale at provincial general mixed auctions, rather than in the sales conducted by numismatic auctioneers. Goods up for auction may be subject to an upset price which is made public as the price at which the bidding will start. A reserve price, on the other hand, is known only to the auctioneer, and if it is not reached, the goods will not be sold. Upset prices are common in Scotland, reserve prices in England. If no upset price is specified and the goods are not subject to a reserve price then the highest bid secures them, even though it may not be as high as the vendor hoped for. If a seller notifies other bidders that he is bidding for his own goods, or that he has employed an agent to bid for him, the bidding is legal. If he does not give notice and bids himself, or gets someone to bid for him, thus forcing up the price, the sale is fraudulent, and the buyer can purchase the goods for the amount of the last bid he made before fraudulent bidding started.

One frequently hears dark, but usually apocryphal, tales of "the ring" in action to depress the bidding and secure items below the price commensurate with their actual value. This is a fraudulent practice and in law is regarded as a criminal conspiracy. In practice, however, it would be very difficult for a group of dealers or other individuals to keep the bidding down merely by sitting on their hands. This practice could only operate successfully in sales which were largely, if not entirely, frequented by dealers. But coin sales, like other specialist collector-orientated auctions, are characterised by a high proportion of private bidders in attendance. Any conspiracy by a ring would merely allow some private bidder to step in and secure the lot at a bargain price. Rings are illegal, but in practice prosecutions are very rare as it is extremely difficult to obtain proof of their operations. What is more likely to happen is that dealers have been known to act in concert to force up the bidding to frighten off some unwelcome interloper. Here again, such tales are legion, but astonishingly lacking in specific details. The golden rule in attending auctions is to know what you are going after, and to have a pretty precise idea of how much you are prepared to pay. Do not be stampeded in the heat of the moment into going way beyond your limit.

Taxation of Profits on Disposal

The Inland Revenue define an asset as "any form of property (other than sterling) wherever situated". A disposal includes a sale, exchange or gift of an asset, or the receipt of a capital sum in respect of them. In layman's terms you dispose of an asset when you sell it, give it away, exchange it or lose it. A transfer of assets between husband and wife doesn't count (unless they are legally separated), nor does the transfer of an asset you leave when you die. If a disposal results in a profit you could be liable to tax. Any profit made on the sale of certain assets, including coins, medals and other collectables, constitutes a capital gain and is subject to Capital Gains Tax (CGT) which is now charged at the same 25% and 40% rates as income tax. However the government allows you to make a total capital gain in the current tax year of £5,500 before tax becomes chargeable. If this is the case, and the total proceeds from disposal do not exceed £10,000, then a simple declaration to this effect is all you need to make in the relevant section of your annual tax return.

Computing the actual capital gain is a complicated matter. Suppose you purchased a coin in 1960 for £5,000 and sold it in 1993 for £12,000. On the face of it, you've made a capital gain of £7,000 and you might think that you were liable to CGT because the gain was over £5,500. However, the *length of time* you've held the asset also has to be taken into consideration. From April 6, 1988 the law was altered so that only gains made after March 31, 1982 are now taxable. In effect, you are taxed as if you acquired the coin on March 31, 1982. The initial value of the coin is deemed to be its market value at that date. If the gain from March 1982 to the time of disposal is greater than the overall gain from acquisition in 1960 to disposal in 1993, you take the lesser of the two figures. If this produces a gain, whereas the old method of working it out would have produced a loss, you will be regarded, for tax purposes, as having made neither a gain nor a loss on disposal. You have a choice of opting for computing from the time of actual acquisition or from March 1982, whichever seems the more advantageous; but once you've made your choice you cannot subsequently change your mind.

How do you establish what the coin was worth in March 1982? The Inland Revenue tend to regard Seaby, Krause or other relevant catalogues as their yardstick. The difference between the nominal or catalogue value in 1982 and what you eventually got for the coin *assuming that the latter was greater*, might be regarded as the capital gain, but even then the position is complicated by inflation in the intervening years eroding the real value of the coin.

At this stage things get really complicated as you have to work out the indexation allowance. This is determined by the Retail Prices Index (RPI), and you need to know the RPI for (a) the month of disposal, and (b) the month in which you acquired the asset, or March 1982, if later. The RPI is announced each month by the Departmenrt of Employment and is published in its *Employment Gazette* which ought to be available in your local public library. Take the RPI for the month of the disposal and subtract the RPI for the month when indexation commenced. Then divide the result by the RPI for the month when indexation began, and work out this figure to the nearest third decimal place. This is known as the indexation factor, which you then multiply by the initial value of your coin. Simple isn't it? In most cases, however, I expect you will have made a capital loss in real terms, so these sums, though necessary to satisfy the Inland Revenue, are largely academic.

Treasure
and the Law

Until the introduction of the new Treasure Act, the legal position regarding articles of value, found long after they were hidden or abandoned, was not as simple and straightforward as it might be supposed. Furthermore, this was a case where the law in England and Wales differed fundamentally from that in Scotland.

Treasure Trove was one of the most ancient rights of the Crown, deriving from the age-old right of the monarch to grave treasure. In England and Wales, the law applied only to objects made of, or containing, gold or silver, whether in the form of coin, jewellery, plate or bullion. Moreover, the object had to be shown to have been deliberately hidden and the owner could not be readily found. The English law therefore excluded precious stones and jewels set in base metals or alloys such as bronze or pewter. It also took no account of artifacts in pottery, stone, bone, wood or glass which might be of immense antiquarian value.

In recent years, as a result of the rise in metal-detecting as a hobby, the archaeological lobby brought pressure to bear on Parliament to change the law and bring it into line with Scotland where the rules on Treasure Trove were far more rigorously interpreted. In Scotland the Crown is entitled to *all* abandoned property, even if it has not been hidden and is of little value. This applies even to objects dumped in skips on the pavement. Strictly speaking you would be committing a criminal offence if you removed an old chair from a skip without the owner's permission, although in practice such helping oneself rarely proceeds to a prosecution. In 1958 an archaeological expedition

Metal detecting can be fun—but be sure you know the rules!

from Aberdeen University found several valuable artifacts on St Ninian's Isle, Shetland. These included silver vessels and ornaments, as well as a porpoise bone which had incised decoration on it. The archaeologists challenged the rights of the Crown to this treasure, arguing that the Crown would have to prove that the articles had been deliberately hidden, and that a porpoise bone was in any case not valuable enough to count as treasure. The High Court, however, decided that as long as the property had been abandoned, it belonged automatically to the Crown. Its value, intrinsic or otherwise, or whether or not it was hidden, did not make any difference. Since then, as a result of this decision in case law, the criteria for Treasure Trove have been very strictly applied in Scotland. It would have only required a similar test case in England or Wales to result in a similar tightening of the rules. This has been resisted, mainly by the detectorist lobby, but inevitably the government considered legislation to control the use of metal detectors, if not to ban them altogether.

In England and Wales a find of gold or silver coins, artifacts or ornaments, or objects which contain some of these metals, which appears to have been concealed by the original owner, was deemed to be Treasure Trove. It was not even necessary for the articles to be buried in the ground; objects concealed in thatched roofs or under the floorboards of buildings have been judged to be Treasure Trove. Such finds had to be notified immediately to the police who then informed the district coroner. He then convened an inquest which decided whether all or part of the find was Treasure Trove. Establishing the gold or silver content was straightforward, but the coroner's inquest had to decide whether the material was hidden deliberately and not just lost or abandoned, and that the owner could not be located. A gold coin found on or near a country footpath might reasonably have been dropped by the original possessor through a hole in pocket or purse and in such cases it was very unlikely that it would be deemed Treasure Trove, even if the coin turned out to be very rare. In this instance the coroner would then have had to determine who was the lawful owner of the find: the actual finder, the owner of the land where it was found or even the tenant of the land. As a rule, however, it was left to the finder and landowner to decide between them who the owner of the coin should be, and in some cases the matter could only be resolved by referring to a civil court. For this reason it was vital that metal detectorists should secure permission *in writing* from landowners before going on to their land, defining rights and obligations on both sides, in order to determine

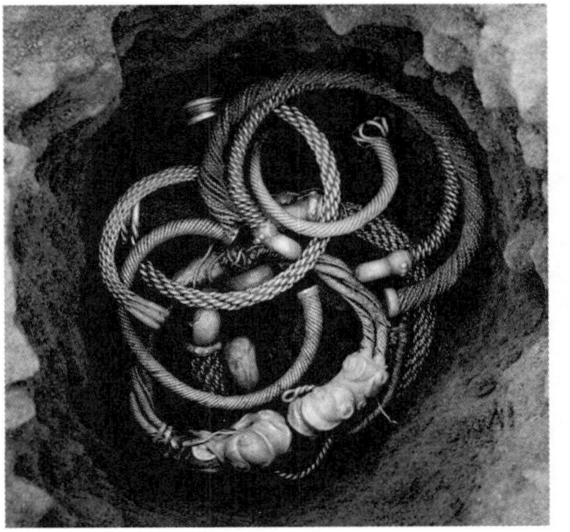

The Snettisham torcs—one of our country's greatest finds.

the disposal or share-out of any finds or proceeds from the sale of finds, *beforehand*.

If the coroner decided that the articles were deliberately concealed, and declared them to be Treasure Trove, the find automatically reverted to the Crown. In practice the find was considered by the Treasure Trove Reviewing Committee of the Treasury. They might decide that although the articles *invariably coins* were gold or silver, they were so common that they were not required by the British Museum or one of the other great national collections, and would return them to the finder to dispose of at his discretion. If some or all of the coins were deemed vital for inclusion in a national collection the finder was recompensed with the full market value of the material. On the other hand, if someone found gold or silver which might be Treasure Trove and failed to declare it at the time, that person was liable to prosecution under the Theft Act should the find subsequently come to light. Not only could he face a heavy fine but the articles would be forfeit to the Crown, and of course no reward or recompense was then payable either.

The anomalies and inconsistencies of existing law on Treasure Trove were eliminated and the position considerably tightened up by the passage, on July 5, 1996, of the Treasure Act.

Announcing that the Treasure Act had received the Royal Assent, Lord Inglewood, National Heritage Minister, said, "This represents the first legislation on treasure trove to be passed in England and Wales and will replace common law precedents and practices dating back to the

Middle Ages. The Act, which offers a clearer definition of treasure and simplified procedures for dealing with finds, will come into force after a code of practice has been drawn up and agreed by both Houses of Parliament". The Act came into force in England, Wales and Northern Ireland on September 24, 1997, replacing the common law of treasure trove.

The act was introduced as a Private Member's Bill by Sir Anthony Grant, after the failure of an earlier attempt by Lord Perth. For the first time, it would be a criminal offence to fail to report within 14 days the discovery of an item which would be declared Treasure Trove. Finders will continue to be rewarded for reporting their discoveries promptly, while landowners and occupiers will also be eligible for rewards for the first time.

The Treasure Act covers man-made objects and defines treasure as objects other than coins which are at least 300 years old and contain at least 10 per cent by weight of gold or silver; coins more than 300 years old which are found in hoards (a minimum of two coins if the precious metal content is more than 10 per cent, and a minimum of 10 coins if the precious metal content is below 10 per cent). The act also embraces all objects found in clear archaeological association with items which are treasure under the above definitions. It also covers any object which would have been Treasure Trove under the previous definitions (e.g. hoards of 19th century gold or silver coins).

The maximum penalty for failing to report the discovery of treasure within 14 days will be a fine of £50,000 or three months imprisonment, or both.

In Scotland the police pass the goods on to the procurator fiscal who acts as the local representative of the Queen's and Lord Treasurer's Remembrancer. If the articles are of little value, historically or intrinsically, the finder will usually be allowed to keep them. If they are retained for the appropriate national collection then a reward equal to the market value is payable.

A favourite haunt of metal-detectorists these days is the beach, and many hobbyists make quite a lucrative living by sweeping the beaches especially just after a Bank Holiday. It's surprising how much loose change gets lost from pockets and handbags over a holiday weekend. Technically the coins recovered from the beach are lost property, in which case they ought to be surrendered to the police, otherwise the finder may be guilty of theft. In practice, however, the law turns a blind eye to coins, on the sensible grounds that it would be impossible to prove ownership. On the other hand, banknotes are treated as lost property since someone could in theory at least identify a note as his by citing the serial number.

In the case of other objects, such as watches and jewellery, of course the law governing lost property is enforced, and the old adage of "finders keepers" does not apply. Any object of value, identifiable as belonging to someone, that is washed up on the foreshore or found in territorial waters is known technically as "wreck". This includes not just a wrecked ship, but any cargo that was being carried by a ship.

If wreck is not claimed by its owner, it falls to the Crown. In this case it is not necessary to prove deliberate concealment, as in the case of Treasure Trove. This law has a specific numismatic application in the case of the gold and silver coins washed up after storms around our shores, from Shetland to the Scillies. Such coins, emanating from wrecks of Spanish treasure ships and Dutch East Indiamen in particular, are well documented, and any such finds ought to be reported immediately to the police.

Stray finds of coins, as well as other objects of value, on public places, such as the street, a public park or a sports ground, are also subject to law. In this case the finder must take all reasonable steps to locate the owner. Anyone who keeps a coin without making reasonable effort to find the owner could be prosecuted for theft. As with the beach, however, such "reasonable effort" would clearly be impractical. Finding coins on private premises is another matter. In this case large bodies, such as the Post Office, British Rail, the British Airports Authority, bus companies, municipal authorities, hospitals, the owners of department stores, theatre and cinema proprietors and the like, may have bye-laws, rules and regulations for dealing with lost property found within their precincts, or in their vehicles. If you found a purse or wallet on a bus or train, or in a telephone kiosk or a shop, common sense (and your conscience) would tell you to hand it over to the driver, conductor, shopkeeper or official in charge. As a rule, unclaimed lost property reverts eventually to the finder, but not always; British Rail and some other organisations have a rule that in such cases the property reverts to the organisation. In any event, failure to disclose the find immediately might render you liable to prosecution for stealing by finding.

Treasure Act
Code of Practice
—a summary

For easy reference a summary of the main points of the new law is reproduced here*. Further information will be found in the *Code of Practice on the Treasure Act*, which can be obtained free of charge from the Department for Culture, Media and Sport (formerly the Department of National Heritage) (telephone: 020 7211 6200). Metal detectorists are strongly advised to obtain a copy of the Code of Practice which, among other things, contains guidance for detectorists, sets out guidelines on rewards, gives advice on the care of finds and has lists of useful addresses.

What is the definition of treasure?

The following finds are treasure under the Act (*more detailed guidance is given in the Code of Practice*):

1. *Objects other than coins:* any object other than a coin provided that it contains at least 10 per cent of gold or silver and is a least 300 years old when found (objects with gold or silver plating normally have less than 10 per cent of precious metal).

2. *Coins:* all coins from the same find provided they are at least 300 years old when found (but if the coins contain less than 10 per cent of gold or silver there must be at least 10 of them; there is a list of these coins in the Code of Practice).

An object or coin is part of the same find as another object or coin if it is found in the same place as, or had previously been left together with, the other object. Finds may have become scattered since they were originally deposited in the ground.

Only the following groups of coins will normally be regarded as coming from the "same find":

(a) hoards that have been deliberately hidden;
(b) smaller groups of coins, such as the contents of purses, that may have been dropped or lost and
(c) votive or ritual deposits.

Single coins found on their own are not treasure and groups of coins lost one by one over a period of time (for example those found on settlement sites or on fair sites) will not normally be treasure.

3. *Associated objects:* any object, whether it is made of, that is found in the same place as, or that had previously been together with, another object that is treasure.

4. *Objects that would have been treasure trove:* any object that would previously have been treasure trove, but does not fall within the specific categories given above. These objects have to be made substantially of gold or silver; they have to have been buried with the intention of recovery and their owner or his/her heirs cannot be traced.

The following types of find are not treasure:

(a) objects whose owners can be traced;
(b) unworked natural objects, including human and animal remains, even if they are found in association with treasure;
(c) objects from the foreshore, which are wreck.

If you are in any doubt, it will probably be safest to report your find.

What about objects found before the Act came into force?

You should report objects that come into any of the four categories just described (if found after September 23, 1997). There is no need to report any objects found before that date unless they may be treasure trove (see 4 above).

What should I do if I find something that may be treasure?

You must report all finds of treasure to the coroner for the district in which they are found *either* within 14 days after the date on which you made the find *or* within 14 days after the day on which you realised that the find might be treasure (for example, as a result of having it identified). The obligation to report finds applies to everyone, including archaeologists.

How do I report a find of treasure?

Very simply. You may report your find to the coroner in person, by letter, telephone or fax. The coroner or his officer will send you an acknowledgement and tell you where you should deliver your find. The Code of Practice has a list of all coroners' addresses, telephone and fax numbers.

There are special procedure for objects from a few areas for which treasure franchises exist, but they should be reported to the coroner in the usual way. The main franchise-holders (the Duchies of Lancaster and Cornwall, the Corporation of London and the City of Bristol) have confirmed that they will pay rewards for finds of treasure from their franchises in the normal way.

Where will I have to take my find?

You will normally be asked to take your find to a local museum or archaeological body. Local agreements have been drawn up for each coroner's district in England and Wales to provide the coroner with a list of such museums and archaeological organisations. The Department is publishing a series of leaflets, roughly one for each country of England and one for Wales, listing the relevant coroners, museums and archaeological services in each area.

The body which receives the find on behalf of the coroner will give you a receipt. Although they will need to know where you made the find, they will keep this information confidential if you or the landowner wish—and you should do so too.

The body receiving the find will notify the Sites and Monuments Record as soon as possible (if that has not already happened), so that the site where the find was made can be investigated by archaeologists if necessary. A list of Sites and Monuments Records is in Appendix 3 of the Code of Practice.

What if I do not report a find of treasure?

If you fail to report a find that you believe or have reasonable grounds for believing to be treasure without a reasonable excuse you may be imprisoned for up to three months or receive a fine of up to level 5 on the standard scale (currently £5,000) or both. You will not be breaking the law if you do not report a find because you do not initially recognise that it may be treasure, but you should report it once you do.

What happens if the find is not treasure?

If the object is clearly not treasure, the museum or archeological body will inform the coroner, who may then decide to give directions that the find should be returned without holding an inquest.

What happens if the find is treasure?

If the museum curator or archaeologist believes the find may be treasure, they will inform the British Museum or the National Museums & Galleries of Wales. The museums will then decide whether they or any other museum may wish to acquire it.

If no museum wishes to acquire the find, the Secretary of State will be able to disclaim it. When this happens, the coroner will notify the occupier and landowner that he intends to return the object to the finder after 28 days unless he receives an objection. If the coroner receives an objection, the find will be retained until the dispute is settled.

What if a museum wants to acquire my find?

If a museum wants to acquire part or all of a find, then the coroner will hold an inquest to decide whether it is treasure. The coroner will inform the finder, occupier and landowner and they will be able to question witnesses at the inquest. Treasure inquest will not normally be held with a jury.

If the find is declared to be treasure, then it will be taken to the British Museum or the National Museums & Galleries of Wales, so that it can be valued by the Treasure Valuation Committee.

How do I know I will receive a fair price for my find?

Any find of treasure that a museum wishes to acquire must be valued by the Treasure Valuation Committee, which consists of independent experts. The Committee will commission a valuation from one or more experts drawn from the trade. You, together with the museum that wishes to acquire the find and any other interested party, will have an opportunity to comment on the valuation and to send in a separate valuation of your own, before the Committee makes its recommendation. If you are dissatisfied you can appeal to the Secretary of State.

What if the coroner or museum loses or damages my find?

They are required to take reasonable steps to ensure that this does not happen; but, if it does, you should nonetheless be compensated.

Who will receive the reward?

This is set out in detail in the Code of Practice.

To summarise:

- where the finder has permission to be on the land, rewards should continue to be paid in full to him or her (the burden of proof as to whether he or she has permission will rest with the finder). If the finder makes an agreement with the occupier/landowner to share a reward, the Secretary of State will normally follow it;
- if the finder does not remove the whole of a find from the ground but allows archaeologists to excavate the remainder of the find, the original finder will normally be eligible for a reward for the whole find;
- rewards will not normally be payable when the find is made by an archaeologist;
- where the finder has committed an offence in relation to a find, or has trespassed, or has not followed best practice as set out in the Code of Practice, he or she may expect no reward at all or a reduced reward. Landowners and occupiers will be eligible for rewards in such cases.

How long will it take before I receive my reward?

The Code of Practice states that you should receive a reward within one year of you having delivered your find, although this may take longer in the case of very large finds or those that present special difficulties. If no museum wants to acquire the find it should be disclaimed within six months or within three months if it is a single object.

***Reproduced from "The Treasure Act, Information for Finders of Treasure (England and Wales)" leaflet DCMSJ0229NJ, published by the Department for Culture, Media and Sport.**

Index
to COIN NEWS

This index of persons, places, events, articles and reviews, as well as new issues detailed in COIN NEWS, covers the period from September 2002 to August 2003. Entries are indicated by numbers signifying the month (e.g. 9-12 relate to September to December 2002 and 1-8 refer to January to August 2003) followed by the page number.

BOOKS

NEW ISSUES

CONTRIBUTORS

AIREDALE CO.

P.O. BOX 7, BINGLEY, WEST YORKSHIRE. BD16 1XU
TELEPHONE: (01535) 272754 FAX: (01535) 275727
E-Mail info@airedalecoins.com Website www.airedalecoins.com
MEMBERS OF THE BRITISH NUMISMATIC TRADE ASSOCIATION

SPECIALIST IN NEW ISSUES
SEND OR TELEPHONE FOR FREE LIST

U.K. EURO PATTERNS

BRITISH PATTERN £1 COINS

COLOURED MAPLES

HOLOGRAM COINS

GERMAN SILVER 10 EURO WORLD CUP 2006—£12.00

SILVER BULLION COINS FROM U.K., CANADA, AUSTRALIA, U.S.A., CHINA, ZAMBIA, SAMALIA, MEXICO, SOUTH AFRICA ETC